Study and Revise

GCSE Intermediate Maths

Sheila Hunt and Philip Hooper

KEY TO SYMBOLS

As you read through this book you will notice the following symbols. They will help you find your way around the book more quickly.

shows you a handy hint to help you learn

explains some of the mathematical jargon that you might meet

points out a potential hazard that could cause a problem

First published in this edition 2004
exclusively for WHSmith by
Hodder & Stoughton Educational
338 Euston Road
London NW1 3BH

Impression number 10 9 8 7 6 5 4 3 2 1
Year 2010 2009 2008 2007 2006 2005 2004

Illustrations: Karen Donnelly, Andrea Norton, Mike Parsons, John Plumb, Chris Rothero

Prepared by Tech-Set Ltd
Printed and bound in the UK by Scotprint

A CIP record for this book is available from the British Library

ISBN 0 340 85861 3

Contents

Contents

Introduction to GCSE Intermediate Maths

Are you struggling to raise that GCSE Maths grade to a C? Do you feel that your C is in the bag, but you secretly dream of a B? If you answer, "Yes" to either of these questions, this could be just the book for you. In this *Study and Revise* book, you will find chapters covering all the topics you need for Intermediate level, whether you follow a modular or linear syllabus.

You do not have to follow the book in any specific order. As soon as you have been given your first piece of Maths coursework, you can turn to the appropriate chapters to help you start to pile on those valuable marks. If yours is a modular syllabus, use the chapters that will help you most with the module you are studying. If your school uses a linear syllabus, i.e. one in which there are only two exams at the end of the course, you may find it more convenient to work through the book in the given order. To help you further still, there is a "Three simple steps to success" section near the end of the book. This provides a suggested revision plan which you can use as it is or adapt to suit your own personal needs.

If you quickly flip through the book, you will soon see some banana skin symbols. Each one of these highlights a common mistake and how to avoid it, thus ensuring that you keep hold of every hard-earned mark.

What else makes this book different? Just look at any chapter at random and you will find all sorts of short cuts, easy methods and original ideas to make learning Maths easier – and yes, maybe more enjoyable – than you ever thought was possible.

Good luck.

Sheila Hunt and Philip Hooper

Chapter 1 Proportion, percentages and ratio

PREVIEW

By the end of this chapter you will be able to:

- **answer questions on direct and inverse proportion**
- **find a given percentage of a number**
- **find one number as a percentage of another**
- **increase or decrease a price or amount by a given percentage**
- **find a percentage profit or loss**
- **calculate the percentage discount on a price**
- **calculate the VAT-inclusive price of an article, given the pre-VAT price**
- **calculate the pre-VAT price, given the VAT-inclusive price**
- **divide a given number or amount in a given ratio**
- **calculate individual shares of a number or amount divided in a given ratio**
- **state ratios in their lowest terms**
- **state ratios in the form 1 : *n* or *n* : 1**
- **work out the lengths involved in scale drawing.**

How much do you know already?

Exercise 1.1

1 1 kilogram is approximately 2.2 pounds. (1 kg ≈ 2.2 lbs)

a) How much is 75 kg that in pounds?

b) 14 pounds = 1 stone. Express your answer to part **a)** in stones and pounds.

c) A man weighs 12 st 8 lbs. Express this in kg.

2 What is 40% of 60?

3 A pie chart is drawn to represent 300 members of an audience. How many degrees represent 80 members?

4 Two litres of a solution contain 850 grams of a chemical.

a) How many litres would contain 1500 g?

b) How many grams are there in 3.3 litres? Give your answer to the nearest hundred grams.

5 In a test, a student scored 45 out of a possible 70 marks. What percentage was this?

6 The plan of a new house and garden is drawn, using a scale of 1 : 25.

a) The length of the kitchen as drawn on the plan is 15 cm. What is its actual length, in metres?

b) The actual garden is 12.5 metres long. How long will it be on the plan?

7 The lengths of the labels of two jars are in the ratio of 5 : 2.

a) If the larger label is 8 cm wide, how wide is the smaller?

b) If the smaller label is 5 cm high, find the height of the larger.

8 A van was bought for £9500 and sold a year later for £7800. Find the depreciation as a percentage of the cost price.

Answers – 1.1

1 a) 165 lbs **b)** 11 stone 11 pounds
c) 80 kg
2 24
3 96°
4 a) 3.53 litres
b) 1402.5 g = 1400 g to the nearest 100 g
5 64%
6 a) 3.75 m **b)** 50 cm
7 a) 3.2 cm **b)** 12.5 cm
8 18%

How did you get on?

All of them right?

Well done! Questions of this type are extremely common at Intermediate level. If you found them easy, you probably have methods that work well for you, and you don't need to change them. However, you may find that we can show you some shortcuts that could save you valuable minutes in the exam, so it's worth looking through the methods we will cover. You just might pick up a tip or two.

Most questions right, but a few blunders?

You are just the sort of person for whom this chapter was written. Use our easy methods to help you score 100% next time.

Don't even ask?

Don't despair. Just work through this chapter and you'll see just how easy it is to score 100%!

Proportion

Example 1.1 – An Easy Example

Five books cost £15. Find the cost of seven books.

This is probably the method you used in the past.

5 books cost £15
1 book costs £15 ÷ 5 = £3
7 books cost £3 × 7 = £21

There's nothing wrong with this method, and it works. However, if you're having problems, see if the **X-Direct** approach can help.

Solution

Using the X-Direct method

Step 1

Set out the information in a table.

To do so, ask yourself 'what does the question tell me?', and 'what do I need to know'?

Make sure that you put the numbers under the right headings. You should arrive at:

	Books	Cost (£)
I know:	5	15
I need:	7	?

Step 2

	Books	Cost (£)
I know:	5	15
I need:	7	?

Draw in the diagonals as shown. Now you can see why this is called the X-Direct method.

Step 3

Multiply the two numbers joined by one diagonal (7 and 15), and divide by the third number (5).

Cost of 7 books $= \frac{7 \times 15}{5} = 21$

So, seven books cost £21.

Once you get the hang of this, it's really quick and easy, as you'll discover when you see it in action.

Example 1.2

A box of chocolates was bought in the USA for $4.58, when the exchange rate was £1 = $1.42. Give the cost in pounds to the nearest penny.

Solution

	£	Cost $
What does the question tell me?	1	1.42
What do I need to find?	?	4.58

Using X-Direct, you can see that the calculation is

$\frac{1 \times 4.58}{1.42} = £3.23$

Since you are multiplying by 1, you can of course leave it out of your written working without affecting the answer, but many people prefer to write everything in until they get used to X-Direct.

Hints & Tips

Try to get into the habit of making a rough estimate ***before*** *you hit the calculator buttons, just to give you some idea of what answer to expect. When using a calculator, it's very easy to press the wrong key without realising it.*

Example 1.3

Paul worked for 42 hours and received £48.30. How much would he receive for working 20 hours at the same rate?

Solution

Estimate: 20 is about half of 42, so he should receive about £24.

	Hours	£
What does the question tell me?	42	48.30
What do I need to know?	20	?

Amount $= \frac{20 \times 48.30}{42} = £23.00$

Example 1.4 – Using X-Direct more than once

How many litres are approximately equal to 30.5 gallons?

1 litre ≈ 1.75 pints *(≈ means 'approximately equals')*
8 pints = 1 gallon

Solution

You need to work backwards on this one.

	Pints	Gallons
I know	8	1
I need	?	30.5

$\frac{8 \times 30.5}{1} = 244$ pints

This gives the answer in pints, and we need to know the number of litres. Consider the relationship between pints and litres.

	Pints	Litres
I know	1.75	1
I need	244	?

30.5 gallons $\approx \frac{244 \times 1}{1.75} = 139.4$ litres

Now you try your luck!

Exercise 1.2

1 3.5 m of tape cost £4.20.
   a) What would 8 m cost?
   b) How much tape would you get for £15?

2 30 cm ≈ 1 foot   3 feet = 1 yard
   1760 yards = 1 mile   1 mile ≈ x metres
   What is the value of x?

3 A large jar of honey weighs 850 grams and costs £4.50 and a small jar costs £1.75 for 300 grams.
   a) Which is better value? Why? Show your working.
   b) Why might someone choose the other size?

Answers – 1.2

1 a) £9.60   b) 12.5 m

2 1584 m

3 a) The larger jar is better value as £1.00 buys 189 g, whereas for the smaller size jar £1.00 only buys 171 g.
   b) Someone might choose the smaller jar if he or she does not eat much honey, or if he or she were just wanting to try it out.

Some words and phrases crop up a lot in Maths, and it is important that you understand them. This makes it much easier for you to understand what a question is asking you to do, and so it gives you a better chance of answering the question correctly.

Whenever you see this sign, you will know that you are about to be given a useful hint about what something means.

TAKE A BREAK

This is a good point to take a break. When you come back, look again at the principles of X-Direct. Start to make a list of situations when you could use the technique. You will be surprised how often it crops up.

Avoiding pitfalls

We have used the symbol of the banana skin to point out potential hazards that could trip you up. Whenever you see it you know there is something that could cause you a problem. It's a warning to be careful and to try to avoid common mistakes.

Inverse proportion

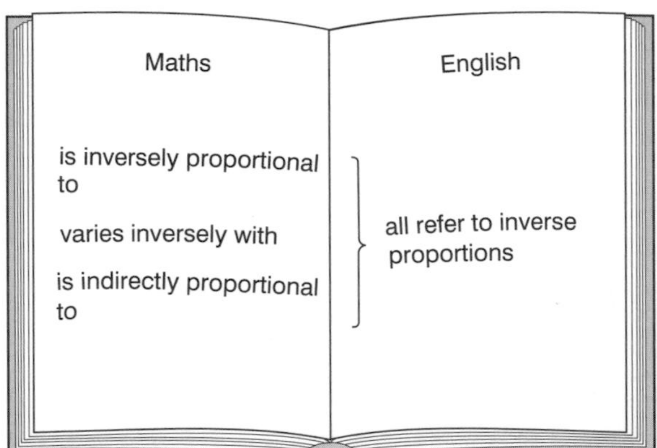

Maths
English
is inversely proportional to
varies inversely with
is indirectly proportional to
all refer to inverse proportions

A problem involving inverse proportion is one of the very rare cases *where you must **not** use X-Direct.*

Example 1.5

A journey takes 6 hours at 40 km/h. How long does it take at 80 km/h?

*Common sense tells you that the faster you go, the less time you take, so you must use **inverse proportion** (i.e. one variable gets bigger as the other gets smaller and vice versa). X-Direct only applies to questions where both variables increase at the same rate, or both decrease at the same rate.*

Solution

Inverse proportion can drive you MAD:

Multiply what you are given $6 \times 40 = 240$

And then

Divide by the other number. $240 \div 80 = 3$

The journey takes 3 hours.

Do not use X-Direct for inverse proportion.

Inverse proportion questions are not nearly as common, but we have inserted them here, so that you don't muddle them with X-Direct.

Exercise 1.3

1. If Rashid and four friends share the bill at a restaurant, the cost per head is £24.00. How much should each person pay if the cost is shared among eight people?
2. Andy and his two other brothers can put up a marquee in three hours. How long would six people take?
3. It takes six days for eight workers to dig a trench. How long would it take twelve workers to carry out the task?

Answers – 1.3

1 £15.00 **2** 1.5 hours

3 8 workers take 6 days, so 1 worker would take (**M**ultiply) 8 × 6 = 48 days, and 12 workers would take (**A**nd then **D**ivide) 48 ÷ 12 = 4 days.

TAKE A BREAK

Now's the time for a break! You probably feel you need it. Don't make it too long, though, because we still have to tackle percentages.

Percentages

Percentages feature very prominently in Intermediate level papers, so this section could help you pick up some useful marks. If you have a method that works for you, by all means stay with it. However, the fact that you are reading this means that you may be having problems, so try X-Direct!

Type 1: Finding the percentage of a number

Example 1.6

What is 30% of £200?

Solution

100% is the original amount of £200.

What we need to know is the amount of money that equals 30% of £200.

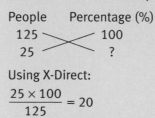

Pounds (£)	Percentage (%)
200	100
?	30

Using X-Direct:

$$\frac{200 \times 30}{100} = 60$$

The answer is £60.

Type 2: Expressing one number as a percentage of another

Example 1.7

In a market survey, 25 stallholders, out of 125 who were asked, said that they were running their stalls at a loss. Express this as a percentage.

Solution

100% is the total number of people asked, i.e. 125.

We need to find 25 as a percentage of 125.

People	Percentage (%)
125	100
25	?

Using X-Direct:

$$\frac{25 \times 100}{125} = 20$$

The answer is 20%.

Percentage profit and loss

Questions are often set asking you to find the percentage profit or loss following a transaction. Unless the question asks for something different, calculate the profit or loss from the **original cost price**.

Example 1.8

A woman bought a coat for £30.00 and sold it for £45.00. Calculate her percentage profit.

Solution

First find the actual cash profit.

£45.00 – £30.00 = £15.00

Then use X-Direct.

£	%
30	100
15	

$$\frac{15 \times 100}{30} = 50\%$$

Alternatively, use the £45.00.

Pounds (£)	Percentage (%)
30	100
45	?

$$\frac{45 \times 100}{30} = 150\%$$

150% – 100% = 50%

Her percentage profit is 50%.
Either method gives you the correct answer.

Example 1.9

Rory has decided to sell off some of his stock of watches. He paid £120.00 for some watches which have not sold well, so is selling them for £75.00. Find his loss as a percentage of the cost price.

Solution

Actual loss = £120.00 – £75.00 = £45.00

Pounds (£)	Percentage (%)
120	100
45	?

$$\frac{45 \times 100}{120} = 37.5\%$$

His percentage loss is 37.5%.

If you used the £75.00 instead, you should get the answer 62.5%. Then you would subtract this from 100% to get the answer 37.5%.

Example 1.10

Kath bought a radio for £80.00 and sold it again for £60.00. Find the percentage loss.

Solution

Start by finding the actual loss.
(i.e. £80.00 – £60.00 = £20.00)

	Pounds (£)	Percentage (%)
Cost	80.00	100
Loss	20.00	?

$$\text{Percentage loss} = \frac{20 \times 100}{80} = 25\%$$

Type 3: The figure you're given doesn't refer to 100%

Example 1.11

Jack buys a camera. The price is cut by 20%, which is a discount of £7.50. Find the old price.

Solution

The original price is 100%.

Percentage (%)	Pounds (£)
100	?
20	7.50

$$\text{Using X-Direct: } \frac{100 \times 7.50}{20} = 37.5$$

The old price is £37.50.
When writing money amounts always use two decimal places, i.e. £37.50 not £37.5.

Can you see that it does not matter where the gap in the table is, as long as you keep the numbers in the correct columns, and the numbers that relate to each other next to each other?

Hints & Tips

Example 1.12

The price of a camera is reduced by 25% to £30. Find its original price.

Solution

This question is similar to the previous one, but find the price after the discount has been given, rather than the discount itself.

If 25% has been taken off the original of 100% then we have 75% left, so £30 relates to 75%.

Pounds (£)	Percentage (%)
30	75
?	100

$$\text{Using X-Direct: } \frac{30 \times 100}{75} = 40$$

So the original price was £40.00.

Exercise 1.4

1 As an experiment to encourage larger audiences to a local theatre, the price of all tickets was reduced by 15%. If the original price of a ticket was £5.70, find the new price.

2 In an audience of 240 people, 108 were children.
   a) What percentage of the audience were children?
   b) What percentage were adults?

3 Rent for a nearby campsite was increased by 20% one year. If the new rent is £3000, find the original charge.

Answers – 1.4

1 £4.85
2 **a)** 45% **b)** 55%
3 £2500

VAT questions

Value Added Tax (VAT) is put on most items that you buy in the shops. VAT questions are very common in exams. VAT is currently 17.5%.

Adding on VAT

Example 1.13

The pre-VAT price of a set of DVDs is £58.40. Find the price including VAT.

Solution

There are two ways of solving this problem: either work out 17.5% and add it on to the original price, or use the complete 'VAT-inclusive' percentage, which will be 100% + 17.5% = 117.5%.

Method 1

Price (£)	Percentage (%)
58.40	100
?	17.5

$$\text{VAT} = \frac{58.40 \times 17.5}{100} = 10.22$$

The price including VAT = £58.40 + £10.22
= £68.62

Method 2

Price (£)	Percentage (%)
58.40	100
?	117.5

$$\text{Price including VAT} = \frac{58.40 \times 117.5}{100}$$
$$= £68.62$$

Removing VAT from the 'VAT-included' price

As you saw in the example above, the 'VAT-included' price is 100% + 17.5% = 117.5% of the original or pre-VAT price.

If you want to find the original price, you need to find the value of 100%, or if you want to find the VAT, you need to find the value of the 17.5%.

Example 1.14

A coffee-maker is priced at £31.49 including VAT. Find its price before VAT was added.

Solution

Price (£)	Percentage (%)
31.49	117.5
?	100

$$\text{Pre-VAT price} = \frac{31.49 \times 100}{117.5} = 26.8$$

The original price was £26.80 (remember not to write this as £26.8).

Example 1.15

Find the VAT on a calculator if the price including VAT is £16.92.

Solution

Price (£)	Percentage (%)
16.92	117.5
?	17.5

$$\text{VAT} = \frac{16.92 \times 17.5}{117.5} = £2.52$$

In this exercise, take VAT to be 17.5%.

Exercise 1.5

1 If the pre-VAT prices of theatre tickets are £11.50 for adults and £8.50 for children, find the prices including VAT.

2 Zena booked a holiday for £1001.10 including VAT. What would the price be without VAT?

3 Yoko paid £426.76 for a coat, including VAT. How much VAT did she pay?

Answers – 1.5

1 Adult's ticket = £13.51, child's ticket = £9.99
2 £852.00
3 £63.56

Percentages as multipliers

Adding a given percentage

3% can be written as a decimal, as 0.03.
Adding 3% gives 103% of the starting amount.

$$103\% = \frac{103}{100} = 1.03.$$

The simplest way of adding 3% to a number is to multiply the number by 1.03.

Subtracting a given percentage

Subtracting 3% from a number gives 97% = 0.97.
So to subtract 3% from a number multiply the number by 0.97.

In summary ...

To add 43% to a number, multiply by 1.43.
To subtract 43% from a number, multiply by 0.57 (that is 1 – 0.43).

Compound percentages

Example 1.16

A number is increased by 10%, then the answer is increased by 20%. What is the total percentage increase?

Solution

Increasing by 10% is the same as multiplying by 1.10, or 1.1, and increasing by 20% is the same as multiplying by 1.20, or 1.2.

$1.1 \times 1.2 = 1.32$

Multiplying by 1.32 is the same as increasing by 32%.

Example 1.17

A number is reduced by 30% then increased by 15%. What is the total percentage decrease?

Solution

$100\% - 30\% = 70\% = 0.7$

$100\% + 15\% = 115\% = 1.15$

$0.7 \times 1.15 = 0.805$

As $1 - 0.805 = 0.195$, multiplying by 0.805 is the same as reducing by 19.5%.

So the total percentage decrease is 19.5%.

Compound interest

Take the original amount, and multiply it by the percentage as a multiplier for the given number of time periods. For example, £2000 invested at 7% per annum works out as follows.

Years	Amount earned
1	2000×1.07
2	$2000 \times 1.07 \times 1.07 = 2000 \times 1.07^2$
3	$2000 \times 1.07 \times 1.07 \times 1.07 = 2000 \times 1.07^3$

After n years the amount of money is 2000×1.07^n.

The formula for this is AP^T, where A is the original amount, P is the percentage (in multiplier form) and T is the time for which the money is invested.

Example 1.18

£5000 is invested in a bank account which pays compound interest of 4% per year. Find, to the nearest pound, the amount of money in the account after 7 years.

Solution

$5000 \times 1.04^7 = £6580$

Exercise 1.6

1 Find the total percentage increase or decrease if a number is changed by these percentages.
 a) increased by 16% then reduced by 25%
 b) reduced by 30% then by a further 12%
 c) reduced by 50% then increased by 50%

2 The amounts below are invested in a bank paying compound interest at the given interest rates. Find the amount in the bank account after the given number of years, giving your answers to the nearest pound.
 a) £3000 at 5% for 6 years
 b) £7500 at 8% for 3 years
 c) £25 000 at 4.5% for 12 years

Answers – 1.6

1 **a)** $1.16 \times 0.75 = 0.87$, so reduced by 13%.
 b) $0.70 \times 0.88 = 0.616$, $1 - 0.616 = 0.384$, so reduced by 38.4%
 c) $0.5 \times 1.5 = 0.75$, so reduced by 25%.

2 **a)** $3000 \times 1.05^6 = £4020$
 b) $7500 \times 1.08^3 = £9448$
 c) $25\,000 \times 1.045^{12} = £42\,397$

Ratio

Ratio is a way of dividing or sharing quantities.

How much do you know already about ratio?

Exercise 1.7

1. Ella distributed a £600 lottery win among three people in the ratio 2 : 3 : 7. How much did each receive?
2. Sam wanted a photo enlarged in all dimensions in the ratio 2 : 5. If the original length was 45 cm, find the new length.
3. Express the ratio 32 : 180 in its simplest form.
4. Express the ratio 40 cm to 1 m in its simplest form.

Answers – 1.7

1. £100, £150 and £350
2. 112.5 cm
3. 8 : 45
4. 2 : 5

Ratios using a ruler

Look carefully at these rulers. Count the number of parts in each one. Add up the two numbers in the ratio. Get the idea?

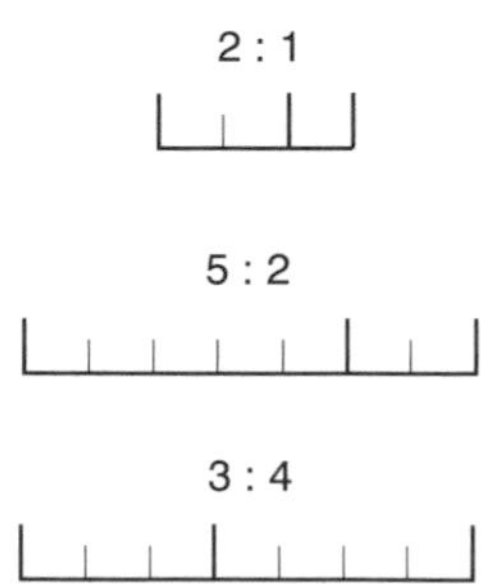

Type 1: The question gives a quantity that relates to the whole of the ruler

Example 1.19

Sanjeev gave £300 to two friends, Marie and Farhad, in the ratio of 3 to 2. How much did each receive?

Solution

Write £300 above the whole of the 3 : 2 ratio ruler.

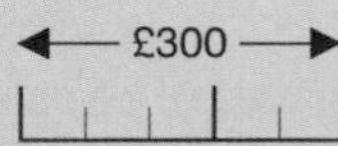

Use X-Direct to find Marie's share.

Share (£)	Sections
300	5
?	3

Marie's share = $\dfrac{300 \times 3}{5}$ = £180.

Or work out the money relating to each section. i.e. £300 ÷ 5 = £60.

Marie receives 3 sections. £60 × 3 = £180

Farhad receives 2 sections. £60 × 2 = £120

Check: *All the amounts must add up to the original £300.*

Example 1.20

A man gave £750 to his grandchildren, Will, Clara and Noel, in the ratio of their ages: 7, 6 and 2 respectively. How much did each receive?

Solution

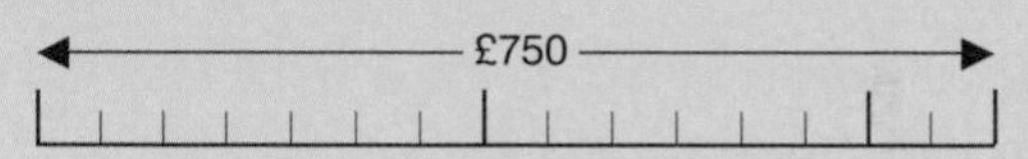

Use X-Direct to find, for example, Will's share.

Share (£)	Sections
750	15
?	7

Will's amount = $\dfrac{750 \times 7}{15}$ = £350

or

Each section represents £750 ÷ 15 = £50.

Will gets £50 × 7 = £350.

Clara gets £50 × 6 = £300.

Noel gets £50 × 2 = £100.

Check: 350 + 300 + 100 = 750

Type 2: The quantity given in the question relates to part of the ruler

Example 1.21

Picture frames are made in two sizes. The width of the smaller is 16 cm. The lengths on the larger size are bigger in the ratio 4 : 5. Find the width of the larger frame.

Solution

Start by marking out a ratio ruler with nine divisions, in the ratio 4 : 5.

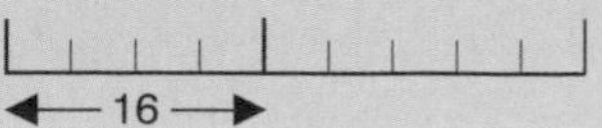

This time you do not have a total, so do not write anything along the top.

Write the smaller width, 16, as shown in the diagram.

Now it is a simple matter of using X-Direct to get the answer.

4 : 5
16 : ?

$\frac{5 \times 16}{4} = 20\text{ cm}$

Giving ratios in their lowest form

Example 1.22

Give the ratio 2 : 8 : 12 in its lowest form.

Solution

Look for common factors. (These are numbers which divide into 2, 8 and 12. If you have forgotten about factors, you need to refer to Chapter 2, Number.)

The only common factor of 2, 8 and 12 is 2, so dividing through by this gives 1 : 4 : 6. There are no other common factors, so we say that 1 : 4 : 6 is its lowest (or simplest) form.

Example 1.23

A ratio is given as 5 : 8.

a) Express this ratio in the form $n : 1$.

b) Express this ratio in the form $1 : n$.

Solution

Once again, X-Direct can help.

a) 5 : 8
? : 1

$\frac{1 \times 5}{8} = 0.625$

Answer in the form $n : 1$ is 0.625 : 1

b) 5 : 8
1 : ?

$\frac{8 \times 1}{5} = 1.6$

Answer in the form $1 : n$ is 1 : 1.6

Example 1.24

Express the ratio 40 : 56 in its simplest form.

Solution

Keep dividing both numbers by common factors, cancelling until their only common factor is 1.

The highest common factor of 40 and 56 is 8. Dividing both numbers by 8 gives 5 and 7.

40 : 56 = 5 : 7

If you don't spot the highest common factor, work out the problem in steps.

40 : 56 = 20 : 28 = 10 : 14 = 5 : 7

When you are expressing ratios in their simplest form, be careful with units.

Example 1.25

Express the ratio 25 cm : 3 km in its simplest form.

Solution

Work in either centimetres or kilometres. In this case, it is probably easier to work in centimetres.

25 cm : 3 km = 25 : 300 000 = 1 : 12 000

Example 1.26

A group of 10 adults and 35 students went on a school trip. Express in its simplest form the ratio of:

a) adults to students **b)** students to adults.

Solution

a) 10 : 35 = 2 : 7
In other words, for every two adults, there will be seven students.

b) 35 : 10 = 7 : 2
In other words for every seven students, there will be two adults.

You must always keep the numbers in the same order as they are given. For example, 2 : 7 is not the same as 7 : 2.

To recap ...

When working with ratios:

1 Mark out a ruler showing you all the parts.

2 If you have a total (i.e. the whole amount) which has to be shared, write the amount over the top. You can then see that dividing the total by the number of parts will give you the 'size' of one share. Then it is just a matter of using X-Direct to calculate the other shares.

3 If you do not have the total, but just an increase or decrease in one part, write this underneath the ruler and solve *either* by using X-Direct or by working out the size of each section.

Exercise 1.8

1 Share £750 in the ratio 5 : 7 : 13.

2 Some money is shared in the ratio 3 : 2. If the larger amount is £450.00, find the smaller.

3 a) A party from a local school plans to visit the circus. If the ratio of teachers to students must be 2 : 15, how many teachers would be needed to accompany a party of 45 students?
b) If 12 teachers were available, what is the maximum number of students that could accompany them?

4 Write the following ratios in their simplest form.
a) 120 : 400 b) 175 : 25

Answers – 1.8

1 £150, £210 and £390
2 £300
3 a) 6 teachers b) 90 students
4 a) 3 : 10 b) 7 : 1

Exercise 1.9

1 A shop sells paper plates at 5p each, or in packets of 10 for 40p, or in packets of 50 for £1.85. Find the cheapest way to buy:
a) 9 plates b) 20 plates
c) 110 plates.

2 In a closing down sale, a shop reduces all its prices by 15%. What is the sale price of an item that originally cost £380.00?

3 A gift of £1800 is to be shared among Anne, Jack and Alun in the ratio of their ages, which are 3, 4 and 2 respectively.
a) How much will each receive?
b) If, instead, the present is deferred for a year, but is still divided in the ratio of the ages of the recipients, how much would each receive then?

4 A job is advertised as paying an hourly rate of £7.50 for a 40-hour week.
a) How much would be paid for working a 40-hour week?
b) Overtime is paid at a rate of time and a half. How much extra would be paid for six hours overtime?
c) If one week a man earned £401.25, how many hours overtime did he work?

5 The price of an item has been reduced in a sale by 20%. If it now costs £70.00, find its original price.

6 In a college, 80 people were asked what grade they expected to get in Maths. Sadly, 22 of them said that they would be lucky not to get a 'U'. Express this number as a percentage of the whole group asked.

7 A packet contains 24 biscuits. Half of the biscuits are put aside, and the remainder are shared by Amy, Ben and Chris in the ratio 3 : 4 : 5.
a) What fraction of the original packet does Ben receive?
b) Chris eats two biscuits. What fraction of his share does he still have?
c) Amy eats one of her biscuits and does not like it, so divides her remaining biscuits equally between Ben and Chris. What fraction of the original packet has Ben received altogether?
d) What fraction of the packet of biscuits did Amy eat?

8 The sides of two pictures are in the ratio 5 : 3.
a) If the larger is 35 cm wide, how wide is the smaller?
b) If the smaller is 10.5 cm long, find the length of the larger.

9 A map is drawn to a scale of 1 : 5000.
a) How long in reality is a road which measures 6 cm on the map?
b) The length of a lake is 200 m. How long should it be on the map?

10 Express the ratio 48 : 80 in its simplest form.

11 In decorating a room, 4 tins of blue paint were used and 8 tins of white. Express this in its simplest form as a ratio:
a) blue to white
b) white to blue.

12 A 192 bus leaves a bus garage every three minutes, a 157 bus leaves every six minutes, a 93 bus leaves every five minutes and a 127 bus every eight minutes. If they all leave the garage at 8.00 a.m., when is the next time that all four buses will leave the garage at the same time?

Answers – 1.9

1 a) In a packet of 10
b) 2 packets of 10
c) 2 packets of 50 and 1 packet of 10

2 £323.00

3 a) Anne gets £600, Jack gets £800, Alun gets £400
b) Anne gets £600, Jack gets £750, Alun gets £450

4 a) £300 **b)** £67.50 **c)** 9 hours

5 £87.50

6 27.5% or 28 %

7 a) $\frac{4}{24} = \frac{1}{6}$ **b)** $\frac{3}{5}$ **c)** $\frac{5}{24}$ **d)** $\frac{1}{24}$

8 a) 21 cm **b)** 17.5 cm

9 a) $5000 \times 6 = 30\,000$ cm = 300 m
b) 4 cm

10 3 : 5

11 a) blue to white = 1 : 2
b) white to blue = 2 : 1

12 The LCM of 3, 6, 5 and 8 = 120. 120 minutes = 2 hours, so the answer is 10.00 a.m.

REVIEW

How much have you learnt?
Tick off each topic in the list when you are confident that you can cope with it.

- ☐ **Answer questions on direct proportion and inverse proportion.**
- ☐ **Find a given percentage of a number.**
- ☐ **Find one number as a percentage of another.**
- ☐ **Increase or decrease a price or amount by a given percentage.**
- ☐ **Find a percentage profit or loss.**
- ☐ **Calculate the percentage discount on a price.**
- ☐ **Calculate the VAT-inclusive price of an article, given the pre-VAT price.**
- ☐ **Calculate the pre-VAT price, given the VAT-inclusive price.**
- ☐ **Divide a given number or amount in a given ratio.**
- ☐ **Calculate individual shares of a number or amount divided in a given ratio.**
- ☐ **State ratios in their lowest terms.**
- ☐ **State ratios in the form 1 : n or n : 1.**
- ☐ **Work out the lengths involved in scale drawing.**

PREVIEW

By the end of this chapter you will be able to:

- **write a number as a product of its prime factors**
- **find the highest common factor (HCF) and lowest common multiple (LCM) of two numbers**
- **add, subtract, multiply or divide fractions**
- **round a decimal fraction to a given number of decimal places or significant figures**
- **round to the nearest 0.5, 1, 10, 50, 100, etc.**
- **state the limits of rounded numbers**
- **make estimates of calculations**
- **compare decimals, fractions and percentages**
- **apply the rules of powers or indices**
- **express a number in standard form**
- **know the order of operations and use your calculator efficiently**
- **express time as a proper decimal**
- **answer questions on rates, such as speed**
- **use formulae to calculate volumes.**

How much do you know already?

Exercise 2.1

1 Write 23.897 correct to two decimal places (2 d.p.).

2 Write 5468 correct to two significant figures (2 sig. figs.).

3 Change $\frac{2}{5}$ to **a)** a decimal **b)** a percentage.

4 Write the following numbers in standard form.
a) 5 240 000 000 **b)** 0.000 005 24

5 Evaluate and write the answer in standard form.
$(3.2 \times 10^9) \times (2.1 \times 10^{12})$

6 Use your calculator to work out $\frac{16.2 + \sqrt{16.3}}{2.8 + 7.1}$.

a) Write down all the figures on your calculator display.
b) Give your answer correct to 3 d.p.
c) Give your answer correct to 3 sig. figs.
d) Without using a calculator, give a rough estimate of the answer. Show how you reached your answer.

7 Evaluate and write the answer in standard form to 3 significant figures.
$(1.4 \times 10^{15}) \div (6.8 \times 10^8)$

8 Write the following numbers in order of size starting with the smallest.
1.3×10^{12}, 6.2×10^8, 1.7×10^{11}, 8.6×10^9, 7.3×10^8

9 The length of a piece of string is measured to the nearest cm. If the length is given as 12 cm, give its longest and shortest possible measurements.

10 An audience is estimated at 700 to the nearest 100. Give the smallest and largest size it could be.

11 Give your answers to the following as a power of 5 where possible.
a) $5^5 \times 5^2$ **b)** $5^5 + 5^2$ **c)** $5^5 \div 5^2$

12 **a)** A car travels at 96 km/h. How far does it go in 3 hours 40 minutes?
b) How long would it take the car travelling at this speed to travel 120 km? Give your answer in hours and minutes.

13 Express 840 as a product of its prime factors.

14 $648 = 2^x \times 3^y \times 5^z$ Find x, y and z.

15 Work out $6^4 \div 6^4$ giving your answer
a) as a power of 6
b) as an integer (i.e. whole number).

16 Find the highest common factor (HCF) and lowest common multiple (LCM) of 36 and 48.

17 What is the reciprocal of $2\frac{1}{2}$?

Answers – 2.1

1 23.90

2 5500

3 **a)** 0.4 **b)** 40%

4 **a)** 5.24×10^9 **b)** 5.24×10^{-6}

5 6.72×10^{21}

6 **a)** 2.044 174 328 **b)** 2.044 **c)** 2.04
d) $\frac{16 + 4}{3 + 7} = \frac{20}{10} = 2$

7 2.06×10^6

8 6.2×10^8, 7.3×10^8, 8.6×10^9, 1.7×10^{11}, 1.3×10^{12}

9 12.5 cm, 11.5 cm

10 650, 750

11 **a)** 5^7
b) You cannot simplify this as a power of 5.
c) 5^3

12 **a)** 352 km **b)** 1 hour 15 minutes

13 $2^3 \times 3 \times 5 \times 7$

14 $x = 3, y = 4, z = 0$

15 **a)** 6^0 **b)** 1

16 HCF = 12, LCM = 144

17 $2\frac{1}{2} = \frac{5}{2}$. The reciprocal is $\frac{2}{5}$ or 0.4.

How did you get on?

All questions right?

Well done! Look through the rest of the chapter because we have some new methods which might appeal to you.

Not quite full marks?

This chapter is not very long, and you shouldn't find it too difficult.

Here are some things you need to remember:

- **Integers** are whole numbers. −2, 0, 2, 3, 5 are integers.
- **Reciprocals** are numbers 'turned upside down'. The reciprocal of 3 is $\frac{1}{3}$ (on a calculator the reciprocal key is marked with 1/x or x^{-1}).
- **Factors** are numbers which divide into other numbers without leaving a remainder. 2 is a factor of 10, and 9 is a factor of 27.

Prime numbers

Prime numbers are whole numbers that have only two factors. The only numbers that divide into a prime number are the number itself and 1.

The first six prime numbers are:

2, 3, 5, 7, 11, 13

Note: 1 is not a prime number. It does not have two factors.

The product of primes

This is sometimes called the product of prime factors.

When two numbers are multiplied together, the answer is called the **product**. The two numbers are called **factors**. Factors that are prime numbers are called **prime factors**. Splitting a number into all its prime factors is sometimes referred to as writing the number as the **product of its prime factors**.

Example 2.1

Write 360 as a product of its prime factors.

This question may also be written in the form '$360 = 2^a \times 3^b \times 5^c$. Find a, b and c.'

Solution

Write down any two factors of 360.

If you have a prime number, ring it.

Split each non-prime number in turn, until all lines end in rings.

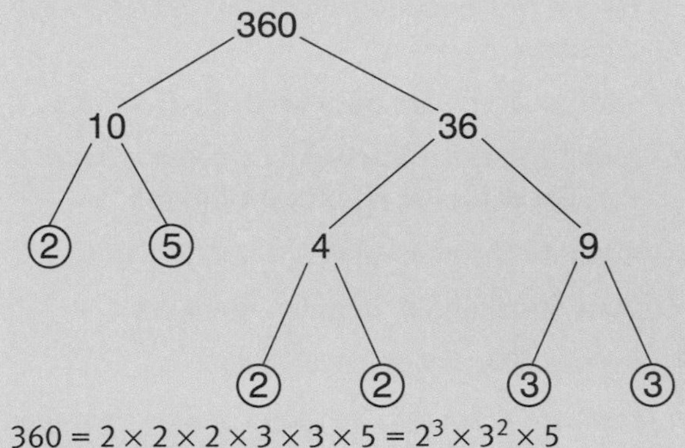

$360 = 2 \times 2 \times 2 \times 3 \times 3 \times 5 = 2^3 \times 3^2 \times 5$

(The answer to the question in the alternative form $2^a \times 3^b \times 5^c$ would be $a = 3$, $b = 2$ and $c = 1$, since $5 = 5^1$.)

***Remember:** Any number written to the power of nought (or zero) is 1.*

e.g. $4^0 = 19^0 = 359^0 = 1$

Highest common factor (HCF)

This is the largest number that divides exactly into two or more numbers. The highest common factor of 12 and 20 is 4. The highest common factor of 50 and 100 is 50.

Example 2.2

Find the highest common factor of 24 and 40.

Solution

Step 1

Split the numbers into prime factors and draw loops round the common factors.

$24 = 2 \times 2 \times 2 \times 3$
$40 = 2 \times 2 \times 2 \times 5$

Step 2

Write down one of each pair of common factors – just once.

$2 \times 2 \times 2 = 8$, so 8 is the highest common factor.

Lowest common multiple (LCM)

This is the smallest number into which two or more numbers will divide exactly.

Example 2.3

Find the lowest common multiple of 10 and 45.

Solution

Step 1
Split each number into prime factors.

$10 = 2 \times 5$
$45 = 3 \times 3 \times 5$

Step 2
Join up any common factors.

$10 = 2 \times 5$
$45 = 3 \times 3 \times 5$

Step 3
Write each common factor **once** and then list any other numbers without partners. Multiply them all together.

$2 \times 3 \times 3 \times 5 = 90$

The LCM of 10 and 45 is 90.

Example 2.4

Find the lowest common multiple of 36 and 120.

Solution

$36 = 2 \times 2 \times 3 \times 3$
$120 = 2 \times 2 \times 2 \times 3 \times 5$

$2 \times 2 \times 2 \times 3 \times 3 \times 5 = 360$

The lowest common multiple of 36 and 120 is 360.

Example 2.5

The trapeze artist Daniella wears her pink dress every fourth day. Her colleague Suzy, wears her identical pink dress once every six days. If they both wear these outfits on 1 May, on what date will they next both be wearing these dresses?

Solution

Find the lowest common multiple of 4 and 6.

$4 = 2 \times 2$
$6 = 2 \times 3$

$\text{LCM} = 2 \times 2 \times 3 = 12$

The will be wearing identical pink dresses in 12 days' time, on 13 May.

Exercise 2.2

1. Express 480 as a product of prime factors.
2. Which of the following are prime numbers?
   2, 3, 10, 27, 29, 65
3. Find the highest common factor of 60 and 90.
4. Find the lowest common multiple of 16 and 40.
5. A bus leaves a depot every 8 minutes and a train leaves the adjacent station every 30 minutes. If a train and a bus both leave at 9.00 a.m., when is the next time that a bus and train both leave their respective depot or station at the same time?

Answers – 2.2

1 $2^5 \times 3 \times 5$
2 2, 3, 29
3 30
4 80
5 $8 = 2 \times 2 \times 2$
$30 = 2 \times 3 \times 5$
$\text{LCM} = 2 \times 2 \times 2 \times 3 \times 5$
9.00 a.m + 120 minutes = 11.00 a.m.

Fractions

Questions on fractions are very common, particularly on non-calculator papers. **You may also need to add and multiply fractions in probability questions.**

The top number of a fraction is called the $\frac{\text{numerator}}{\text{denominator}}$
The bottom number of a fraction is called the

Improper fractions

These are fractions where the numerator is bigger than the denominator. In some books they are called 'top heavy' fractions.

$\frac{35}{8}$ $\frac{13}{6}$

Mixed numbers

Numbers such as $4\frac{3}{8}$ and $2\frac{1}{6}$ are made up of a whole number and a fraction.

Improper fractions can be changed to mixed numbers.

$\frac{35}{8} = 35 \div 8 = 4 \text{ r } 3 = 4\frac{3}{8}$ $\quad 4\frac{3}{8} = \frac{4 \times 8 + 3}{8} = \frac{35}{8}$

$\frac{13}{6} = 2 \text{ r } 1 = 2\frac{1}{6}$ $\quad 2\frac{1}{6} = \frac{2 \times 6 + 1}{6} = \frac{13}{6}$

Equivalent fractions

Two or more fractions that have the same value are **equivalent**.

$\frac{1}{2} = \frac{2}{4} = \frac{10}{20}$ and so on.

Cancelling means finding the simplest form of the fraction to write it in the lowest terms.

Most questions that involve fractions will ask for the answer in its simplest form, or lowest terms. This means that you need to divide the numerator and the denominator by all their common factors until their only remaining common factor is 1.

$\frac{6}{18} = \frac{1}{3} \quad \frac{8}{20} = \frac{2}{5}$

Each time you cancel, you must divide the numerator and the denominator by the same factor.

You will often need to cancel fractions when you are solving probability questions.

Common denominator

When you add or subtract fractions, you must start by making sure that they each have the same denominator. This is their common denominator. The most efficient way is to find the lowest common multiple of the denominators. (If you do not spot it quickly, you can always find a common denominator by multiplying together all the individual denominators, but you may be storing up trouble for yourself – you may have to manipulate very large numbers.)

Example 2.6

Find common denominators for these pairs of fractions.

a) $\frac{5}{6}$ and $\frac{1}{3}$

b) $\frac{5}{6}$ and $\frac{1}{4}$

c) $\frac{2}{5}$ and $\frac{1}{3}$

Solution

a) The lowest common multiple of 3 and 6 is 6. Leave $\frac{5}{6}$ as it is, change $\frac{1}{3}$ to $\frac{2}{6}$.

b) The LCM of 6 and 4 is 12. Another possible denominator is 24, but using $\frac{10}{12}$ and $\frac{3}{12}$ will probably result in an easier calculation than using $\frac{20}{24}$ and $\frac{6}{24}$.

c) The LCM of 5 and 3 is 15, so the fractions should be changed to fifteenths, i.e. $\frac{6}{15}$ and $\frac{5}{15}$.

To recap ...

Adding and subtracting fractions

- All fractions must have a common denominator.
- Add or subtract the whole numbers and the fractions where possible. (Change whole numbers to fractions if necessary when subtracting.)

  Change improper fractions to mixed numbers and cancel if necessary.

  $5\frac{3}{16} + 2\frac{7}{8} = 7\frac{3}{16} + \frac{14}{16} = 7\frac{17}{16} = 8\frac{1}{16}$

  $7\frac{1}{5} - 2\frac{3}{4} = 5\frac{1}{5} - \frac{3}{4} = 5\frac{4}{20} - \frac{15}{20} = 4\frac{24}{20} - \frac{15}{20} = 4\frac{9}{20}$

Multiplying and dividing fractions

- Change any mixed numbers to improper fractions.
- If dividing, turn the second fraction upside down and change the ÷ to a ×.
- Cancel if possible, i.e. divide top and bottom by the same number, each time.
- Multiply numerators and multiply denominators.
- Change back to mixed numbers and cancel if possible.

  $2\frac{1}{4} \times 2\frac{2}{5} = \frac{9}{4} \times \frac{12}{5} = \frac{9}{1} \times \frac{3}{5} = \frac{27}{5} = 5\frac{2}{5}$

  $6\frac{1}{4} \div 1\frac{2}{3} = \frac{25}{4} \div \frac{5}{3} = \frac{25}{4} \times \frac{3}{5} = \frac{5}{4} \times \frac{3}{1} = \frac{15}{4} = 3\frac{3}{4}$

Exercise 2.3

1. $2\frac{3}{4} + 2\frac{3}{5}$
2. $7\frac{5}{12} - 4\frac{5}{6}$
3. $4\frac{2}{3} \times 2\frac{2}{5}$
4. $4\frac{2}{3} \div 5\frac{5}{6}$

Answers – 2.3

1. $5\frac{7}{20}$
2. $2\frac{7}{12}$
3. $11\frac{1}{5}$
4. $\frac{4}{5}$

Reciprocals

A reciprocal is a number turned 'upside down'.

Example 2.7

Write the reciprocal of **a)** 4 **b)** $1\frac{1}{2}$

Solution

a) The reciprocal of 4 is $\frac{1}{4}$.

b) Change $1\frac{1}{2}$ to an improper fraction.

$1\frac{1}{2} = \frac{3}{2}$

The reciprocal of $\frac{3}{2}$ is $\frac{2}{3}$.

Using a calculator

Most calculators have a special button for reciprocals. You will usually find it marked x^{-1} or $^1/_x$.

As procedures vary from calculator to calculator, ask your teacher to show you how to use it, or try to unscramble the instructions that came with your calculator.

Exercise 2.4

Join up these numbers and their reciprocals.

2	100
$\frac{1}{3}$	$\frac{1}{5}$
5	$\frac{1}{10}$
0.01	$\frac{1}{2}$
10	3

(Hint: You may find it easier to change the decimals to fractions, e.g. $0.01 = \frac{1}{100}$)

Answers – 2.4

2 and $\frac{1}{2}$ or 0.5, $\frac{1}{3}$ and 3, 5 and $\frac{1}{5}$ or 0.2,
0.01 and 100, 10 and $\frac{1}{10}$ or 0.1

Approximation

Decimal places

The number of decimal places is the number of digits (figures) that there are in a number, **to the right of the decimal point**.

Example 2.8

Write 4.782 correct to 1 d.p.

Solution

The number currently has 3 decimal places. Write the number, and put a ring round the digit which is **one figure to the right** of the required decimal place e.g. 4.7⑧2.

Now decide whether to round up or down by looking at the number that you have ringed. If its value is less than 5, you usually round *down*, but if it is 5 or more, you usually round *up*.

4.782 = 4.8 correct to 1 d.p.

Example 2.9

Write 7.304 correct to 2 d.p.

Solution

Write the number and put a ring round the digit in the **third** decimal place.

7.30④ as it is 4, round down.

7.304 = 7.30 correct to 2 d.p.

As the question asks for 2 d.p. you must include the zero.

If the question asks you to give an amount of money to the nearest penny, you are really rounding to two decimal places. If you have to round to the nearest 0.1 cm, you need one decimal place.

Significant figures

The first significant figure is the first digit greater than zero starting from the left.

Example 2.10

Write 28.3762 correct to 3 sig. figs.

Solution

Ring the figure **to the right** of the required number of significant figures. If its value is 5 or more, round up; if it is 4 or less round down.

28.3⑦62 = 28.4 to 3 sig. figs.

It may help you to notice that large numbers, bigger than 9999, are usually written with a space or a comma before every third number, starting from the right.

Example 2.11

Write 7 143 680 correct to 2 sig. figs.

Solution

7 1④3 680

The original number is approximately 7 million, so you must be careful to indicate this in your answer by including appropriate zeros. Try writing the original number with a decimal point at the end, and write the approximation directly below.

7 143 680.

7 100 000.

7 143 680 to 2 sig. figs. is 7 100 000.

Remember the noughts. Don't write your answer as 71.

Example 2.12

Write 0.000 759 6 correct to:

a) 1 sig. fig. **b)** 2 sig. figs. **c)** 3 sig. figs.

Solution

Note that 7 is the first significant figure as it is the first non-zero digit starting from the left.

a) 0.000 759 6 = 0.0008 to 1 sig. fig.
b) 0.000 759 6 = 0.00076 to 2 sig. figs.
c) 0.000 759 6 = 0.000760 to 3 sig. figs.

Remember to include the final zero as it is the third significant figure.

Rounding

Although these rules apply when you are using decimal places or significant figures, you must always read the question carefully. If, for instance, your answer suggests that 5.2 buses are required to carry a certain number of people, you will probably need to round up to 6 to avoid stranded passengers!

If your final answer requires, say, two decimal places, either use your calculator's memory or else round to four decimal places until you reach the final answer, to avoid inaccuracies.

Approximation to the nearest unit

Some questions state that a number has been rounded to the nearest hundred, ten, 0.1, ... and then ask you to give the highest and lowest possible values for the number. The easiest way is to take the hundred, ten, ... and halve it. Then, starting with your original number, add this 'half' to it and subtract this 'half' from it.

Example 2.13

The size of an audience was recorded as 650 to the nearest 50. What were the smallest and largest numbers of people that could have been there?

Solution

Find half of 50. $50 \div 2 = 25$

Smallest value $= 650 - 25$
$= 625$ Take away half of 50.

Largest value $= 650 + 25$
$= 675$ Add on half of 50.

The number of people in the audience must have been between 625 and 675.

Example 2.14

A length of 78.6 cm is stated as being correct to the nearest mm. What are the smallest and largest values it could take?

Solution

Think of 1 mm as 0.1 cm.

$0.1 \div 2 = 0.05$

Smallest value $= 78.6 - 0.05$
$= 78.55$

Largest value $= 78.6 + 0.05$
$= 78.65$

The value must be between 78.55 cm and 78.65 cm.

Exercise 2.5

1 The length of a rope is given as 30 m to the nearest metre. What is the shortest length that it could be?

2 A school is described as having 620 pupils to the nearest ten pupils. What is the smallest number of pupils it could have?

3 A club with 130 members is applying for a grant. It can state its membership:
a) exactly
b) to the nearest hundred
c) to the nearest fifty.

Which option would you choose?

Answers – 2.5

1 29.5m
2 615 pupils
3 a) 130 **b)** 100 **c)** 150
Option **c)** is likely to produce the largest grant.

Multiplying and dividing decimals

Be very careful when multiplying decimals.

Example 2.15

0.3×0.2

Solution

If you think that the right answer is 0.6, try thinking of 0.3 and 0.2 as fractions.

$0.3 \times 0.2 = \frac{3}{10} \times \frac{2}{10} = \frac{6}{100} = 0.06$

$0.3 \times 0.2 = 0.06$

Example 2.16

1.3×1.4

Solution

$\frac{13}{10} \times \frac{14}{10} = \frac{182}{100} = 1.82$

Confused about the point? Here is an easy way.

Work out the multiplication as if there were no decimal points.

$13 \times 14 = 182$

Count the digits after the points in both the numbers in the question. The decimal point in the answer should be followed by the same number of digits as there are in the two numbers together. Count back, from the right, along the digits and insert a decimal point. In Example 2.16 there are two digits after the points altogether in the question, so insert the decimal point in the answer accordingly:

1.82

Exercise 2.6

Answer these questions without using a calculator.

1 0.45×0.2
2 1.3×0.4
3 0.03×0.2
4 0.001×0.01
5 12.6×0.04

Answers – 2.6

1 0.09
2 0.52
3 0.006
4 0.0001
5 0.504

You might also slip up when dividing decimals.

If you divide by a decimal, it isn't always obvious where to put the decimal point in the answer. It is easier to change the numbers so that the divisor (number by which you are dividing) is a whole number. This won't affect the answer as long as you multiply both the original numbers by the same amount.

e.g. $6 \div 3 = 2$, $60 \div 30 = 2$ (Hands up all those who thought it was 20!) and $600 \div 300 = 2$.

Example 2.17

$360 \div 0.05$

Solution

You must change the 0.05 to a whole number. The easiest way to do this is to multiply it by 100, so that 0.05 becomes 5.

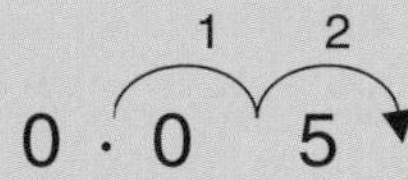

Since you have multiplied 0.05 by 100, you must multiply 360 by the same number.

$360 \div 0.05 = 36\,000 \div 5 = 7200$

$360 \div 0.05 = 7200$

If it surprises you that the answer is bigger than the original number, imagine a cake. You start with **one** cake, but if you cut it in half, you get **two** pieces. If 100 people were to share the cake equally, they would each have 0.01 of the cake, and you would have **one hundred** pieces. Each piece would be smaller than the original cake, but you would have more pieces. The smaller the size of each piece, the more pieces you will have.

Exercise 2.7

1 0.4×0.2
2 $5.3 \div 0.002$
3 $0.06 \div 0.5$

Answers – 2.7

1 0.08
2 2650
3 0.12

Comparing and ordering decimal numbers

The easiest way of doing this is to put extra zeros at the end of each decimal until they all have the same number of decimal digits as the longest number. Remember, putting extra zeros at the end of the decimal (after the decimal point) does not change the value of the number.

So to compare 4, 4.4 and 4.04, put in extra zeros until they are all the same length as the longest number (4.04):

4.00   4.40   4.04

Now you can compare in terms of hundredths.

The order, from smallest to largest, is:

4.00   4.04   4.40

Now take off the extra zeros, to give the answer in terms of the original numbers:

4   4.04   4.4

Listing the numbers vertically may be easier.

Example 2.18

Arrange the following numbers in order, from smallest to largest:

5.5   5.05   5.555   5.055   5   5.55

Solution

Put extra zeros at the end of each number until they all have the same number of decimal digits as the longest number:

5.500   5.050   5.555   5.055   5.000   5.550

Now it is easy to arrange the numbers as you can read them all as thousandths.

The correct order is

5.000   5.050   5.055   5.500   5.550   5.555

Give your answer in terms of the original numbers.

5   5.05   5.055   5.5   5.55   5.555

Fractions, decimals and percentages

Changing decimals to fractions

This is easy if you remember that the columns after the decimal point are tenths, hundredths, thousandths, and so on.

Think of money.

£0.2 is written £0.20 and is the same as two ten-pence pieces.

£0.25 is the same as twenty-five single pence or twenty-five hundredths of a pound.

Example 2.19

Change 0.625 to a fraction, giving your answer in its lowest terms.

Solution

Numerator: Write the decimal, starting with the first non-zero digit on the left.

Denominator: Write a 1 instead of the decimal point, and a 0 in place of all the original digits.

$0.625 = \frac{625}{1000}$

Then cancel down to get $\frac{5}{8}$.

Comparing fractions, decimals and percentages

Example 2.20

Write the following in order of size, starting with the smallest.

0.91, 0.905, $\frac{10}{11}$, 90%

Solution

The easiest way is to turn them all into decimals.

$\frac{10}{11} = 10 \div 11 = 0.909\,09...$

$90\% = 90 \div 100 = 0.9$

The order is 90%, 0.905, $\frac{10}{11}$, 0.91.

Indices

Indices are used as a mathematical shorthand. So instead of writing $2 \times 2 \times 2$ we can write more simply 2^3. In the number 2^3, the 3 is called the **power** or **index** (the plural of index is **indices**), while the 2 is called the **base number**.

Also, remember that 2^3 means $2 \times 2 \times 2$, **not** 2×3.

Rules of indices

1 *You can only simplify indices when the base number is the same.*

2 *When dividing or multiplying powers of the same number remember TIP and DIM.*

TIP: Times ⇒ Indices Plus
DIM: Divide ⇒ Indices Minus

When multiplying or dividing indices of the same base number, to multiply simply add the indices, and to divide just subtract the indices.

Example 2.21

Simplify the following.

a) $3^2 \times 3^5$ **c)** $3^2 + 3^5$
b) $3^7 \div 3^2$ **d)** $4^3 - 4^2$

Solution

a) $3^2 \times 3^5 = 3^7$
b) $3^7 \div 3^2 = 3^5$
c) $3^2 + 3^5$ cannot be simplified as a power of 3.
d) $4^3 - 4^2$ cannot be simplified as a power of 4.

Negative indices

Example 2.22

Work out $2^3 \div 2^6$.

Express your answer

a) as a power of 2 **b)** as a fraction.

Solution

$3 - 6 = -3$, so $2^3 \div 2^6 = 2^{-3}$

Change the sign of the power and make it 'one over', i.e. write its reciprocal.

$2^{-3} = \frac{1}{2^3} = \frac{1}{8}$.

Standard form or standard index form

This is a shorthand method of writing very large or very small numbers. It involves rewriting the number as a number between 1 and 10, multiplied by a power of 10.

Remember:

$10^1 = 10$
$10^2 = 100$
$10^3 = 1000$
$10^8 = 100\,000\,000$
and so on.

Be careful! $10^0 = 1$

Example 2.23

Write 34 200 in standard form.

Solution

Rewrite your original number, inserting a decimal point after the first non-zero digit.

3.4200

Note that the decimal point was originally at the right-hand end of the number.

34200.

So to change 3.4200 into 34200, how many places must the point move?

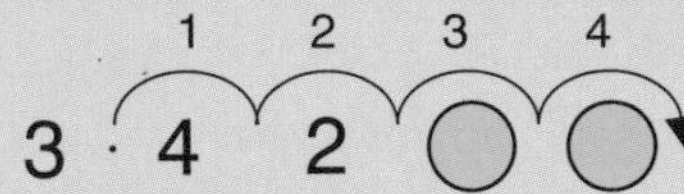

The answer is 4.

$34\,200 = 3.42 \times 10^4$

When rewriting a number in standard form, the simplest way is:

1 Start with a number between 1 and 10 based on the number you are given.

2 Count the number of decimal places you need to return the decimal point to its starting position.

3 Write this as a power of 10.

Example 2.24

Write 0.000 067 in standard form.

Solution

Rewriting the original number and inserting the required decimal point gives:

000 006.7

The decimal point must be moved back five places to get to its starting position. Just remember: negative direction, negative power.

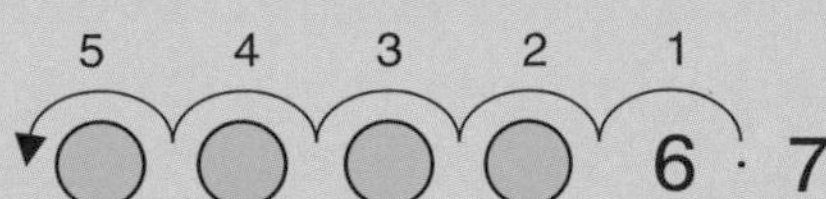

$0.000\,067 = 6.7 \times 10^{-5}$

If your original number is smaller than one, write the power of 10 with a negative sign. Remember that if you need to travel back to the start in a negative direction, you need a negative sign.

As a rule, if you need to count back (i.e. to the left) the index will be negative. If you count forwards (i.e. to the right) the index will be positive.

Most calculators use EXP for standard form, but some have a button marked EE.
Some calculators work like this:

3.42×10^4 3 · 4 2 EXP 4 =

6.7×10^{-5} 6 · 7 EXP (-) 5 =

Check on your calculator if you are in any doubt.

If you can say, 'times 10 to the ...,' replace it with EXP or EE. **Do not** press

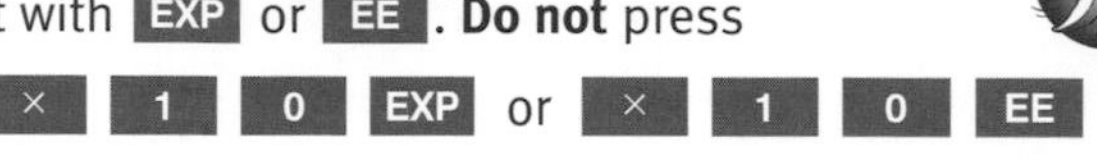

If your calculator has a different procedure from this, make sure you can follow it.

Exercise 2.8

1 Evaluate $(3.4 \times 10^{22}) \div (1.6 \times 10^9)$. Give your answer in standard form, correct to three significant figures.

2 A book was measured to the nearest centimetre. Its length was given as 30 cm. What was its longest possible length?

3 The speed of light is approximately 2.998×10^8 metres per second. How many metres does it travel in half a minute?

4 **a)** The planet Mercury is approximately 5.79×10^{10} metres from the sun and Pluto is approximately 5.90×10^{12} metres from the sun. Write the ratio of the distance from the sun of Mercury to Pluto in the form $n : 1$ in standard form, giving your answer correct to three significant figures.

b) Correct to four significant figures, the mass of the Earth is 5.798×10^{24} kg and that of Jupiter is 1.899×10^{27} kg. Write the ratio of the mass of the Earth to that of Jupiter in the form $1 : n$ in standard form, giving your answer correct to three significant figures.

Answers – 2.8

1 2.13×10^{13}

2 30.5 cm

3 8.994×10^9

4 **a)** $9.81 \times 10^{-3} : 1$ **b)** $1 : 3.28 \times 10^2$

Standard form without a calculator

Adding and subtracting numbers in standard form

You need to know how to add and subtract numbers written in standard form without using a calculator.

The simplest method is to convert the numbers into regular form, add or subtract them, then convert the answer into standard form.

Example 2.25

Evaluate $2.2 \times 10^7 + 1.6 \times 10^6$. Write your answer in standard form.

Solution

$$\begin{aligned} 2.2 \times 10^7 + 1.6 \times 10^6 &= 22\,000\,000 + 1\,600\,000 \\ &= 23\,600\,000 \\ &= 2.36 \times 10^7 \end{aligned}$$

Multiplying numbers written in standard form

Remember that when you are multiplying numbers, you can take them in any order. This means that when you multiply two numbers in standard form you can multiply the first parts of the numbers, then the second parts of the numbers. Then you must make sure your final answer is in standard form.

Example 2.26

Evaluate $(3.1 \times 10^9) \times (4.0 \times 10^7)$ without using a calculator. Write your answer in standard form.

Solution

Remove the brackets and write the first parts of the two numbers next to each other, then the second parts of the numbers:
$3.1 \times 4.0 \times 10^9 \times 10^7 = 12.4 \times 10^{16}$

This must now be written in standard form.
$1.24 \times 10 \times 10^{16} = 1.24 \times 10^{17}$

Dividing numbers written in standard form

Divide the first parts of the numbers, then the second parts of the numbers, then make sure that your final answer is in standard form.

Example 2.27

Evaluate $\dfrac{6.2 \times 10^8}{2.0 \times 10^3}$

Write your answer in standard form.

Solution

$(6.2 \times 10^8) \div (2.0 \times 10^3) = (6.2 \div 2.0) \times (10^8 \div 10^3)$
$= 3.1 \times 10^5$

Exercise 2.9

Evaluate the following without using a calculator, giving your answers in standard form.

1. $5.4 \times 10^6 + 2.3 \times 10^5$
2. $3.8 \times 10^8 + 8.6 \times 10^7$
3. $6.7 \times 10^{10} - 8.6 \times 10^9$
4. $1.8 \times 10^{-3} - 7.9 \times 10^{-4}$
5. $1.6 \times 10^{-8} + 9.3 \times 10^{-9}$
6. $(4.2 \times 10^3) \times (1.5 \times 10^4)$
7. $(7.4 \times 10^{-3}) \times (6.5 \times 10^{-5})$
8. $\dfrac{3.6 \times 10^{11}}{1.2 \times 10^5}$
9. $\dfrac{7.2 \times 10^{-5}}{2.4 \times 10^4}$

Answers – 2.9

1 5.63×10^6 **2** 4.66×10^8
3 5.84×10^{10} **4** 1.01×10^{-3}
5 2.53×10^{-8} **6** 6.3×10^7
7 4.81×10^{-7} **8** 3×10^6
9 3×10^{-9}

TAKE A BREAK

This is a good point to take a short break. The next section should be easy, so you shouldn't feel too bad about starting again.

BODMAS or BIDMAS

You may have learned about BODMAS or BIDMAS. It is a useful word to help you remember the order in which every scientific calculator will work.

Brackets	**B**rackets
Of as in 3 to the power **of** 4 i.e. $3^4 = 81$	**I**ndices
Divide	**D**ivide
Multiply	**M**ultiply
Add	**A**dd
Subtract	**S**ubtract

Using your calculator

Examiners often set questions like this.

Evaluate $\dfrac{\sqrt{31.92}}{51.7 - 7.3^2}$

It is important to remember that your calculator will find the square or square root, then multiply or divide, then add or subtract.

Using brackets and sometimes [=], you can force it to change this order.

Example 2.28

Evaluate $\dfrac{18 + 2}{5}$

Solution

You can see that the answer is $20 \div 5 = 4$ but ...

what would your calculator do? If you keyed in $18 + 2 \div 5$ your calculator would show 18.4, as it would calculate $2 \div 5$ before adding it to 18.

You can avoid this by keying in

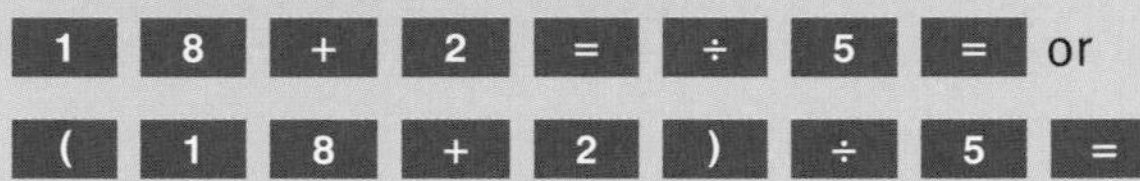

Either way you get the answer 4, because the 18 and the 2 are added before their sum is divided by 5.

Example 2.29

Evaluate $\dfrac{60}{6 - 1}$

Solution

Key in

to get the answer 12.

Take care with questions involving square roots, such as $\dfrac{30}{12 - \sqrt{4}}$ for which the answer is 3.

On some calculators, you need to press [√] [4], whereas on others you need to reverse this and press [4] [√]. Experiment with your calculator until you get the right answer.

Example 2.30

Evaluate $\dfrac{7.1 + 1.65}{2.4 \times 4.6}$

Give your answer correct to 3 significant figures.

Solution

BODMAS/BIDMAS tells us that brackets are always done first, so you can insert brackets to make the calculation clearer.

$$\frac{(7.1 + 1.65)}{(2.4 \times 4.6)}$$

Then, using a calculator, work out
$(7.1 + 1.65) \div (2.4 \times 4.6)$

You should get the answer 0.793 (to 3 s.f.)

Remember: *With any calculation, it is a good idea to make an estimate first, so you can check that your answer is sensible.*

Exercise 2.10

Work out the following. Give each answer correct to **a)** 2 decimal places **b)** 2 significant figures.

1 $\dfrac{5.2 \times 6.3}{2.1 \times 0.7}$ **2** $\dfrac{3.6 + 0.2}{8.1 - 0.6}$

3 $\dfrac{2.5^2 + 6.2}{2 \times 1.6}$

Answers – 2.10

1 a) 22.29 **b)** 22
2 a) 0.51 **b)** 0.51
3 a) 3.89 **b)** 3.9

Converting time to a decimal number

A common mistake with hours and minutes is to write 2 hours and 45 minutes as 2.45. **This is wrong!**

Remember there are 60 minutes in an hour.

Think of 45 minutes as $\frac{45}{60}$ of an hour.

So 45 minutes = 45 ÷ 60 = 0.75 of an hour (three-quarters of an hour)

and 2 hours 45 minutes is 2.75 hours.

Or use the fraction button! 2 hours 45 minutes

= [2] [a b/c] [4] [5] [a b/c] [6] [0]

If you press [=], it simplifies the fraction. Then you may need to convert this to a decimal. Most calculators will do this if you press the fraction key [a b/c] again, but on some you need to press the [2nd f] or [shift] key followed by a different button.

Using formulae

To find the value of a letter, cover it or cross through it. If the other letters are:

a) on the same level, multiply them
b) on different levels, divide the top by the bottom.

Distance, speed, time

Distance travelled is found by multiplying the speed by the time. The two quantities multiplied together form the denominator, i.e. the base of the triangle. The other quantitity goes above, as shown.

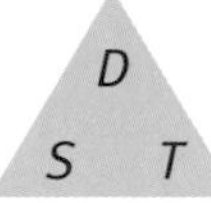

$D = S \times T \qquad S = \dfrac{D}{T} \qquad T = \dfrac{D}{S}$

*Remember **D**owning **St**reet.*

Amount, rate, time

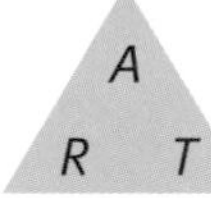

$A = R \times T \qquad R = \dfrac{A}{T} \qquad T = \dfrac{A}{R}$

*Remember **ART**.*

Example 2.31

A car travels at 120 km/h. How far does it travel in 3 hours and 25 minutes?

Solution

Firstly, **do not** write 3 hours 25 minutes as 3.25.

3 hours 25 minutes = 3 + $\frac{25}{60}$ or

You are asked for the distance, D. Look at S and T. Cover or cross out *D*.

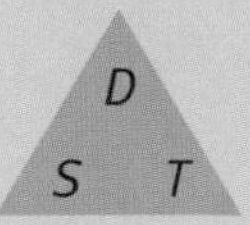

S and *T* are on the same level, so you multiply them.

$D = S \times T$
$= 120 \times 3\frac{25}{60}$
$= 410$ km

Example 2.32

Tariq's tap is leaking at a rate of $25\,\text{cm}^3$ per second. How long does it take to fill a 1 litre bowl? (1 litre = $1000\,\text{cm}^3$)

Solution

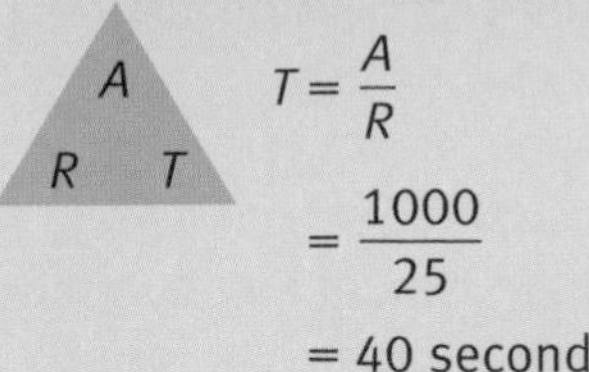

$$T = \frac{A}{R} = \frac{1000}{25} = 40 \text{ seconds}$$

Don't mix units. In this example the rate is in cm^3, so change the litre into cm^3.

Similarly, if the question involves cm and m, change the metres into centimetres.

Example 2.33

A coach travels 210 kilometres in 3 hours and 30 minutes. Find the average speed in kilometres per hour.

Solution

3 hours 30 minutes = 3.5 hours (not 3.3 hours)

$$S = \frac{D}{T} = \frac{210}{3.5} = 60\,\text{km/h}$$

These techniques will probably be useful in Physics, too.

Example 2.34

Find the density of a metal rod that weighs 200 g and has a volume of $16\,\text{cm}^3$.

Solution

First you need the density formula.

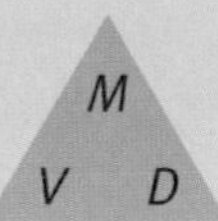

Maths can be **V**ery **D**ifficult if you are **V**ery **D**ense.

Cover up the D and you can see that $\frac{M}{V} = D$

$D = \frac{200}{16} = 12.5\,\text{g/cm}^3$

(12.5 grams per cubic centimetre)

Remember: Include the units in your working and answer or you may lose a mark.

Example 2.35

The volume of a plastic figure is about $84\,\text{cm}^3$. The density of the material used to make the figure is $0.168\,\text{g/cm}^3$. What is its mass?

Solution

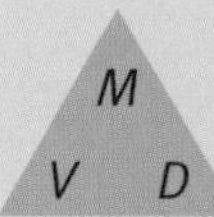

$M = V \times D = 84 \times 0.168 = 14.1\,\text{g}$

Example 2.36

A length of wood weighing 3.6 kg has a density of $1.5\,\text{g/cm}^3$. Calculate its volume.

Solution

The mass is given in kg, but the density has been measured in grams. Change one or the other so that the calculation uses the same units. Here it is probably easier to work in grams.

$$V = \frac{M}{D} = \frac{3600}{1.5} = 2400\,\text{cm}^3$$

Exercise 2.11

1 a) Write 3 hours 24 minutes in decimal form.
b) Write 5.7 hours in hours and minutes.

2 Sally plans to spend 40% of each weekday either at school or studying at home. How many hours a day is this? Give your answer:
a) as a decimal **b)** in hours and minutes.
c) If the school day lasts 6 hours 30 minutes altogether, how many hours per day does she plan to spend studying at home?
d) What percentage of the day is spent studying at home, to the nearest 1%?

3 a) How long does it take a car moving at a speed of 96 km/h to travel 796.8 km?
b) Another car takes 7 hours 15 minutes for the same journey. Find its average speed.

4 Water flows out of a leaking tank at the rate of 5.2 litres per second. If the full tank holds 135 litres, how long will it take for it to empty?

5 **a)** Without a calculator, give a rough estimate for 5389×96. Show your method.
b) Without a calculator, work out the exact answer to 5389×96. Show enough working to show that you have not used a calculator.

6 A car travels 18.6 km on 4.4 litres of petrol.
a) How far does it go on 20 litres?
b) How many litres will it use to go 100 km?

7 Write the following numbers in standard form.
a) 2 380 000 000 000
b) 0.000 000 007 23
c) 14 678.3 (Give the answer correct to 3 s.f.)

8 Jemma took tests in English, Maths and French. In English she scored $\frac{47}{72}$, in Maths $\frac{38}{60}$ and in French 64%.
a) Which was her best result?
b) Which was her worst result?

9 $192 = 2^x \times 3^y \times 5^z$. Find the values of x, y and z.

10 People can pass through a turnstile at the rate of 7 per minute. How many would you expect to pass through in $1\frac{1}{2}$ hours?

11 How long would it take to complete a journey of 90 miles at 40 mph? Give your answer in hours and minutes.

12 15 litres of a liquid has drained out of a container in 40 minutes. Find the average rate of drainage in litres per hour.

13 Without using a calculator work out $(3 \times 10^8) \times (9.7 \times 10^5)$

Answers – 2.11

1 **a)** 3.4 hours **b)** 5 hours 42 minutes
2 **a)** 9.6 hours **b)** 9 hours 36 minutes
c) 3 hours 6 minutes or 3.1 hours **d)** 13%
3 **a)** 8.3 hours = 8 h 18 mins **b)** 110 km/h
4 26 seconds
5 **a)** $5400 \times 100 = 540\,000$ **b)** 517 344
6 **a)** 84.5 km **b)** 23.7 litres
7 **a)** 2.38×10^{12} **b)** 7.23×10^{-9} **c)** 1.47×10^4
8 Convert all the scores to percentages:
$\frac{47}{72} = 65\%$, $\frac{38}{60} = 63\%$.
a) English was her best result,
b) Maths was her worst.
9 $x = 6, y = 1, z = 0$
$192 = 64 \times 3 \times 1$; $64 = 2^6$, $3 = 3^1$, $1 = 5^0$.
(**NB:** Any number to the power of 0 is 1.)
10 Amount (number of people) = Rate × Time
$= 1\frac{1}{2} \times 60 \times 7 = 630$ people
11 Time = Distance ÷ Speed = $90 \div 40$
= 2.25 hours = 2 hours 15 minutes
Remember, 0.25 hours = $\frac{1}{4}$ hour = 15 minutes.
12 Rate = Amount (of liquid) ÷ Time
$= 15 \div \frac{40}{60} = 22\frac{1}{2}$ litres per hour
13 $3 \times 9.7 = 29.1$ $10^8 \times 10^5 = 10^{13}$
$29.1 \times 10^{13} = 2.91 \times 10 \times 10^{13} = 2.91 \times 10^{14}$

REVIEW

How much have you learnt?
Tick off each topic in the list when you are confident that you can cope with it.

- ☐ **Write a number as a product of prime factors.**
- ☐ **Find the highest common factor (HCF) and lowest common multiple (LCM) of two numbers.**
- ☐ **Add, subtract, multiply or divide fractions.**
- ☐ **Round a decimal fraction to a given number of decimal places or significant figures.**
- ☐ **Round to the nearest 0.5, 1, 10, 50, 100, etc.**
- ☐ **State the limits of rounded numbers.**
- ☐ **Make estimates of calculations.**
- ☐ **Compare decimals, fractions and percentages.**
- ☐ **Apply the rules of powers or indices.**
- ☐ **Express a number in standard form.**
- ☐ **Know the order of operations and use your calculator efficiently.**
- ☐ **Express time as a proper decimal.**
- ☐ **Answer questions on rates, such as speed.**
- ☐ **Use formulae to calculate volumes.**

Number review

1 Use your calculator to evaluate these.

a) $\dfrac{5.76 - 1.42}{6.72 + 2.33}$ **b)** $\sqrt{(4.72 - 3.17)^2 + 1.76}$

2 Which of the following numbers is the largest?
$\frac{2}{3}$, $\frac{5}{8}$, $\frac{7}{11}$

3 Two people score points in the ratio of 7 : 2. If the higher score was 42, what was the lower?

4 Convert 6 feet 2 inches into centimetres.
1 cm ≈ 0.394 inches
12 inches = 1 foot

5 Express $\frac{33}{60}$ as a percentage.

6 A group of 248 people is going on holiday by bus. Each bus costs £310 and can accommodate 52 people. Find the approximate total cost. Do not use a calculator and show all working.

7 When going on holiday, a man converts £620 into 1000 euro.

a) If his friend changes £590, how many euro will he receive?

b) If they have a total of 260 euro at the end of the holiday, what would this be worth in pounds?

8 A train travels 288 kilometres in 2 hours 10 minutes. What was its average speed in km/h?

9 Write 0.000 007 02 in standard form.

10 A club of 130 people hires coaches for an event. If each coach can hold 30 people, how many coaches must be hired?

11 The price of a jacket, usually set at £75, is reduced by 15% in a sale. Find the sale price.

12 Find the HCF and LCM of 75 and 250

13 Arrange these numbers in order of size, starting with the smallest. : 7.07, 7.01, 7.071, 7.1, 7.008, 7.7, 7.707

14 A student scored 28 out of 70 in a test. If the pass mark was 45%, did the student pass or fail?

15 Without using a calculator, work out the following fractions.

a) $2\frac{2}{5} + 2\frac{3}{10}$ **b)** $6\frac{3}{8} - 2\frac{3}{4}$

c) $2\frac{4}{5} \times 2\frac{1}{7}$ **d)** $4\frac{1}{4} \div 1\frac{1}{2}$

16 Put these numbers in order of size, starting with the largest.
0.6, 61%, $\frac{4}{7}$, $\frac{2}{3}$

17 Which fraction comes halfway between $\frac{1}{2}$ and $\frac{5}{8}$? (Hint: First find the common denominator.)

18 Without using a calculator, work out which is bigger, and by how much, 0.3×0.2 or $0.3 \div 0.2$. (You can cheat by using a calculator, but you won't be able to on the day of the non-calculator paper.)

19 Write 37.6×10^7 in standard form.

20 The price of a jacket costing £40.00 is reduced by 15%. On the last day of the sale it is reduced by a further 10% of the sale price.

a) What is its new price?

b) Write the total reduction as a percentage of the cost price.

Answers – Number review

1 **a)** 0.48 **b)** 2.04

2 $\frac{2}{3}$

3 12

4 187.8 cm

5 55%

6 $250 \div 50 = 5$ buses are needed;
$5 \times 300 = £1500$

7 **a)** 951.61 euro **b)** £161.20

8 133 km/h

9 7.02×10^{-6}

10 5 (Remember to round up!)

11 £63.75

12 HCF is 25, LCM is 750

13 7.008, 7.01, 7.07, 7.071, 7.1, 7.7, 7.707

14 The student scored 40%, so the student failed.

15 **a)** $4\frac{7}{10}$ **b)** $3\frac{5}{8}$ **c)** 6 **d)** $2\frac{5}{6}$

16 Change each number to a decimal. Only work out the minimum number of decimal places that you need. In this case it will be two. 61% = 0.61, $\frac{4}{7} = 0.57...$, $\frac{2}{3} = 0.66...$.

So the answer is $\frac{2}{3}$, 61%, 0.6, $\frac{4}{7}$
Remember to write the answer in its original form, e.g. 61% and not 0.61.

17 Change the $\frac{1}{2}$ into $\frac{4}{8}$. Then, using equivalent fractions, change each number into sixteenths.
$\frac{4}{8} = \frac{8}{16}$ and $\frac{5}{8} = \frac{10}{16}$. Halfway between is $\frac{9}{16}$.

18 $0.3 \times 0.2 = 0.06$, $0.3 \div 0.2 = 3 \div 2 = 1.5$, so $0.3 \div 0.2$ is larger by 1.44

19 Remember that when writing in standard form the number must be between 1 and 10.
$37.6 \times 10^7 = 3.76 \times 10^1 \text{ x } 10^7 = 3.76 \times 10^8$

20 **a)** 15% of £40.00 = £6.00, so after the first reduction, the jacket costs £34.00. It is then reduced by a further £3.40, so the final price is £30.60.

b) £40.00 – £30.60 = £9.40

Cost (£)	Percentage (%)
40	100
9.40	?

$9.40 \times \frac{100}{40} = 23.5\%$

Chapter 3 Algebra

PREVIEW

By the end of this chapter you will be able to:

- **explain the meaning of the words coefficient, constant and variable**
- **solve simple linear equations in one unknown**
- **solve equations involving algebraic fractions**
- **solve simultaneous equations in two unknowns**
- **factorise algebraic expressions**
- **solve quadratic equations by factorising**
- **find the rule for forming a sequence with equal differences**
- **find the rule for forming a sequence with unequal differences**
- **find the nth term of a sequence**
- **find the value of an unknown in a formula by substitution**
- **rearrange formulae**
- **make expressions and equations from statements.**

How much do you know already?

Exercise 3.1

1 Solve for x.
$7x + 2 = 10x - 13$

2 Solve for x and y.
$4x + 3y = 41$
$5x - 2y = 34$

3 Solve this equation for x.
$x^2 - 17x - 18 = 0$

4 Rearrange the formula below to make c the subject.
$t = ad - c^2$

5 Find the next two numbers in each of the following sequences, and give formulae for the nth term.
a) 2, 5, 8, 11, ... **b)** 4, 7, 12, 19, ...

6 Given that

$$a = \frac{cm - d}{e - c}$$

find a, when $c = -0.7$, $m = 3.4$, $d = -0.15$ and $e = -2$. Give your answer correct to two decimal places.

Answers – 3.1

1 $x = 5$
2 $x = 8, y = 3$
3 $x = 18, x = -1$
4 $c = \sqrt{ad - t}$
5 **a)** 14, 17; nth term $3n - 1$
b) 28, 39; nth term $n^2 + 3$
6 1.72

How did you get on?

All of them right?
Have you considered taking a Maths degree?

Four or more right?
Why aren't you taking the Higher paper?

Fewer than four right?
The bad news is that this is probably the most difficult chapter in the book. The good news is that our easy methods will make it less difficult and will boost your marks.

To recap ...

$ab = a \times b$

$\frac{a}{b} = a \div b$

$\frac{a}{b + c} = a \div (b + c)$

$3a = 3 \times a$

$3a^2 = 3 \times a \times a = 3 \times a^2$

$(3a)^2 = 3a \times 3a = 9a^2$

$(-a)^2 = -a \times -a = a^2$

Evaluating formulae

This type of question is very common. The questions are easy if you use your calculator properly, but you must be very careful with formulae that involve negative numbers. Work through this example.

Example 3.1

Find z when

$$z = \frac{rs - t}{r + t}$$

and $r = -6.2$, $s = 3.4$ and $t = -5.3$. Give your answer correct to 1 d.p.

Solution

$z = 1.4$

If you did not get this right, you probably either:

a) slipped up with the signs (if you did, learn how to use the +/– or the (–) key on your calculator), or

b) did not calculate $rs - t$ and $r + t$ **before** you divided the top by the bottom.

In questions like this it is a good idea to put brackets around the numerator and the denominator:

$$\frac{(rs - t)}{(r + t)}$$

Simple equations

How much do you know already about equations?

Here are some straightforward equations for you to try, just to see how much algebra you understand.

Exercise 3.2

Evaluate (find the value of) x in the following equations.

1 $x + 2 = 20$ **2** $x - 3 = 15.5$

3 $2x + 1 = 15$ **4** $5x - 2 = 33$

5 $16 = 24 - 2x$ **6** $5x + 20 = 5$

7 $\frac{x}{2} = 10$ **8** $\frac{x}{3} + 1 = 5$

9 $5x + 2 = 3x + 18$ **10** $2x - 1 = 5x - 28$

Answers – 3.2

1 18 **2** 18.5

3 7 **4** 7

5 4 **6** –3

7 20 **8** 12

9 8 **10** 9

If you managed to get the whole exercise right without any help, you can skip the next section and turn to 'Simplifying expressions' on page 30. However, if things did not go so well, don't despair. Carefully work through the next few examples.

Be fair to both sides

Remember: the golden rule – whatever you do to one side of the equation you must do to the other.

Example 3.2

Find x if $5x + 3 = 23$

Solution

$5x + 3 = 23$

$-3 \quad -3$ Take 3 from both sides.

$5x = 20$

$\div 5 \quad \div 5$ Divide both sides by 5.

$x = 4$

Check: Put this answer into the original equation.

$5 \times 4 + 3 = 23$

The answer is correct.

Example 3.3 – Using a subtraction sign

Find x if $2x - 5 = 17$

Solution

$2x - 5 = 17$

$+5 \quad +5$ Add 5 to both sides.

$2x = 22$

$\div 2 \quad \div 2$ Divide both sides by 2.

$x = 11$ **Check** your answer!

Example 3.4 – With a negative coefficient of x

Solve the equation $4 = 16 - 3x$ to find x.

Solution

$4 = 16 - 3x$

$+3x \quad +3x$ Add $3x$ to both sides.

$4 + 3x = 16$

$-4 \quad -4$ Subtract 4 from both sides.

$3x = 12$

$\div 3 \quad \div 3$ Divide both sides by 3.

$x = 4$ **Check** your answer!

Example 3.5 – Negative answer

Find x if $3x + 10 = 4$

Solution

$3x + 10 =$	4	
-10	-10	Subtract 10 from both sides.
$3x =$	-6	
$\div 3$	$\div 3$	Divide both sides by 3.
$x =$	-2	Because $-6 \div 3 = -2$!
		Check your answer!

Example 3.6 – Fractional answer

Find x if $6x - 1 = 2$

Solution

$6x - 1 =$	2	
$+1$	$+1$	Add 1 to both sides.
$6x =$	3	
$\div 6$	$\div 6$	Divide both sides by 6 (not $6 \div 3$).
$x =$	$\frac{1}{2}$	**Check** your answer!

A common error here would be to give the answer as 2. This is one reason why you must always check your answer. You should always divide by the **coefficient** of x (which in this case is 6) at this point.

Two terms that you will find useful to know are:

- ***variable*** *– a letter used to stand for an unknown number. Often the letter used is x, but you can use any letter*
- ***coefficient*** *– a number in front of a variable. For example, the coefficient of x in $4x$ is 4, the coefficient of a^2 in $-5a^2$ is -5.*

Example 3.7 – Using fractional coefficients

Given that $\frac{x}{2} + 1 = 11$, find the value of x.

Solution

$\frac{x}{2} + 1 =$	11	
-1	-1	Subtract 1 from both sides.
$\frac{x}{2} =$	10	
$\times 2$	$\times 2$	Multiply both sides by 2.
$x =$	20	**Check** your answer!

Balancing: questions with variables on both sides

In this type of question, you need to take the variables (usually x) on to one side and the rest of the numbers on to the other.

Example 3.8 – Negative answer

Find the value of x which satisfies
$4x + 7 = 2x + 37$

Solution

$4x + 7 =$	$2x + 37$	
$-2x$	$-2x$	Take $2x$ from both sides.
$2x + 7 =$	37	
-7	-7	Subtract 7 from both sides.
$2x =$	30	
$\div 2$	$\div 2$	Divide both sides by 2.
$x =$	15	**Check** your answer!

Example 3.9 – With larger coefficient of x on the right

Find the value of x for which $x - 1 = 4x - 10$

Solution

$x - 1 =$	$4x - 10$	
$-x$	$-x$	You could have subtracted $4x$ from both sides, but this would produce a negative coefficient of x.
$-1 =$	$3x - 10$	
$+10$	$+10$	
$9 =$	$3x$	
$3x =$	9	Swap the equation round.
$\div 3$	$\div 3$	Divide both sides by 3.
$x =$	3	**Check** your answer!

Now go back and try Exercise 3.2 again. You should find it easier this time.

TAKE A BREAK

It's probably time for a break now. This is a long chapter, so don't try to do too much at any one sitting.

Simplifying expressions

When simplifying expressions, you can only add or subtract like with like.

For example, an expression like $3a + 2b - a - b$ can be simplified to give $2a + b$.

An expression like $2a - 4b + 3c$, however, **cannot** be simplified.

Example 3.10

Simplify the following.

a) $x + x$ **b)** $x + x + y + 3$
c) $x^2 + x$ **d)** $x^2 + x^2 + x + 2x$
e) $x^2 + xy + xy + y + 3$

Solution

a) $x + x = 2x$

b) $x + x + y + 3 = 2x + y + 3$

c) $x^2 + x$ cannot be simplified

d) $x^2 + x^2 + x + 2x = 2x^2 + 3x$

e) $x^2 + xy + xy + y + 3 = x^2 + 2xy + y + 3$

How good are you at simplifying expressions?

Exercise 3.3

Simplify the following expressions where possible.

1 $3a + 2a + 5a + b$

2 $10c + 5a - 2a$

3 $2a^2 - a$

4 $6t + 5t^2 - 8t$

5 $5b^2 + 3b - 7b^2$

6 $12x - x^2 - 3x + 10x^2$

Answers – 3.3

1 $10a + b$

2 $10c + 3a$

3 Cannot be simplified.

4 $5t^2 - 2t$

5 $3b - 2b^2$

6 $9x^2 + 9x$

Expanding single brackets

Multiply the number outside the bracket with each term inside.

Example 3.11

Expand $3(2x + 5)$

Solution

$3(2x + 5)$ $3(2x + 5)$

$3(2x + 5) = 3 \times 2x + 3 \times 5$

$3(2x + 5) = 6x + 15$

You only need the last line; the other steps are optional.

Example 3.12

Expand $a(b - c)$

Solution

$a(b - c)$ $a(b - c)$

$a(b - c) = a \times b + a \times -c$

$a(b - c) = ab - ac$

Remember: The sign is always attached to the number that follows it – which is why we have ringed $-c$.

Example 3.13

Expand $-4(3x + 2y)$

Solution

$-4(3x + 2y)$ $-4(3x + 2y)$

$-4(3x + 2y) = -4 \times 3x - 4 \times 2y$

$-4(3x + 2y) = -12x - 8y$

Remember: The minus sign belongs to the 4.

Example 3.14

Simplify $2x(y - 4) - 3(2x - 1)$

Solution

$2x(y - 4) - 3(2x - 1) = 2xy - 8x - 6x + 3$
$= 2xy - 14x + 3$

Remember: $-1 \times -3 = +3$

Example 3.15

Simplify $2x - (x - 4)$

Solution

As there is no number immediately outside the brackets, it is a good idea to put in a 1. That way there is less chance of getting the sign wrong when you expand the brackets.

$2x - (x - 4) = 2x - 1(x - 4)$
$= 2x - x + 4$
$= x + 4$

Remember: $-1 \times -4 = +4$

Exercise 3.4

Simplify the following expressions.

1. $3(2x + 4) + 2(x + 3)$
2. $2(x + y) + 3(x + 2y)$
3. $2x(y + 4) + y(x - 3)$
4. $a(2 + a) - 3(a - a^2)$
5. $3(2a + 3) - (a - 3)$

Answers – 3.4

1. $8x + 18$
2. $5x + 8y$
3. $3xy + 8x - 3y$
4. $4a^2 - a$
5. $5a + 12$

Simple equations with brackets

To find x, expand the brackets, simplify and solve (or evaluate) as before.

Example 3.16

Find x where $3(2x - 1) - 4(x - 1) = 15$

Solution

$$3(2x - 1) - 4(x - 1) = 15$$
$$6x - 3 - 4x + 4 = 15$$
$$2x + 1 = 15$$
$$2x = 14$$
$$x = 7$$

The FaBuLouS way to solve equations

This is not necessarily the only way to solve more complicated equations, but it can be very useful if you are faced with a 'where do I start?' situation.

Keep in mind the word FaBuLouS.

Hints & Tips

F stands for **F**ractions – get rid of them.

B stands for **B**rackets – work them out, i.e. expand them.

L stands for **L**ike terms – collect all the variables that belong together on one side of the equation and the other numbers on the other side.

S stands for **S**ort it out. At this stage you should have greatly simplified the initial equation, e.g. if $10x = 30$ the answer would be $x = 3$.

Example 3.17

$$\frac{5(2x + 3)}{4} = 8$$

Solution

$5(2x + 3) = 32$	(Multiply each side by 4 to eliminate the fraction.)
$10x + 15 = 32$	(Expand the brackets.)
$10x = 32 - 15 = 17$	(Collect like terms together.)
$x = \frac{17}{10} = 1.7$	(Divide both sides by 10.)

Example 3.18

$$\frac{4(3x - 1)}{5} = 2x$$

Solution

First, eliminate the **F**raction by multiplying both sides by 5.

$4(3x - 1) = 10x$

Next expand the **B**rackets.

$12x - 4 = 10x$

Now collect the **L**ike terms, x terms on one side of the equals sign, numbers on the other.

$$2x = 4$$
$$x = 4 \div 2$$
$$x = 2$$

Example 3.19

$$\frac{2(6x - 5)}{5} = 3x$$

Solution

(Don't try to cancel the 5s. The 5 in the numerator is joined to the $6x$ by a subtraction sign.)

$2(6x - 5) = 15x$	**F**ractions
$12x - 10 = 15x$	**B**rackets
$-10 = 3x$ or $3x = -10$	**L**ike terms
$x = -10 \div 3$	**S**ort it out
$x = -3\frac{1}{3}$	

You could have written the decimal part as $0.\dot{3}$ or 0.3 recurring. Only write 0.3 or 0.33 etc. if the question asks for the answer as a decimal to a specific number of places.

Exercise 3.5

Solve each equation for x.

1. $5(x + 20) = 25$
2. $4(x - 2) = 2(x + 10)$
3. $2 - (x - 3) = -7$
4. $2(x - 1) = 5(x + 2)$
5. $7 - (x - 3) = 3x - 2$
6. $3(x - 4) = 5(x + 3)$
7. $4(x - 2) + 2(x + 5) = 14$
8. $2(x - 1) - 3(x - 2) = 3(x + 5) + 2(3x - 8)$
9. $\frac{3(4x + 1)}{2} = 7$ Give your answer as a fraction.
10. $\frac{2(5x + 2)}{3} = 2x$

Answers – 3.5

1 -15 **2** 14
3 12 **4** -4
5 3 **6** -13.5
7 2 **8** 0.5
9 $3(4x + 1) = 14$, $12x + 3 = 14$, $12x = 11$, $x = 11 \div 12 = \frac{11}{12}$
10 $2(5x + 2) = 6x$, $10x + 4 = 6x$, $10x - 6x = -4$, $4x = -4$, $1 = -x$, so $x = -1$

Factorising using single brackets

Factorising means splitting a number into its **factors** (see Chapter 2). When you factorise you need to find the **highest common factor**, i.e. the biggest number or letter that 'goes into' all the terms.

Example 3.20

Find the highest common factor (HCF) of each pair of numbers.

a) 4 and 10 **b)** 20 and 5
c) a and a^2 **d)** y^2 and y^3

Solution

a) 2 $4 = 2 \times 2$, $10 = 5 \times 2$ so the HCF of 4 and 10 is 2.

b) 5 $20 = 2 \times 2 \times 5$, $5 = 1 \times 5$, so the HCF of 20 and 5 is 5.

c) a $a^2 = a \times a$ so the HCF of a and a^2 is a.

d) y^2 $y^2 = y \times y$ and $y^3 = y \times y \times y$, so their HCF is $y \times y = y^2$.

Example 3.21

Factorise $2x + 6$

Solution

Look for the highest common factor of $2x$ and 6: 2 goes into both terms. So $2x + 6 = 2(\quad)$

Hints & Tips

Now: 2 times *what* makes $2x$? x
2 times *what* makes $+6$? $+3$

When factorised, $2x + 6 = 2(x + 3)$
Check by expanding (multiplying out) the brackets that $2(x + 3) = 2x + 6$.

Example 3.22

Factorise $x^2 + 5x$

Solution

What goes into both x^2 and $+5x$? x does.
So $x^2 + 5x = x(\quad)$
Now: x times *what* makes x^2? x
x times *what* makes $+5x$? $+5$
So $x^2 + 5x = x(x + 5)$
Check by expanding $x(x + 5)$.

Example 3.23

Factorise $y^2 - y$

Solution

What goes into both y^2 and $-y$? y does.
So $y^2 - y = y(\quad)$
Now: y times *what* makes y^2? y
y times *what* makes $-y$? -1
So $y^2 - y = y(y - 1)$

Example 3.24

Factorise fully $12c^2 - 16c$

Solution

What goes into both $12c^2$ and $-16c$?

4 goes into 12 and 16, c goes in to c^2 and c.

So $4c$ goes into both $12c^2$ and $-16c$ (i.e. $4c$ is the HCF of $12c^2$ and $-16c$).
$2c$ is also a common factor, but it is not the **highest** common factor.

So $12c^2 - 16c = 4c(\quad)$

Now: $4c$ times *what* makes $12c^2$? $3c$
$4c$ times *what* makes $-16c$? -4

So $12c^2 - 16c = 4c(3c - 4)$

Example 3.25

Factorise fully $x^2y + xy^2$

Solution

What goes into both $x^2y + xy^2$? x and y, or xy

So write $xy(\quad)$

xy times *what* makes x^2y? x

xy times *what* makes $+xy^2$? $+y$

So $x^2y + xy^2 = xy(x + y)$

Example 3.26

Factorise fully $9d^3 - 3d^2$

Solution

The HCF of $9d^3$ and $-3d^2$ is $3d^2$.

$3d^2$ times what makes $9d^3$? $3d$

$3d^2$ times what makes $-3d^2$? -1

So $9d^3 - 3d^2 = 3d^2(3d - 1)$

Exercise 3.6

Factorise the following expressions fully:

1 $12x - 4$ **2** $x^2 + 7x$

3 $4x^2 - 6x$ **4** $6y^3 + 9y^2$

Answers – 3.6

1 $4(3x - 1)$ **2** $x(x + 7)$

3 $2x(2x - 3)$ **4** $3y^2(2y + 3)$

Making expressions and equations from statements

Expressions

Before you look at the solutions of the next example, see if you can work out the expressions by yourself.

Example 3.27

Molly knows that her cousin is eight years younger than she is. If Molly is x years old, write down an expression for the age of her cousin. (**Remember:** When asked for an expression, your answer will be in terms of a variable, such as x.)

Solution

$x - 8$

Example 3.28

Lou and Jake work in a shoe shop. Lou is paid three times as much per week as Jake. If Jake earns y pounds per week, find Lou's weekly wage in pounds.

Solution

$3y$

Example 3.29

Ali earns £5 per hour for his Saturday job.

a) If he works n hours, how much does he get paid, in pounds?

b) If he also gets £10 in tips, how much money will he take home?

Solution

a) $5n$ **b)** $5n + 10$

Example 3.30

Shona weighs twice as much as her younger sister Minal, who weighs x kg.

a) Write an expression for Shona's weight.

b) Write an expression for their combined weight. Simplify your expression.

c) If their combined weight is 138 kg, write an equation in x and solve it to find the weight of each of them.

Solution

You can replace 'is' or 'are' in a sentence by '='. In plain English, it would make sense to say, 'Shona ***is*** *twice as heavy as' instead of 'Shona weighs twice as much as', so we can write 'Shona's weight = 2 × Minal's weight'.*

a) As Minal's weight is x kg, Shona's is $2x$ kg.

b) Their combined weight is $x + 2x = 3x$ kg.

c) $3x = 138$

$x = 46$, so $2x = 92$

Minal weighs 46 kg, Shona weighs 92 kg.

Some questions may ask you for mass instead of weight. Don't be put off. The method is the same.

Exercise 3.7

1 Kathy and Bob took a test. Kathy scored ten marks more than Bob.
   a) If Bob's mark was y, find, in terms of y:
      i) Kathy's mark **ii)** their total mark.
   b) If their total score was 65, write an equation in y and solve this to find their individual marks.

2 Vic and Noel each bought a book of raffle tickets. Vic won three times as many prizes as Noel.
   a) If Noel won n prizes, write an expression for the number won by Vic.
   b) Write an expression for the total number of prizes won.
   c) If, between them, they collected 68 prizes, how many prizes did Vic receive?

3 Eva is 20 years older than her niece Olivia. Take Eva's age as x years.
   a) Write an expression in x for Olivia's age, in years.
   b) In terms of x, how old will each be in two years' time?
   c) In two years' time Eva will be twice as old as Olivia. Write this statement as an equation, and solve it to find their current ages.

4 Wendy and her friend Sabina are saving up to go on holiday. They find that Sabina has £30.00 less than Wendy. After six months of really saving hard, each has managed to save an extra £20.00. Take the amount that Wendy starts with as £x.
   a) Write an expression for the amount of money in pounds that Sabina has at the start.
   b) Write an expression for the amount of money in pounds that Wendy has after six months.
   c) Write an expression for the amount of money in pounds that Sabina has after six months.
   d) After six months Wendy has twice as much money as Sabina. Write this as an equation and solve it to find the value of x.

Answers – 3.7

1 **a) i)** $y + 10$ **ii)** $2y + 10$
   b) $2y + 10 = 65$, $2y = 55$, $y = 27.5$, so Kathy scored 37.5, Bob scored 27.5.

2 **a)** $3n$ **b)** $4n$
   c) $4n = 68$, $n = 17$, Vic won 51 prizes.

3 **a)** $x - 20$ **b)** Eva: $x + 2$, Olivia: $x - 18$
   c) $x + 2 = 2(x - 18)$, ages 18 and 38

4 **a)** $x - 30$ **b)** $x + 20$
   c) $x - 10$ because $x - 30 + 20 = x - 10$
   d) $x + 20 = 2(x - 10)$ so $x = 40$

TAKE A BREAK

Time for another rest.

Simultaneous equations

Simultaneous equations are two equations involving two variables (**usually** x and y). You must find values of x and y that satisfy both equations simultaneously. We'll now look at the elimination method of solving simultaneous equations.

Elimination

This is the most common method. It always works as long as you make sure that all the variables are on the same side of the equations. If, for instance, you have $4x = 22 - 2y$, you rearrange it to $4x + 2y = 22$.

When the coefficients of either x or y are the same

Example 3.31

Solve the following simultaneous equations.

$4x + 2y = 22$
$3x + 2y = 19$

Solution

Remember:

1 One of the unknowns must have the same coefficient in both equations (ignoring whether it is positive or negative). In our example there is a 2y in both. (Hints & Tips)

*Remember **STOP: S**ame **T**ake **O**pposite **P**lus*

2 If the signs of these are the same, you take away one equation from the other, and if the signs are opposite you add (plus) them.

*3 In our example, each y-term is positive (same sign – '**s**ame **t**ake, **o**pposite **p**lus'), so take away.*

$4x + 2y = 22$ Box the terms that will cancel out.
$3x + 2y = 19$
$x = 3$ $(4x - 3x = x,\ 22 - 19 = 3)$

Next the easier equation.

$3x + 2y = 19$
$9 + 2y = 19$ because $3x = 3 \times 3 = 9$
$2y = 10$
$y = 5$

Check: Use the other equation ($4x + 2y = 22$).
$4 \times 3 + 2 \times 5 = 22$

The answer is $x = 3$, $y = 5$.

Exercise 3.8

1. $5x + 4y = 21$
   $5x + 3y = 17$
2. $6x + 5y = 86$
   $6x + 2y = 56$
3. $5x + 2y = 35$
   $2x + 2y = 20$

Answers – 3.8

1. $x = 1, y = 4$
2. $x = 6, y = 10$
3. $x = 5, y = 5$

When the coefficients of *x* and of *y* are different

Example 3.32

Find the values of x and y that satisfy these equations.

$3x + 2y = 16$
$x + y = 5$

Solution

Notice that we number the equations to make the working clear.

Hints & Tips

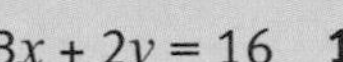

$3x + 2y = 16$ **1**

$x + y = 5$ **2**

Ignoring the signs, are the coefficients of either variable (letter) the same? No.

It is usually easier to multiply the equation with the lower coefficient to make the coefficients of either x or y the same (ignoring signs). As we have chosen to eliminate y, we have multiplied the second equation by 2. (If instead you chose to eliminate x, you would have to multiply the second equation by 3.)

Remember: You need to multiply the whole equation.
If $x + y = 5$ then $2x + 2y = 10$.

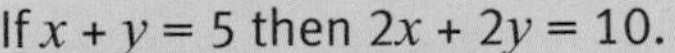

$3x + 2y = 16$ **1**
$2x + 2y = 10$ **2 × 2**
$x = 6$

The signs of the ys are the same, so we've taken one equation from the other. **STOP**

Having found x we need to find y, so substitute x back into the easier of the two original equations.

$x + y = 5$
$6 + y = 5$
$y = -1$

Check in equation **1**: $3 \times 6 + 2 \times -1 = 16$

This is true so the answers for x and y are correct.

Example 3.33

$2x + 5y = 36$
$4x + 5y = 42$

Solution

If you subtract the equations as they stand, you should get $-2x = -6$. Although this is correct, you may find all those negative signs confusing. However, if you subtract the first equation from the second, you will have $2x = 6$. If it helps, rewrite the equations before you start.

$4x + 5y = 42$
$2x + 5y = 36$

If you get as far as $2x = 6$, you will have no trouble in deciding that $x = 3$. Now replace either the $4x$ or the $2x$ with $4 \times 3 = 12$ or $2 \times 3 = 6$, and try to find y. You should arrive at the answer $y = 6$.

$x = 3, y = 6$

Again, check your answer.

Example 3.34

$5x - 2y = 26$
$3x - 2y = 10$

Solution

Even if the letter which you plan to eliminate is negative in both equations, you still subtract.

$5x - 2y = 26$ **1**
$3x - 2y = 10$ **2**

$-2y - -2y = -2y + 2y = 0$
and this will eliminate the y terms.

$5x - 2y = 26$ **1**
$3x - 2y = 10$ **2**

Subtracting equation **2** from equation **1** gives

$2x = 16$
$x = 8$

Now comes the tricky part.

From equation **1** we get

$40 - 2y = 26$

To avoid being left with a negative y-term, you may find it easier to rearrange the equation.

$40 = 26 + 2y$
$40 - 26 = 2y$
$14 = 2y, 7 = y$
$y = 7$

Alternatively, you can leave the y in the usual place and work out $-2y = -14$, $-y = -7$. Multiplying both sides by -1 gives the correct answer, $y = 7$.

If the answer had been, for example, $-y = 10$, then the final answer should be $y = -10$. (Multiplying both sides by -1 would change the sign preceding each of them.)

Example 3.35

$5x - 7y = -26$
$3x - 7y = -24$

Solution

$5x - 7y = -26$ **1**
$3x - 7y = -24$ **2**

You now know what to do with the two $-7y$ terms. Eliminate them by subtracting the equations, leaving
$2x = ?$

Don't panic! Just take things a step at a time.

$-26 - -24 = -26 + 24 = -2$

$2x = -2$
$x = -1$

Replacing $x = -1$ in equation **2** (though you could have chosen to use equation **1**) gives

$-3 - 7y = -24$

If you are feeling really adventurous, you could multiply everything by -1, to give $3 + 7y = 24$. It's then relatively easy to solve and find that $y = 3$.

However, not many people will feel that confident, so you may feel safer in breaking the equation down.

$-3 - 7y = -24$
$-3 = -24 + 7y$ (to ensure finishing with y
$-3 + 24 = 7y$ and not $-y$)
$21 = 7y,\ 3 = y,\ y = 3$

Example 3.36

$3x - 2y = -6$
$2x - 5y = 7$

Solution

The same rules for multiplying coefficients still apply. Usually people prefer to eliminate the negative variable.

$3x - 2y = -6$ **1** $\times 5$ This will eliminate the
$2x - 5y = 7$ **2** $\times 2$ negative y-values.

$15x - 10y = -30$
$4x - 10y = 14$

The next line is tricky. $-30 - 14 = -44$

$11x = -44$
$x = -4$

Use either equation here, but probably **2** is slightly more attractive, because 7 is positive.

$-8 - 5y = 7$	or	$-8 - 5y = 7$
$-5y = 15$		$-8 = 7 + 5y$
$-y = 3$		$-8 - 7 = 5y$
$y = -3$		$-15 = 5y$
$x = -4,\ y = -3$		$-3 = y$
		$y = -3$

If you are feeling more confident by now, try substituting $x = -4$ into equation **1**. You should finish up with $y = -3$.

Exercise 3.9

Find x and y in the following equations.

1 $x + 8y = 17$
$x + y = 10$

2 $5x + 2y = 26$
$3x + 2y = 18$

3 $6x + 5y = 67$
$2x + y = 15$

4 $4x - 5y = -23$
$2x - 5y = -19$

5 $4x - 3y = 3$
$x - 3y = 12$

Answers – 3.9

1 $x = 9,\ y = 1$
2 $x = 4,\ y = 3$
3 $x = 2,\ y = 11$
4 $x = -2,\ y = 3$
5 $x = -3,\ y = -5$

Example 3.37

$5x - 4y = 32$
$3x + 4y = 0$

Solution

Ignoring the signs, the coefficients of y are the same. The signs are opposite for the $4y$s so the equations must be added.

$5x - 4y = 32$
$3x + 4y = 0$
$8x = 32$
$x = 4$

STOP:
'**S**ame **T**ake, **O**pposite **P**lus'

We have eliminated y because $-4y + 4y = 0$

Having found x you must find y.

Using the simpler second equation, $3x + 4y = 0$

$12 + 4y = 0$
$4y = -12$
$y = -3$

Check your answers by substituting them into the original equations.

Example 3.38

$4x - 3y = 17$
$3x + 2y = 17$

Solution

Again, the same rules for multiplying coefficients apply.

$4x - 3y = 17$ **1**
$3x + 2y = 17$ **2**

You could multiply equation **1** by 3 and equation **2** by 4 to obtain $12x$, or you could decide to eliminate the y-terms and rid the world of a negative.

$4x - 3y = 17$ **1** × 2
$3x + 2y = 17$ **2** × 3

$8x - 6y = 34$
$9x + 6y = 51$

Now **STOP!** You have $-6y$ and $+6y$, so you need **O**pposite **P**lus.

Remember: The signs referred to are those in front of the letter that you plan to eliminate. The signs attached to the terms that you are keeping are not involved in **STOP**.

$17x = 85$
$x = 5$

Replacing $x = 5$ in equation **2** gives

$15 + 2y = 17$, $2y = 2$, $y = 1$

Exercise 3.10

Find x and y in the following equations.

1 $x + 5y = 35$
$2x + 3y = 14$

2 $7x - 2y = 110$
$x + 2y = 50$

3 $5x + 4y = 47$
$2x + 3y = 23$

4 $3x + 4y = 65$
$2x + 5y = 76$

5 $3x + 4y = 57$
$x - 2y = -21$

6 $7x - 4y = 68$
$5x + 4y = 76$

Answers – 3.10

1 $x = -5, y = 8$
2 $x = 20, y = 15$
3 $x = 7, y = 3$
4 $x = 3, y = 14$
5 $x = 3, y = 12$
6 $x = 12, y = 4$

Example 3.39

a) Ellie and Hannah have been rummaging around in charity shops for bargains. Ellie has bought three sweaters and six pairs of shorts and Hannah has bought two sweaters and three pairs of shorts. Taking the cost of a sweater as £x and the cost of a pair of shorts as £y, form expressions to show the cost of what each girl has bought and solve them.

b) If Ellie spent £12.00 and Hannah spent £7.50, form two equations and work out what each bought.

Solution

a) Sometimes simultaneous equations are wrapped up in words, but a careful reading of the question leads us to these expressions.

Ellie: $3x + 6y$, Hannah: $2x + 3y$

b) $3x + 6y = 12$ **1**
$2x + 3y = 7.5$ **2**
$4x + 6y = 15$ **3** (**2** × 2)

We have $+6y$ in **1** and **3**. To avoid negatives, it is easier to work out **3** – **1**, and not the other way round.

$x = 3$

We could substitute in any of the equations. **1** and **3** have just whole numbers, so may be easier.

$12 + 6y = 15$ **3**
$6y = 3$
$y = 0.5$

A sweater costs £3.00 and a pair of shorts costs 50p or £0.50 (but not £0.5!).

Exercise 3.11

1 On Tuesday, Anna lifted five small weights and four large weights, totalling 175 kg. Her great rival, Judy, lifted 178 kg in the form of eight small weights and three large weights. Taking the weight, in kg, of a small weight as x and of a large weight as y, form two equations in x and y, and solve them to find the weight of:
a) a small weight **b)** a large weight.

2 Handy Andy, the odd job man, helps to assemble a marquee using short and long rods that are x and y metres long respectively. The tallest pole is 22.5 m and is made up of four short and six long rods. The shortest pole uses five short and four long rods and is 18.5 m. Use this information to find the length of short and long rods.

Answers – 3.11

1 $x = 11, y = 30$
2 $x = 1.5, y = 2.75$

Fractions and decimals

So far in this section we have used examples where the answer is given in decimal form, but sometimes you need to give the answer as a fraction.

Example 3.40

$6x - 5y = -8$
$3x - 5y = -9$

Solution

$6x - 5y = -8$ **1**
$3x - 5y = -9$ **2**

The $-5y$ in each line means that we must subtract.

$3x = 1$ $(-8 - -9 = -8 + 9 = 1)$
$x = 1 \div 3$

This is 0.3 recurring if it is written as a decimal, but it's more accurate to write $x = \frac{1}{3}$.

Using this value in **2** gives

$1 - 5y = -9$
$1 = -9 + 5y$
$1 + 9 = 5y$
$10 = 5y$
$y = 2$

Exercise 3.12

1 $4x - 5y = -24.5$
$3x - 10y = -29$

2 $3x + 2y = 6\frac{2}{3}$
$3x + 4y = 11\frac{1}{3}$

3 $-2x + 5y = -31.7$
$-2x - 6y = 39.8$

Answers – 3.12

1 $x = -4, y = 1.7$
2 $x = \frac{3}{2}, y = 2\frac{1}{3}$
3 $x = -0.4, y = -6.5$

To recap ...

1 Make the coefficients for either the x or y terms the same, ignoring signs. Multiply if necessary.
2 Use STOP to find either x or y.
3 Substitute this value in one equation to find the other value.
4 Check your answer and make sure that it is correct.

Remember: *You can also solve simultaneous equations graphically by finding the point where two lines cross. You can find out more about that on page 61.*

TAKE A BREAK

Time for tea? Take a break before continuing.

Solving simultaneous equations by substitution

Another method of solving simultaneous equations is the substitution method. If the x and y are on different sides of the equations, you may find this method is easier.

Example 3.41

$3x + 2y = 55$
$x = 3y$

Solution

$3x + 2y = 55$ **1**
$x = 3y$ **2**

If $x = 3y$ (**2**), then $3x = 3 \times 3y = 9y$.
Rewrite **1** to make $9y + 2y = 55$, $11y = 55$, $y = 5$.
Then use equation **2** to work out $x = 3 \times 5 = 15$.

Example 3.42

$2x + 5y = 41$
$y = x + 4$

Solution

$2x + 5y = 41$ **1**
$y = x + 4$ **2**

This time you need to replace $5y$ in **1** and write $2x + 5(x + 4) = 41$

$2x + 5x + 20 = 7x + 20 = 41$, $7x = 21$, $x = 3$ and $y = 3 + 4 = 7$.

Exercise 3.13

Solve these equations by the elimination or the substitution method.

1 $x + 4y = 26$
$y = 3x$

2 $3x + y = -1.5$
$6x - y = 6$

3 $x - y = -6$
$x = -5y$

4 $6x + 5y = 14$
$x = 5y$

5 $7x + 3y = 41$
$x + y = 7$

6 $x - y = 2$
$5y = x + 2$

Answers – 3.13

1 $x = 2, y = 6$
2 $x = 0.5, y = -3$
3 $x = -5, y = 1$
4 $x = 2, y = 0.4$
5 $x = 5, y = 2$
6 $x = 3, y = 1$

Trial and improvement

This is a method of solving an equation by substituting numbers into a given formula until you find one that is the solution to the required level of accuracy.

Example 3.43

Find the solution near $x = 3$ to the equation $x^2 + 2x = 18$ to one decimal place.

Solution

First create a table for x and the left hand side of the formula (in this case $x^2 + 2x$), and for comments.

x	$x^2 + 2x$	Comments
3	$3^2 + 2 \times 3 = 15$	Too low

This answer is less than 18, so try a number slightly larger, such as 3.5:

3.5	$3.5^2 + 2 \times 3.5 = 19.25$	Too high

This is too big, so try a smaller number, say 3.3:

3.3	$= 17.49$	Too low

Try 3.4:

3.4	$= 18.36$	Too high

The x-value that will give an answer of 18 is somewhere between 3.3 and 3.4. Correct to 1 decimal place, the answer will be either 3.3 or 3.4. To find out which one it is, substitute the number half way between these two numbers, 3.35:

3.35 $= 17.923$

This is too low, so the x-value that gives an answer of 18 lies between 3.35 and 3.4. This would round to 3.4 (to 1 d.p.), so the answer is $x = 3.4$.

Example 3.44

Find the solution of $2x^3 - x = 400$ to one decimal place. Start with the value $x = 6$.

Solution

x	$2x^3 - x$	Comments
6	426	Too high
5.7	364.686	Too low
5.8	384.424	Too low
5.9	404.858	Too high

So the value of x that satisfies the equation lies somewhere between 5.8 and 5.9. So substitute the number half way between these values, 5.85

5.85	394.553...	Too low

So the solution must lie between 5.85 and 5.9, which rounds to 5.9 to 1 decimal place.

Exercise 3.14

Use trial and improvement to solve the following equations correct to 1 decimal place.

1 $3x^2 + 7x = 89$ Start with $x = 4$

2 $x^2 + 3x = 34$ Start with $x = 5$

Answers – 3.14

1 $x = 4.4$
2 $x = 4.5$

Multiplying out (expanding) double brackets

We are using **FOIL** (**F**irst **O**uter **I**nner **L**ast) to expand double brackets. Follow through this example.

(If you've learnt another method, feel free to use it).

Example 3.45

Expand $(x + 1)(2x + 3)$

Solution

Using **FOIL**: **F**irst **O**uter **I**nner **L**ast

$$(x + 1)(2x + 3) = x \times 2x + x \times 3 + 1 \times 2x + 1 \times 3$$
$$= 2x^2 + 3x + 2x + 3$$
$$= 2x^2 + 5x + 3$$

A common mistake when expanding brackets is to add the last terms instead of multiplying them.

You can leave out the first line of working – we included it just to show how we found the terms.

Hints & Tips

Using double brackets to factorise

In this section we shall show you how to rewrite a quadratic expression (i.e. one containing an x^2), putting it into two brackets. As you have just spent the last section revising how to make a quadratic expression out of two brackets, this may seem a rather curious activity, but the exam may test either skill, and a few more marks are always worth having!

There are, as usual, several approaches. Try the exercise that follows, and if you can do it go on to the section on 'Rearranging formulae' on page 47.

Exercise 3.15

Factorise the following expressions.

1. $x^2 + 6x + 8$
2. $x^2 + 9x + 20$
3. $x^2 - 9x + 20$
4. $x^2 + 11x - 12$
5. $x^2 - 7x - 30$

Answers – 3.15

1. $(x + 4)(x + 2)$
2. $(x + 5)(x + 4)$
3. $(x - 5)(x - 4)$
4. $(x + 12)(x - 1)$
5. $(x - 10)(x + 3)$

How to factorise

When you multiply out double brackets, you usually finish up with three terms, i.e. an x^2 term, an x term and a term without x, sometimes called a **constant**, e.g. $(x + 3)(x + 2) = x^2 + 5x + 6$.

Factorising is the reverse of this process, as the following steps show.

1. The x^2 term is usually made by putting an x in the first place in each pair of brackets. At Intermediate level there should not be any coefficient in front of the x, so you can immediately write down two pairs of brackets like this.

   $(x \quad)(x \quad)$

2. The other two numbers will involve the factors of the constant. Split the constant into pairs of factors. For the expression $x^2 + 5x + 6$, the constant is 6. The possible pairs of factors are:

   1 2
   6 3

3. Separating the terms will be two signs. These could be two positives, two negatives, or one of each.

$(x + ?)(x + ?)$	$(x - ?)(x - ?)$
$(x + ?)(x - ?)$	$(x - ?)(x + ?)$

   To decide which type you have, first look at the *second sign* in the original equation.

$x^2 + ?x + ?$	$x^2 - ?x - ?$
$x^2 + ?x - ?$	$x^2 - ?x + ?$

   In the example $x^2 + 5x + 6$, the second sign is positive.

Type 1: The second sign in the expression is positive
If the second sign is positive, both signs in the brackets will be the same. (*Plus* and *same* both have four letters.)

- If the first sign is positive, both signs in the brackets are positive.
- If the first sign is negative, both signs in the brackets are negative.

Now go back to the pairs of factors which you wrote down and put positive or negative signs in front of each number, according to which sign you are going to need.

$x^2 + 5x + 6$

Since the first sign is positive:

+1 +2
+6 +3

One pair of factors when added must total the coefficient of x, in this case 5.

When you add up the pairs, you can see that only 2 + 3 gives the required total 5, so the answer is

$x^2 + 5x + 6 = (x + 3)(x + 2)$ or $(x + 2)(x + 3)$

Check your answer by expanding the brackets to ensure that you get back to the same expression as you started with.

Example 3.46

Factorise $x^2 + 12x + 20$

Solution

The pairs of factors making up 20 are:

1	2	4
20	10	5

The second sign is + (positive), so both signs are the same.
The first sign is +, so both signs will be +.
Inserting the + signs and totalling the pairs gives:

+1	+2	+4
+20	+10	+5
21	12	9

As the original expression has $12x$, the answer is:

$x^2 + 12x + 20 = (x + 10)(x + 2)$

Example 3.47

Factorise $x^2 - 9x + 20$

Solution

List the factors of 20.

1	2	4
20	10	5

The second sign is positive, so both signs are the same. The first sign is negative, so both signs will be negative.

−1	−2	−4
−20	−10	−5
−21	−12	−9

$x^2 - 9x + 20 = (x - 5)(x - 4)$ or $(x - 4)(x - 5)$

Exercise 3.16

Factorise the following expressions.

1 $x^2 + 11x + 10$ **2** $x^2 - 6x + 8$

3 $x^2 - 13x + 36$ **4** $x^2 + 11x + 24$

Answers – 3.16

1 $(x + 10)(x + 1)$ **2** $(x - 4)(x - 2)$

3 $(x - 9)(x - 4)$ **4** $(x + 8)(x + 3)$

Type 2: The second sign in the expression is negative

If the second sign is negative, both signs in the brackets will be different. (*Different* and *minus* both have i as their second letter.)

Example 3.48

Factorise $x^2 + 11x - 12$

Solution

List the factors of 12.

1	2	3
12	6	4

The second sign is negative, so the signs will be different. To decide which way round to put the factors, look at the first sign in the expression. If it is positive, this means that the larger factor is positive. If it is negative, this means that the larger factor is negative.

As 11 is positive, put + in front of the larger number in each pair of factors, and − in front of the smaller. Then total them in the usual way.

−1	−2	−3
+12	+6	+4
11	4	1

$x^2 + 11x - 12 = (x + 12)(x - 1)$

Example 3.49

Factorise $x^2 - 7x - 30$

Solution

List the factors of 30.

1	2	3	5
30	15	10	6

The second sign is negative, so the signs in the brackets will be different.

The first sign is −, so the larger factor is negative.

1	2	3	5
−30	−15	−10	−6
−29	−13	−7	−1

$x^2 - 7x - 30 = (x - 10)(x + 3)$

To recap ...

1. Look at the sign of the constant term (the *second* sign).
   plus $\Rightarrow$ same sign
   minus $\Rightarrow$ different signs
2. List the pairs of factors.
3. By looking at the x term, give the factors the appropriate signs.
4. Complete the brackets.

Exercise 3.17

Factorise each of these expressions.

1 $x^2 + 8x - 9$ **2** $x^2 + 7x - 18$

3 $x^2 - 3x - 28$ **4** $x^2 - 24x - 25$

Answers – 3.17

1 $(x + 9)(x - 1)$
2 $(x + 9)(x - 2)$
3 $(x - 7)(x + 4)$
4 $(x - 25)(x + 1)$

Unfortunately, examiners won't tell you whether you have a Type 1 or Type 2 expression. However, if you always start by looking at the second sign and then following the usual procedure, you should be able to cope with anything they might throw at you.

Factorising quadratics

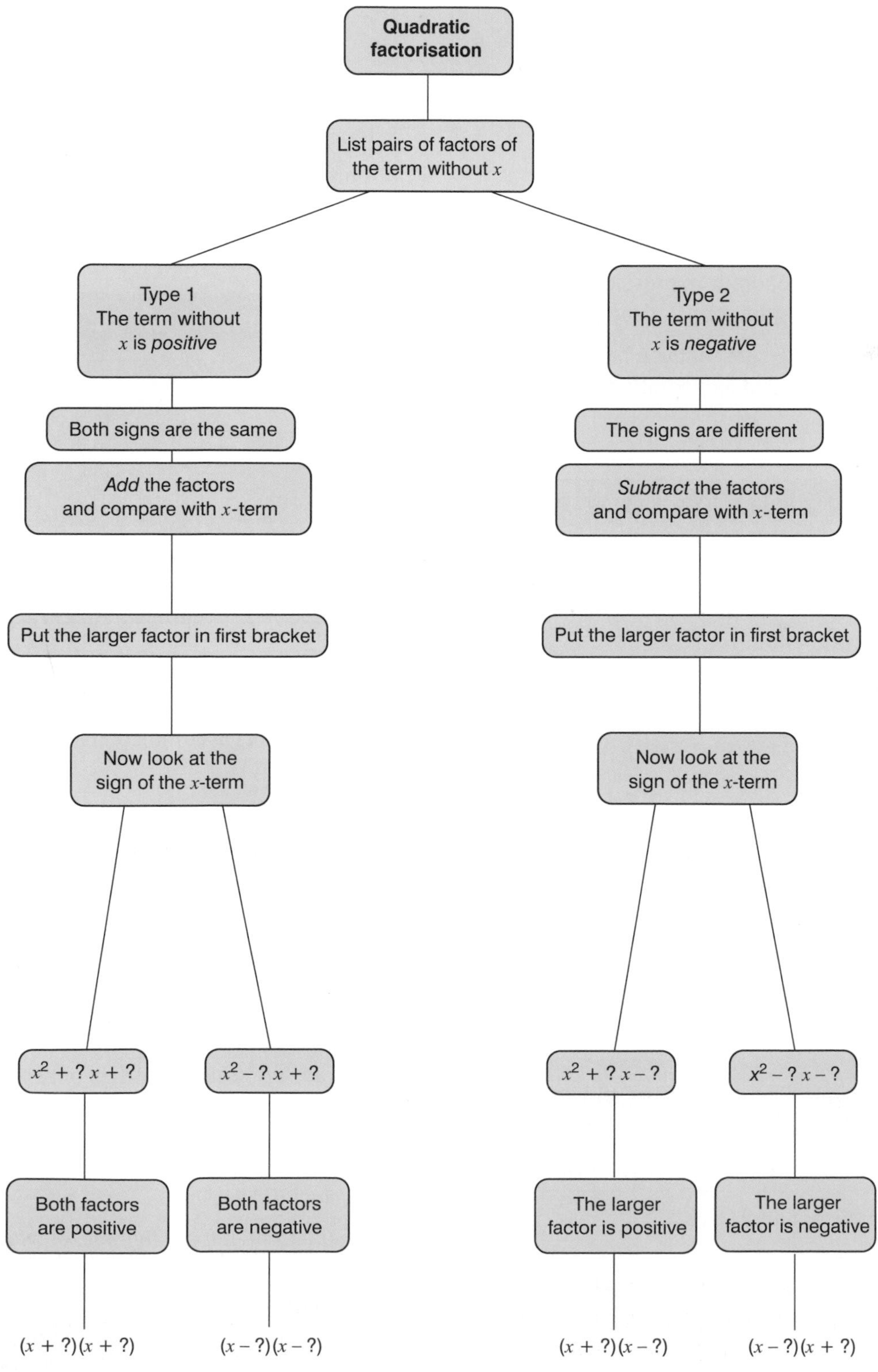

Here are some mixed examples for you to try.

Exercise 3.18

Factorise these expressions.

1 $x^2 + 14x + 45$　　**2** $x^2 + 5x - 6$

3 $x^2 - 11x + 24$　　**4** $x^2 - x - 12$

Answers – 3.18

1 $(x + 9)(x + 5)$
2 $(x + 6)(x - 1)$
3 $(x - 3)(x - 8)$
4 $(x - 4)(x + 3)$

Solving quadratic equations

If you can factorise quadratic expressions, then quadratic equations should be a piece of cake!

You just need to make sure that you have an equation with zero on one side and a quadratic expression on the other.

Example 3.50

Solve $x^2 + 11x + 10 = 0$

Solution

Factorise the equation:

$(x + 10)(x + 1) = 0$

Whenever two numbers are multiplied together and the answer is zero, one or the other must be zero.

$(x + 10)$ and $(x + 1)$ represent these two numbers which are multiplied together to make zero.

Therefore, either $(x + 10) = 0$ or $(x + 1) = 0$.

If $x + 10 = 0, x = -10$.
If $x + 1 = 0, x = -1$.

Example 3.51

Solve $x^2 - 9x - 22 = 0$

Solution

Factorising the equation gives:

$(x - 11)(x + 2) = 0$

Therefore $(x - 11) = 0$, or $(x + 2) = 0$.

Therefore $x = 11$, or $x = -2$.

Exercise 3.19

Here are the expressions from Exercise 3.17 rewritten as quadratic equations. Solve them to find the values of x.

1 $x^2 + 8x - 9 = 0$

2 $x^2 + 7x - 18 = 0$

3 $x^2 - 3x - 28 = 0$

4 $x^2 - 24x - 25 = 0$

Now you're off to a flying start, try these.

5 $x^2 - 3x - 10 = 0$

6 $x^2 + 8 = 9x$

7 $x^2 + 6x = 7$

Hint: Remember to rearrange **6** and **7** before you try to factorise.

Answers – 3.19

1 $(x + 9)(x - 1) = 0$, so $x + 9 = 0$, or $x - 1 = 0$; $x = -9$, or $x = 1$
2 $(x + 9)(x - 2) = 0$, so $x = -9$ or $x = 2$
3 $(x - 7)(x + 4) = 0$, so $x = 7$ or $x = -4$
4 $(x - 25)(x + 1) = 0$, so $x = 25$ or $x = -1$
5 $(x - 5)(x + 2) = 0$, so $x = 5$ or $x = -2$
6 $(x - 8)(x - 1) = 0$, so $x = 8$ or $x = 1$
7 $(x + 7)(x - 1) = 0$, so $x = -7$ or $x = 1$

Don't worry if you find factorising hard. With practice it gets easier and you will gradually get used to the most commonly occurring pairs of factors.

TAKE A BREAK

Are you still with us? If so, you can celebrate by taking a few minutes off.

Difference of two squares

This is an expression made up of two squared terms separated by a minus sign. Remember that minus means the difference. Sometimes it may look like a quadratic expression but with no x-term (that is, the coefficient of x is zero).

A general form of the difference of two squares is $x^2 - y^2$

To solve or factorise the difference of two squares, start by writing two empty pairs of brackets next to each other. (　　)(　　)

Now take the square root of the first term and write it inside both pairs of brackets at the beginning.

$x^2 - y^2 = (x \quad)(x \quad)$

Then take the square root of the second term and put it at the end of both pairs of brackets.

$x^2 - y^2 = (x \quad y)(x \quad y)$

Now put a '+' between the terms in the first bracket and a '–' between the terms in the second:

$x^2 - y^2 = (x + y)(x - y)$

Why does it work that way?

$(x + y)(x - y) = x^2 - xy + xy - y^2 = x^2 - y^2$

so $(x + y)(x - y) = x^2 - y^2$

Example 3.52

Factorise the following expressions:

a) $x^2 - 4$

b) $a^2 - b^2$

c) $y^2 - 9d^2$

d) $2x^2 - 50$

Solution

a) $(x + 2)(x - 2)$

b) $(a + b)(a - b)$

c) $(y + 3d)(y - 3d)$

d) You need to take a factor of 2 out first.
$2(x^2 - 25) = 2(x + 5)(x - 5)$

Example 3.53

a) Factorise $x^2 - 16$

b) Hence or otherwise solve $x^2 - 16 = 0$

Solution

a) $(x + 4)(x - 4)$

b) The word 'Hence' in the question implies that your answer to **a)** will help you to answer this part.

$(x + 4)(x - 4) = 0$
$x + 4 = 0$ or $x - 4 = 0$
$x = -4$ or $x = 4$

The 'otherwise' method:

$x^2 = 16$
$x = \pm\sqrt{16}$
$x = 4$ or $x = -4$

Remember that $4 \times 4 = 16$ and $-4 \times -4 = 16$. To get full marks you need to include the positive **and** the negative answers.

Example 3.54

a) Factorise $x^2 - y^2$

b) Without using a calculator, evaluate $321^2 - 221^2$

Solution

a) $(x + y)(x - y)$

b) $(321 + 221)(321 - 221) = 542 \times 100 = 54\,200$

This is much easier than squaring 321 and 221 and then finding the difference.

Exercise 3.20

1 Factorise the following expressions.

a) $x^2 - 1$
b) $c^2 - 36$
c) $y^2 - 49d^2$
d) $3x^2 - 48$

2 a) Factorise $x^2 - 64$.
b) Hence or otherwise solve $x^2 - 64 = 0$.

3 a) Factorise $x^2 - y^2$.
b) Without using a calculator, evaluate $348^2 - 338^2$.

Answers – 3.20

1 a) $(x + 1)(x - 1)$
b) $(c + 6)(c - 6)$
c) $(y + 7d)(y - 7d)$
d) You need to take out a factor of 3 first.
$3(x^2 - 16) = 3(x + 4)(x - 4)$

2 a) $(x + 8)(x - 8)$
b) $x = -8$ or $x = 8$

3 a) $(x + y)(x - y)$
b) $(348 + 338)(348 - 338) = 686 \times 10 = 6860$

Algebraic fractions

There are fractions that include variables in the numerator, denominator or both. Here are a few examples:

$$\frac{p}{q} \quad \frac{p+q}{s+t} \quad \frac{p^2}{q^2} \quad \frac{x+1}{x+2} \quad \frac{(x+1)(x+3)}{(x+2)(x-4)}$$

You may cancel algebraic fractions only when the terms on the top and bottom are all products. Do not cancel if they are sums or differences.

For example, you can cancel the x in $\frac{px}{qx}$ to give $\frac{p}{q}$.

What you are really doing is dividing the numerator and denominator by x.

You cannot cancel the x in $\frac{p+x}{q-x}$ because you cannot divide the numerator and denominator through by x.

Example 3.55

Simplify the following fractions, where possible.

a) $\frac{xy}{x^2}$ b) $\frac{pqr}{qr^2}$

c) $\frac{ab+d}{ab+c}$ d) $\frac{x^2+1}{x^2+x}$

e) $\frac{(x+1)(x-2)}{(x-3)(x+1)}$

Solution

a) As both the numerator and denominator are divisible by x, we can cancel an x from both top and bottom.

$$\frac{xy}{x^2} = \frac{y}{x}$$

b) As both numerator and denominator are divisible by q and r, the fraction can be simplified.

$$\frac{pqr}{qr^2} = \frac{p}{r}$$

c) This cannot be simplified because the numerator and denominator have no common factors.

Leave ab in both top and bottom.

d) This cannot be simplified because the numerator and denominator have no common factors.

Don't cross out the x^2 in the top and bottom.

e) As the terms in both the numerator and the denominator include the common factor $(x + 1)$, the fraction can be simplified.

$$\frac{(x-2)}{(x-3)}$$

If you are still not sure, try substituting simple numbers for letters and see if cancelling gives the right answer.

Exercise 3.21

Simplify the following, where possible.

1 $\frac{x^2y}{x^3z}$

2 $\frac{pq+r}{qr^2+p}$

3 $\frac{ab^2}{bc}$

4 $\frac{y^2+z}{y^2+x}$

5 $\frac{(x+2)(x-3)}{(x-1)(x+2)}$

Answers – 3.21

1 $\frac{y}{xz}$

2 Cannot be simplified

3 $\frac{ab}{c}$

4 Cannot be simplified

5 $\frac{(x-3)}{(x-1)}$

Simplifying more complicated algebraic fractions

Always try to factorise the numerator and denominator of algebraic fractions, then simplify.

Exercise 3.22

Simplify the following.

1 $\frac{x^2+x}{2x+2}$

2 $\frac{3y+9}{y^2-9}$

3 $\frac{x^2-x-12}{4x-16}$

4 $\frac{x^2+10x+21}{x^2+2x-35}$

Answers – 3.22

1 $\frac{x^2+x}{2x+2} = \frac{x(x+1)}{2(x+1)} = \frac{x}{2}$

2 $\frac{3y+9}{y^2-9} = \frac{3(y+3)}{(y+3)(y-3)} = \frac{3}{y-3}$

3 $\frac{x^2-x-12}{4x-16} = \frac{(x-4)(x+3)}{4(x-4)} = \frac{x+3}{4}$

4 $\frac{x^2+10x+21}{x^2+2x-35} = \frac{(x+7)(x+3)}{(x+7)(x-5)} = \frac{x+3}{x-5}$

Rearranging formulae

Many students think that rearranging formulae (or formulas, you will find both words used) is difficult. However, if you can solve simple equations like the examples at the beginning of the chapter, you shouldn't have any problems. In fact, if you have survived this far into this algebra chapter, you have learned more than enough techniques to solve any of the formula questions that the examiners might dream up.

How much do you know already?

Exercise 3.23

In each of the following questions, rearrange the formula to make the letter in brackets the subject.

1 $a = b + c$ (b)

2 $d = e - f$ (e)

3 $a = x - y$ (y)

4 $ab = z$ (b)

5 $\frac{a}{x} = z$ (a)

6 $\frac{s}{t} = p$ (t)

7 $b = ac + d$ (a)

8 $y(x - z) = s$ (x)

9 $t = b - ak$ (k)

10 $v = h^2 + t$ (h)

11 $s = c + \sqrt{b}$ (b)

12 $e = b - \sqrt{c}$ (c)

13 $b = \frac{c}{e - f}$ (e)

14 $c = 2\pi r$ (r)

Answers – 3.23

1 $b = a - c$

2 $e = d + f$

3 $y = x - a$

4 $b = \frac{z}{a}$

5 $a = xz$

6 $t = \frac{s}{p}$

7 $a = \frac{b - d}{c}$

8 $x = z + \frac{s}{y}$ or $x = \frac{s + yz}{y}$

9 $k = \frac{b - t}{a}$

10 $h = \sqrt{v - t}$

11 $b = (s - c)^2$

12 $c = (b - e)^2$

13 $e = \frac{c}{b} + f$ or $e = \frac{c + bf}{b}$

14 $r = \frac{c}{2\pi}$

How did you get on?

All or most of them right?

Well done! You should be able to cope with any formula rearrangement question which appears on an Intermediate paper.

The first nine right, but the last few defeated you?

Your only problem is one of confidence. Solving the first nine formulae shows that you can think logically, and that is all you need to do to solve the more involved examples. As you get to grips with the routines that we're about to demonstrate, you will soon begin to wonder why you ever had any problems with formula rearrangement.

The first six right but the rest wrong?

You have the basic ideas well established, but you just need more practice in combining the processes.

Don't even ask?

If it's any comfort, most Intermediate level students (and a good many Higher level students too) start off in much the same position as you are now. However, almost everyone can rearrange formulae, given a little help.

Rearranging formulae and changing signs

You already know how to add, subtract, multiply or divide both sides of an equation.

An alternative way of looking at this is to imagine particular terms being moved from one side to another. In doing so, this sign is changed in the following way:

$$+ \Rightarrow -, \quad - \Rightarrow +, \quad \times \Rightarrow \div, \quad \div \Rightarrow \times$$

Remember: *Change sides, change signs.*

Example 3.56

Rearrange this formula, making b the subject.

$a = b + c$

Solution

As b is the subject, move c across to the other side making it $-c$.

$a - c = b$

$b = a - c$

It is usually a good idea to isolate the term you want and get rid of all the surplus letters and terms that are on the same side of the equation.

Example 3.57

Make e the subject of this formula.

$d = e - f$

Solution

This time e is the subject, so move $-f$ to the other side, changing it to $+f$.

$d + f = e$

$e = d + f$

Example 3.58

Make y the subject of this formula.

$a = x - y$

Solution

Here we need y (the subject) to be positive, so move $-y$ to the other side and change it to $+y$. It makes the later operations much easier.

$a + y = x$

Now move the a across to the other side to give:

$y = x - a$

Example 3.59

Make b the subject of this formula.

$ab = z$

Solution

This time $\times a$ moves to the other side as $\div a$, giving:

$b = \frac{z}{a}$

A common mistake is to write $b = \frac{a}{z}$

You can avoid this by first writing down anything that hasn't been moved.

The z has remained in the same place, so start by writing $b = z$.

As the a is moving, it is a that changes from $\times$ to $\div$, not z.

Example 3.60

Make a the subject of this formula.

$\frac{a}{x} = z$

Solution

This is much easier than it might first appear. Simply move $\div x$ across as $\times x$, giving:

$a = zx$

To 'undo' dividing by x, just multiply by x.

If the required letter is on the bottom, you have to get it to the top as soon as possible.

Example 3.61

Make t the subject of this formula.

$\frac{s}{t} = p$

Solution

Move $\div t$ across as $\times t$, giving:

$s = tp$

Then move $\times p$ across as $\div p$, giving:

$\frac{s}{p} = t$

or $t = \frac{s}{p}$

Short cut

Can you see that t and p have changed places? This is easier to understand if you use numbers.

$\frac{20}{10} = 2$ so $\frac{20}{2} = 10$

If you don't want to use this short cut you don't have to.

Example 3.62

Make a the subject of this formula.

$b = ac + d$

Solution

First move the d to the other side.

$b - d = ac$

Next move the c across:

$\frac{b-d}{c} = a$ and so $a = \frac{b-d}{c}$

Example 3.63

Make k the subject of this formula.

$t = b - ak$

Solution

First move the ak across (which will make it $+ak$, and so easier to handle).

$t + ak = b$

Next move the t to the other side:

$ak = b - t$

Finally, move the $\times a$ across, giving:

$k = \frac{b-t}{a}$

Example 3.64

Make h the subject of this formula.

$v = h^2 + t$

Solution

Start in exactly the same way as before.

$v - t = h^2$

To 'undo' a squared number, you must find its square root. Take the square root of both sides, giving:

$\sqrt{v-t} = h$ and so $h = \sqrt{v-t}$

Example 3.65

Make b the subject of this formula.

$s = c + \sqrt{b}$

Solution

Start in exactly the same way.

$s - c = \sqrt{b}$

To 'undo' the square root, you have to square both sides. As the term on the left-hand side is $s - c$, you get:

$(s - c)^2 = b$ and so $b = (s - c)^2$

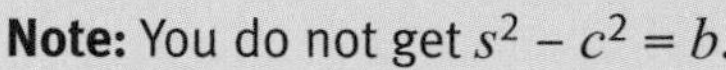

Note: You do not get $s^2 - c^2 = b$.

Example 3.66

Make c the subject of this formula.

$e = b - \sqrt{c}$

Solution

As you have a negative subject, start by moving it over into a positive value.

$e + \sqrt{c} = b$

Then you have to shoot the e over.

$\sqrt{c} = b - e$

Finally, squaring both sides gives:

$c = (b - e)^2$

Example 3.67

Make e the subject of this formula.

$b = \frac{c}{e} - f$

Solution

Start in the usual way by moving over the f.

$b + f = \frac{c}{e}$

Now, because the required subject is on the bottom, i.e. dividing, you must bring it to the top.

$e(b + f) = c$ Remember the brackets.

Because you need e by itself, $(b + f)$ must be moved to the other side to give:

$e = \frac{c}{b+f}$

Example 3.68

Make r the subject of this formula.

$V = \frac{4}{3}\pi r^3$

Solution

This is about the most complicated example which you might get, but you have already practised all the necessary skills, so it shouldn't prove to be too much of a problem.

You may find it easier to rewrite the expression as:

$V = \frac{4}{3}\pi r^3 = \frac{4\pi r^3}{3}$

Start by bringing the 3 across to the top.

$3V = 4\pi r^3$

Then divide by 4π.

$\frac{3V}{4\pi} = r^3$

Just as you 'undo' a square number by finding the square root, you 'undo' a cube by finding the cube root.

$\sqrt[3]{\frac{3V}{4\pi}} = r$

It is worth persevering with this example, since it occurs quite often on exam papers.

Help! Where do I start?

Remember FaBuLouS, which we looked at on page 32? Check back if you've forgotten what the F, B, L and S stand for.

Although FaBuLouS isn't always the best or quickest solution to rearranging formulae, it can be a life-saver if you're faced with a complicated formula to rearrange and you don't know where to start.

Example 3.69

Express h in terms of w. (The question could also say, 'Make h the subject of the formula.')

$\frac{w}{7} = h + 2$

Solution

Using FaBuLouS, start with the **F**raction.

$w = 7(h + 2)$

Then work out the **B**rackets.

$w = 7h + 14$

Now group **L**ike terms. Keep everything with h on one side and move the 14 over to make

$w - 14 = 7h$

Then **S**ort it out by dividing by 7.

$\frac{w - 14}{7} = h$

$h = \frac{w - 14}{7}$

Sometimes there is more than one right answer. Instead of multiplying out the brackets, you could have moved down the 7.

$w = 7(h + 2)$

$\frac{w}{7} = h + 2$

$\frac{w}{7} - 2 = h$, or $h = \frac{w}{7} - 2$

As you have the h by itself, it doesn't matter which version you use.

How much have you learnt?

Exercise 3.24

In the following examples, rearrange the formula to make the letter in the bracket the subject.

1	$d = ab - r$	(r)
2	$A = \pi r^2$	(r)
3	$aw^2 = v$	(a)
4	$C = 20h + t$	(t)
5	$C = 20h + t$	(h)
6	$c^3 - a = b$	(c)
7	$ah - t = w$	(t)
8	$y - xw = t$	(x)

Answers – 3.24

1 $r = ab - d$

2 $r = \sqrt{\frac{A}{\pi}}$

3 $a = \frac{v}{w^2}$

4 $t = C - 20h$

5 $h = \frac{C - t}{20}$

6 $c = \sqrt[3]{a + b}$

7 $t = ah - w$

8 $x = \frac{y - t}{w}$

TAKE A BREAK

Even we have to admit it – that was difficult!
This time, you can comfort yourself with a short rest and the knowledge that it's downhill from here on.

Sequences

DINO and **COSTAS** are two useful words to help you solve sequences. Look at the following examples.

Sequences with equal spacing

Example 3.70

The following numbers form a sequence.

9, 16, 23, 30, ...

a) What is the difference between consecutive terms?
b) What is the next term in the sequence?
c) What is the nth term?
d) What is the 25th term?

Solution

a) 9, 16, 23, 30, ...

The difference between consecutive terms is 7.

b) The next term is given by $30 + 7 = 37$.

c) Here we can use **DINO**, as this helps to find the nth term of sequences that are equally spaced. Here the numbers are equally spaced with a difference of 7. Put a ring before the first term:

◯, 9, 16, 23, 30, ...

What number would go in here if there were a number before the 9?

Answer: $9 - 7 = 2$

②, 9, 16, 23, 30, ...

DI stands for the difference (7), N stands for n and O stands for the number in the ring (2).

DINO gives $7n + 2$.

Check: If you put $n = 1$, you should get the first term, $7 \times 1 + 2 = 9$.
$n = 2$ gives the second term, 16, etc.

d) To find the 25th term, put $n = 25$, which gives $7 \times 25 + 2 = 177$

Example 3.71

The following numbers form a sequence.

1, 8, 15, 22, 29, ...

a) Find an expression for the nth term.
b) If the kth term is 120, find the value of k.

Solution

a) Using DINO, DI = 7, O = −6.
So the nth term is $7n - 6$.

b) The kth term is 120. It is also $7k - 6$.
So $7k - 6 = 120$, therefore $k = 18$.

Sequences with unequal spacing

Example 3.72

a) What is the next term in this sequence?

3, 6, 11, 18, ...

b) What is the nth term in the sequence?

Solution

a) Look at the differences between the terms. You can see that the difference increases by 2 every term, so the next difference must be 9. The next term must be $18 + 9 = 27$.

b) Here we can try **COSTAS**, as this helps to find the nth term of sequences with unequal spacing. COSTAS stands for Cube Or Square, Times, Add, Subtract.

Write the sequence down, with the number of each term above it. First try squaring the n (as squaring is easier than cubing), and comparing to see if you can see a link between the squared numbers and each term. (If you cannot, try cubing them.)

n	1	2	3	4
n^2	1	4	9	16
	3	6	11	18

Now you can see that you have to add 2 to n^2 to get the term. So the nth term is $n^2 + 2$.

Quadratic sequences

Sequences with a term in n^2 are called quadratic sequences. They come up more often in coursework than in the exam, but be prepared!

Example 3.73

Find an expression for the nth term in the following sequence.

2, 16, 54, 128, ...

Solution

Write the numbers 1, 2, 3, 4 above the corresponding terms, leaving spaces in between.

n	1	2	3	4
	2	16	54	128

Using COSTAS, start by squaring n.

n	1	2	3	4
n^2	1	4	9	16
	2	16	54	128

Comparing the n^2 line with the bottom line, you can see there is no link between the numbers in the two lines. You don't need the n^2 line, so put a line through it.

Now try cubes.

n	1	2	3	4
~~n^2~~	~~1~~	~~4~~	~~9~~	~~16~~
n^3	1	8	27	64
	2	16	54	128

Using the TAS of COSTAS (Times, Add, Subtract), you can see that to find the bottom line you need to multiply the numbers in the n^3 row by 2.

So the nth term is $2 \times n^3$, or $2n^3$.

The 3–5–7 sequence

This is a quicker method for some of the COSTAS sequences. It works for sequences in which the differences between terms are 3 then 5 then 7 etc.

n^2 is the sequence 1, 4, 9, 16, ... and the differences are 3, 5, 7, 9, ... so all the following sequences are based on adding a number to n^2.

Example 3.74

Find the nth term of the sequence below.

10, 13, 18, 25, ...

Solution

The differences in the sequence are 3, 5, 7, ...

Subtracting 1 from the first term gives 9.

The nth term of the sequence is $n^2 + 9$.

Quadratic sequences – another way

Example 3.75

Find the formula for the nth term of this sequence.

2, 8, 18, 32, 50, ...

Solution

Write out the sequence, working out the differences.

2   8   18   32   50

6   10   14   18

Now work out a second row of differences.

4   4   4

When there are two rows of differences, you can be confident that the sequence will be quadratic.

If you halve the number in the second row, you will get the coefficient of n^2.

$4 \div 2 = 2$

$n =$	1	2	3	4	5
$n^2 =$	1	4	9	16	25
$2n^2 =$	2	8	18	32	50

This is the same as the original list of numbers, so the nth term of the sequence is $2n^2$.

Example 3.76

Find the formula for the nth term of the following sequence.

4, 7, 12, 19, 28, 39

Solution

$n =$	1	2	3	4	5	6
	4	7	12	19	28	39

1st difference

3   5   7   9   11

2nd difference

2   2   2   2

There are 2 rows of differences, so the formula involves n^2.

The second difference is 2.

$2 \div 2 = 1$, so the sequence involves $1n^2$.

$n =$	1	2	3	4	5	6
$n^2 =$	1	4	9	16	25	36
original sequence	4	7	12	19	28	39, ...

It is easy to see that the difference between the two rows is 3, so the formula is $n^2 + 3$.

Example 3.77

Find the formula for the nth term of this sequence.

2, 6, 12, 20, 30, 42

Solution

$n =$ 1 2 3 4 5 6

2 6 12 20 30 42, ...

1st difference

4 6 8 10 12

2nd difference

2 2 2 2

There are 2 rows of differences, so the formula involves n^2.

The second difference is 2 and dividing this by 2 gives $1n^2$.

$n =$	1	2	3	4	5	6
$n^2 =$	1	4	9	16	25	36
original sequence	2	6	12	20	30	42
The difference is	1	2	3	4	5	6

Don't be put off by the fact that the differences between each pair of numbers aren't the same. If you look at each value of n, i.e. 1, 2, 3, ..., the heading, 1st, 2nd, ... you can see that it's the same as the term number, so the formula is $n^2 + n$.

Fibonacci sequences

In these sequences, each term is the sum of the two previous terms.

You will not be asked for the nth term of a Fibonacci sequence, and you do not have to remember the name.

Example 3.78

Find the next three terms in the sequence below.

1, 1, 2, 3, 5, 8, ...

Solution

Adding the two previous terms in each case, the next three terms are 13, 21, 34.

Now try the following exercise.

Exercise 3.25

1 Look at the sequence 1, 4, 7, 10, 13, ...
 a) Find the 16th term.
 b) Give a formula for the nth term.
 c) Find which term gives the number 139.

2 For the sequence 8, 11, 16, 23, 32, ... , find:
 a) the 14th term **b)** the nth term.

3 For the sequence 5, 12, 19, 26, ... , find:
 a) the 25th term **b)** the nth term.

4 Find the nth term of the sequence 3, 12, 27, 48, ...

5 Find the next two terms in the sequence 2, 4, 6, 10, 16, ...

6 Find the nth term in the sequence 4, 11, 30, 67, ...

Answers – 3.25

1 **a)** 46
 b) $3n - 2$
 c) 47th ($3n - 2 = 139$ so $n = 47$)

2 **a)** 203 **b)** $n^2 + 7$

3 **a)** 173 **b)** $7n - 2$

4 $3n^2$

5 26, 42

6 $n^3 + 3$

The sequence of triangular numbers

This is a favourite sequence of examiners, both in the exams themselves and as part of a coursework task.

Example 3.79

Find the next two numbers, and give the nth term.

1, 3, 6, 10, 15, 21

Solution

$n =$ 1 2 3 4 5 6

1 3 6 10 15 21, ...

1st difference

2 3 4 5 6

The difference is increasing by 1 each time. If you are feeling particularly enthusiastic, you can try working out the formula by yourself, but as it's a little more complicated, we've been kind and given it.

Try using $\frac{n(n+1)}{2}$. The first term is $\frac{1 \times 2}{2}$ followed by $\frac{2 \times 3}{2}, \frac{3 \times 4}{2}, \frac{4 \times 5}{2} \ldots$

The clue to spotting the sequence is that the difference increases by 1 each time.

Sequences with fractions

Example 3.80

Find the nth term in the following sequence.

$\frac{3}{5}, \frac{5}{9}, \frac{7}{13}, \frac{9}{17}, \ldots$

Solution

These sequences are very easy if you treat the top and bottom lines as two different sequences and don't try to deal with them as if they were fractions.

What would the nth term of each line be? Try to work it out before looking at the answer.

The nth term of the top sequence is $2n + 1$.

The nth term of the bottom line is $4n + 1$.

Therefore the formula for the nth term of the sequence is

$\frac{2n+1}{4n+1}$.

Exercise 3.26

For each of the following sequences, find:

a) the next two numbers in the sequence
b) the difference
c) the nth term.

1 7, 11, 15, 19, ...

2 2, 8, 14, 20, ...

3 13, 10, 7, 4, ...

4 4, 7, 12, 19, ...

5 $\frac{1}{7}, \frac{4}{11}, \frac{9}{15}, \frac{16}{19}, \ldots$

Answers – 3.26

1 a) 23, 27 **b)** +4 **c)** $4n + 3$

2 a) 26, 32 **b)** +6 **c)** $6n - 4$

3 a) 1, −2 **b)** −3 **c)** $-3n + 16$

4 a) 28, 39
b) The difference between the numbers increases by 2 each time.
c) $n^2 + 3$

5 a) $\frac{25}{23}, \frac{36}{27}$
b) Top row, difference increases by 2 each time. Bottom row, add 4 each time.
c) $\frac{n^2}{4n+3}$

If you had trouble with Algebra before you started on this chapter, try Exercise 3.1, on page 28, again to see if you find it easier.

REVIEW

How much have you learnt?
Tick off each topic in the list when you are confident that you can cope with it.

- ☐ **Explain the meaning of variable, coefficient and constant.**
- ☐ **Solve simple linear equations in one unknown.**
- ☐ **Solve equations involving algebraic fractions.**
- ☐ **Solve simultaneous equations in two unknowns.**
- ☐ **Factorise algebraic expressions.**
- ☐ **Solve quadratic equations by factorising.**
- ☐ **Find the rule for forming a sequence with equal differences.**
- ☐ **Find the rule for forming a sequence with unequal differences.**
- ☐ **Find the nth term of a sequence.**
- ☐ **Find the value of an unknown in a formula by substitution.**
- ☐ **Rearrange formulae.**
- ☐ **Make expressions and equations from statements.**

PREVIEW

By the end of this chapter you will be able to:

- **solve simultaneous equations graphically**
- **interpret a straight-line graph involving two variables**
- **calculate and interpret the gradient of a straight-line graph**
- **calculate and interpret the y-intercept on a straight-line graph**
- **find a set of values to satisfy an inequality**
- **show regions on a graph that satisfy a set of inequalities**
- **match simple graphs and their equations**
- **match rates of flow in containers with their graphs.**

How much do you know already?

Exercise 4.1

1 Complete the following table for $y = 2x - 3$

x	0	1	2	3	4
y					

2 By adding a suitable line to this graph, solve the following simultaneous equations.

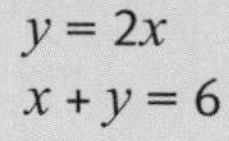

$y = 2x$
$x + y = 6$

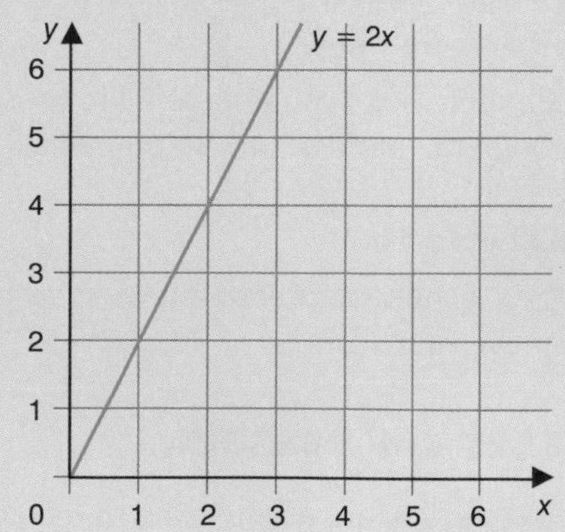

3 The graph below illustrates a family's telephone expenses.

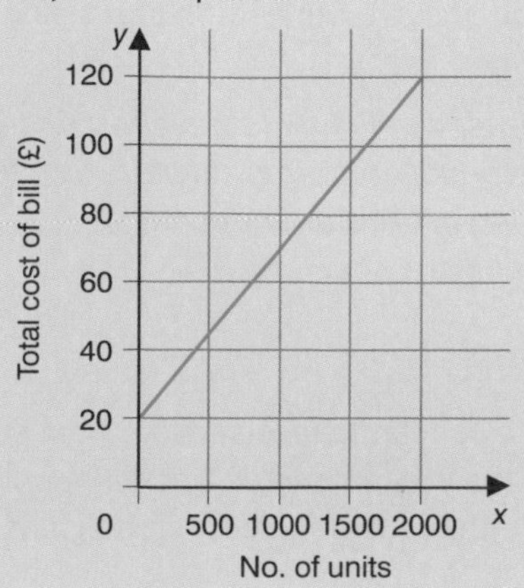

a) The bill is £80.00. How many units were used?
b) Find the gradient of the graph.
c) What does this gradient represent?

4 From the graph below, solve $x^2 - 2x = 5$
Give both answers correct to 1 d.p.

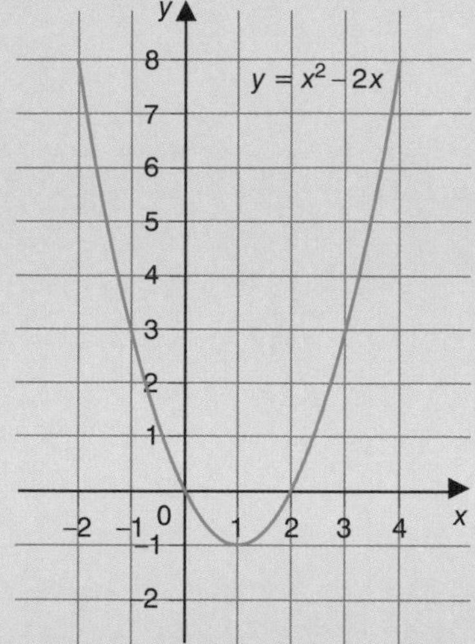

5 Find the set of values of x for which:
a) $3 - x > 4 - 2x$ **b)** $x^2 < 25$ **c)** $x^2 \geq 36$

6 Indicate the region R which satisfies the following inequalities.

$x + y \leq 7 \quad 2y \geq x + 2 \quad x \geq 1$

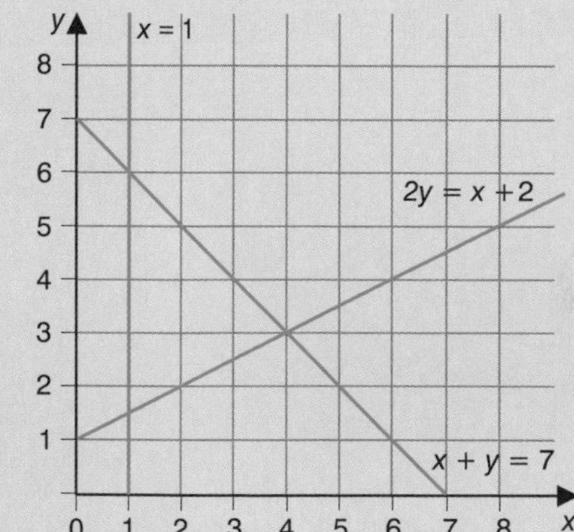

7 Match each equation to its graph.
a) $y = -x^2$ **b)** $y = x + 1$
c) $x + y = 3$ **d)** $y = x^3$

i)
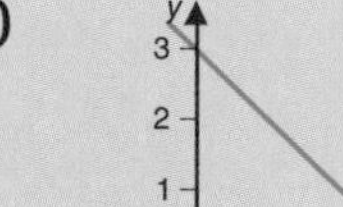

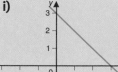

ii)
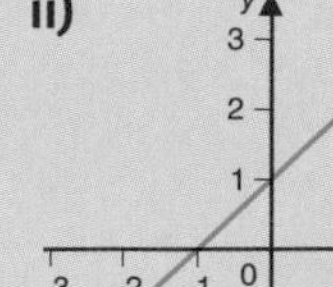

iii)
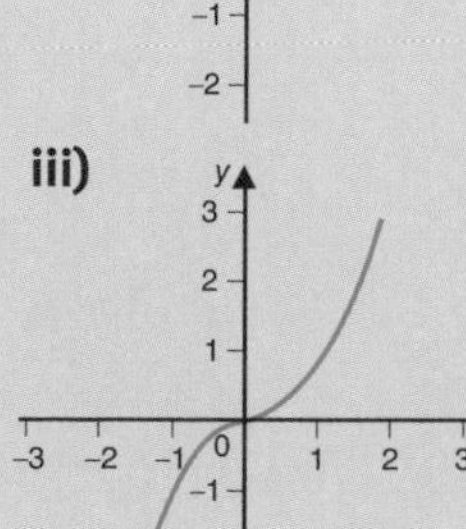

iv)
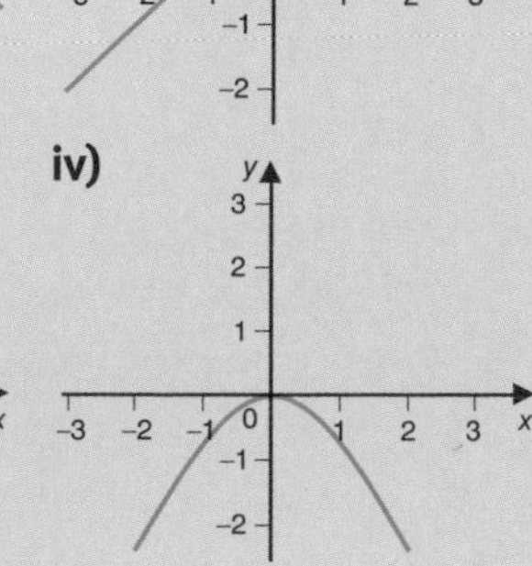

8 Liquid flows into some containers at a constant rate. Sketch the graph of the depth of liquid against time for these containers.

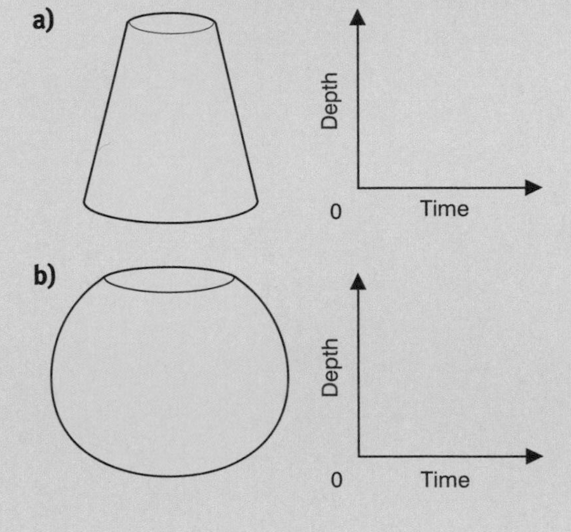

Answers – 4.1

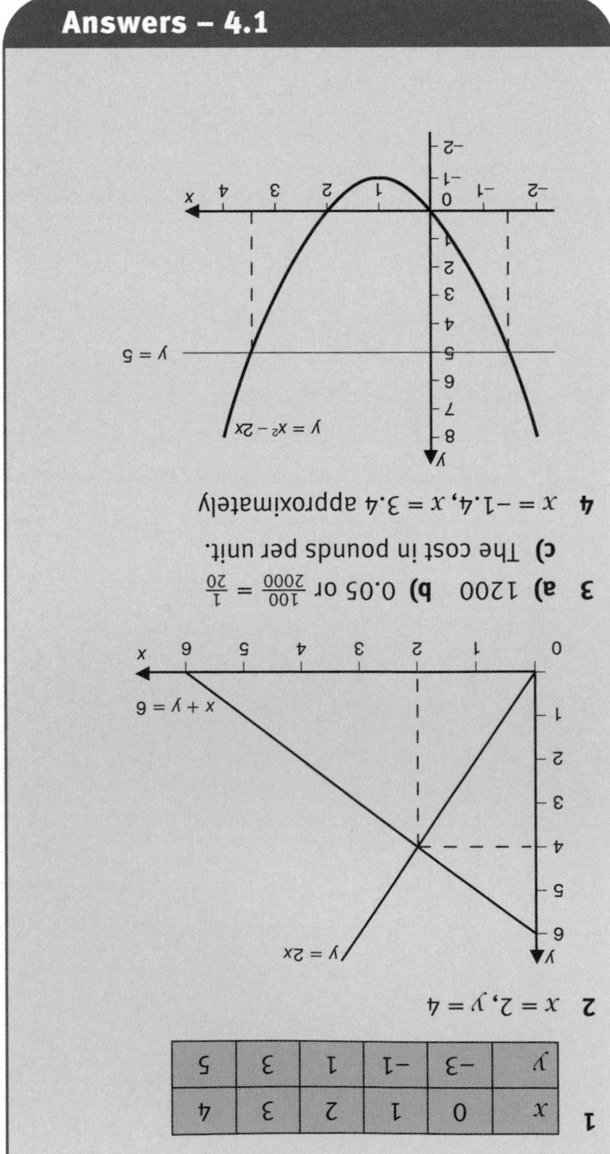

1

x	0	1	2	3	4
y	−3	−1	1	3	5

2 $x = 2, y = 4$

3 **a)** 1200 **b)** 0.05 or $\frac{100}{2000} = \frac{1}{20}$ **c)** The cost in pounds per unit.

4 $x = -1.4, x = 3.4$ approximately

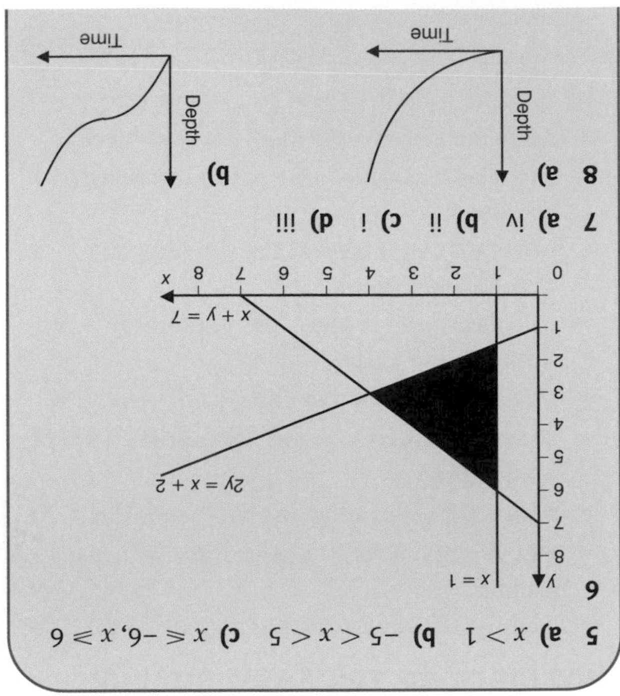

5 **a)** $x > 1$ **b)** $-5 < x < 5$ **c)** $x \leqslant -6, x \geqslant 6$

6

7 **a)** iv **b)** ii **c)** i **d)** iii

8 **a)** **b)**

How did you get on?

All or most of them right?

Well done! You should be able to solve any question of the type shown above that you might find on your exam paper, but it's a good idea to flip through the rest of the exercises in this chapter just to make sure.

Half or more right?

It shouldn't take you long to fill in the gaps. Just work through the parts of the chapter which you need.

Don't even ask?

This is a short chapter and if you stay positive, you'll improve your score.

Vases and vessels

In exams, you are often asked to recognise or draw graphs which describe the depth of liquid in a container when it is filled at a constant rate. Occasionally you are given the graph and asked to draw the container.

The rate of increase of the height depends on the cross-sectional area. The wider the cross-sectional area, the slower the rate at which the height increases.

Cylinders

Cylinders have a constant cross-section. They stay the same width all the way up and do not get narrower or wider. Therefore the rate of increase in height is constant.

Other common shapes

Here are the shapes that often come up. Get to know their graphs.

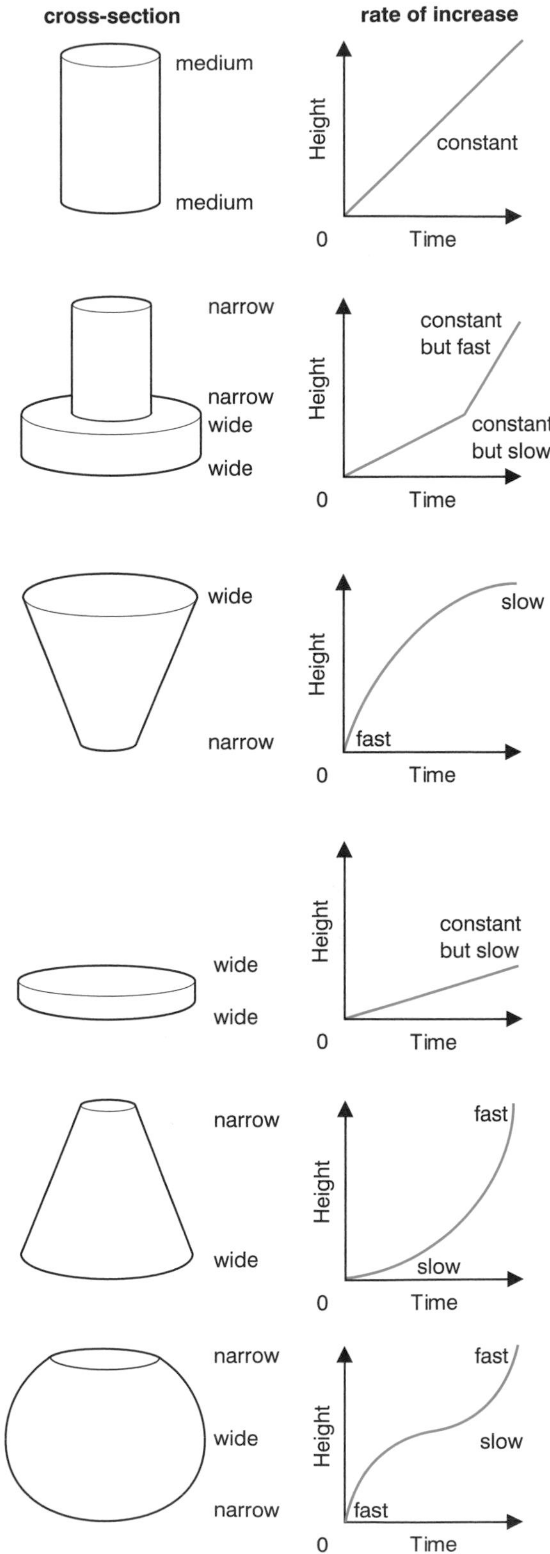

Gradients

The gradient of a line is also known as the slope of the line. If a line has a gradient of 2 units, then for every one unit you go along, you go up two.

Finding the gradient of a straight line

Pick two points on the line, and construct a right-angled triangle. To find the gradient use 'GRADients are gradUAL'.

$$\text{GRADient} = \frac{\text{Up}}{\text{ALong}}$$

If you find it easier, you can think of 'Gradients are GROTty', or Gradients are:

Rise (i.e. how much you go up or down)
Over (divided by)
Tread (how much you go along)

$$\text{Gradient} = \frac{\text{Rise}}{\text{Tread}}$$

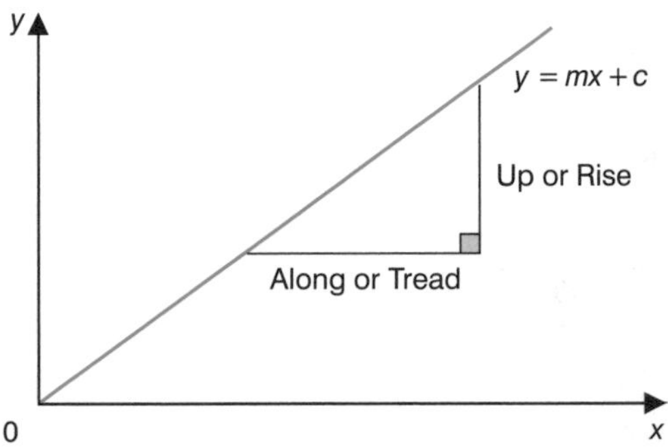

Remember: If the line slopes up, the gradient is positive. If the line slopes down, the gradient is negative.

Remember **N** for negative gradients.

Distance between two points

Given two points, you can use their coordinates to find the distance between them. Here is how to do it.

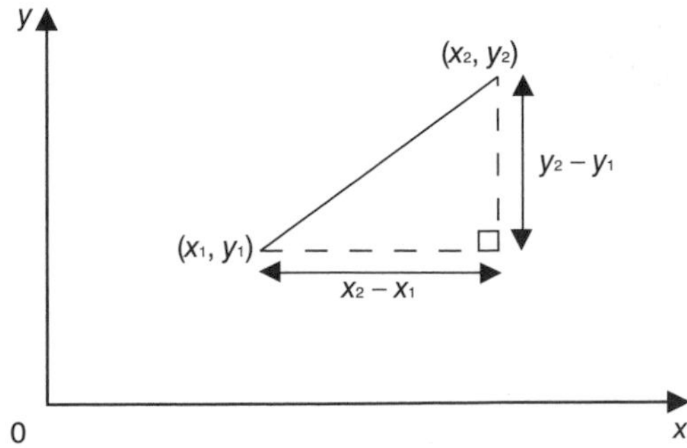

The two points have been joined up, then the right-angled triangle has been drawn with sides parallel to the axes.

The lengths of the sides are $(x_2 - x_1)$ and $(y_2 - y_1)$. To find the distance between the points use Pythagoras' theorem or the formula

$$\sqrt{(x_2 - x_1)^2 + (y_2 - y_1)^2}$$

Example 4.1

Find the distance between the points (4, 5) and (8, 10),

a) leaving your answer as an exact number

b) giving your answer correct to 1 decimal place.

Solution

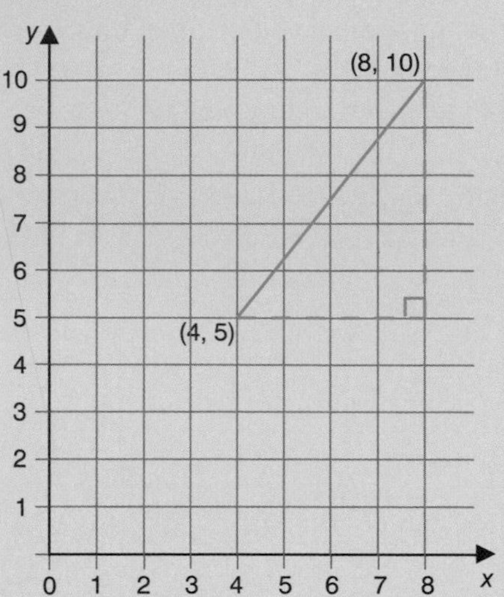

a) $\sqrt{[(8-4)^2 + (10-5)^2]} = \sqrt{16+25} = \sqrt{41}$

b) $\sqrt{41} = 6.4$ to 1 d.p.

Remember: *If you are squaring a negative number on the calculator, with most calculators you need to put the negative number in brackets before you square it.*

Hints & Tips

Finding the midpoint of two points

To find the x-value of the midpoint of the two points (x_1, y_1) and (x_2, y_2), take the mean of x_1 and x_2, and to find the y-value of the midpoint take the mean of y_1 and y_2.

So the midpoint of (x_1, y_1) and (x_2, y_2) is

$$\left(\frac{x_1 + x_2}{2}, \frac{y_1 + y_2}{2}\right)$$

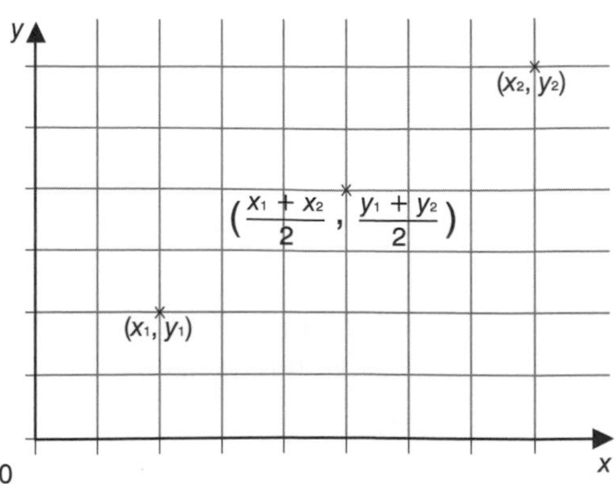

Example 4.2

Find the midpoint of (4, 5) and (−2, 7).

Solution

$$\frac{4 + -2}{2} = 1$$

$$\frac{5 + 7}{2} = 6$$

So the midpoint is (1, 6).

Exercise 4.2

1 Find the distances between the following pairs of points, giving your answers as square roots.
a) (2, 7) and (4, 10)
b) (−3, 0) and (6, 7)
c) (−6, −2) and (−1, 5)

2 Find the distances between the following pairs of points, giving your answers to 2 significant figures.
a) (5, 2) and (6, 9)
b) (−4, −3) and (6, −8)
c) (540, 521) and (348, 892)

3 Find the midpoints of the following pairs of points.
a) (8, 5) and (2, 7)
b) (−3, −5) and (−9, −1)
c) (0, 3) and (7, 2)

Answers – 4.2

1 a) $\sqrt{13}$ **b)** $\sqrt{130}$ **c)** $\sqrt{74}$
2 a) 7.1 **b)** 11 **c)** 420
3 a) (5, 6) **b)** (−6, −3) **c)** (3.5, 2.5)

The gradient and equation of a line

You may have seen the equation $y = mx + c$.

In this equation, m stands for the gradient and c is the y-**intercept**, or the point where the line crosses the y-axis.

The examiner may use different letters, e.g. $y = ax + b$. Do not be put off by this. The letter or number with the x always stands for the gradient, and the letter or number on its own gives the y-intercept.

Make sure that the equation is in the form $y = ax + b$ before you start. If, for instance, your equation is $2x + y = 7$, rewrite it as $y = -2x + 7$.

If lines are parallel, they have the same gradient.

Example 4.3

Find the gradient and the y-intercept of the line $y = 2x + 1$

Solution

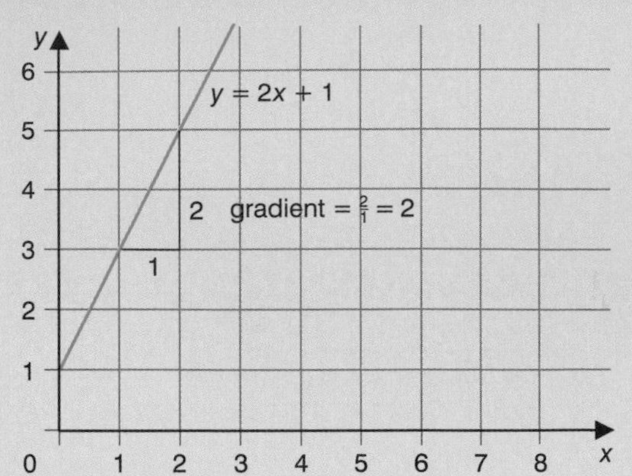

Start by drawing a right-angled triangle on the graph.

Compare the equation with $y = mx + c$.

The gradient is 2. The y-intercept is 1.

Example 4.4

Find the gradient and the y-intercept of the line $y = 1 - 2x$

Solution

Examples of this form are easier to solve if you turn them round i.e. $y = -2x + 1$

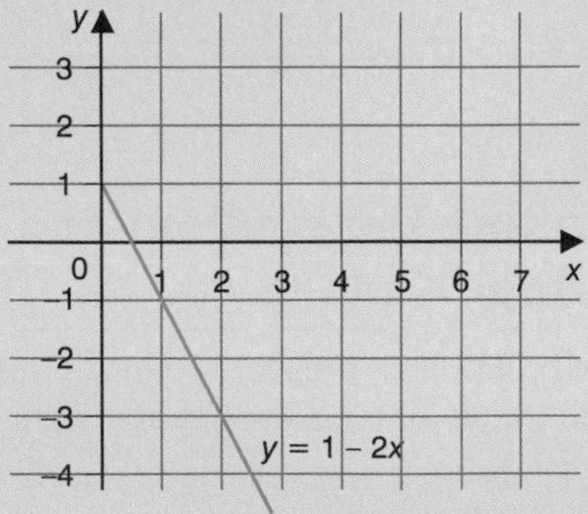

The gradient = −2. The y-intercept = 1.

Exercise 4.3

1 For each of the following equations, find the gradient and the y–intercept.

a) $y = 3x + 7$
b) $y = 0.5x + 2$
c) $y = 4 - x$
d) $2x + y = 11$

2 Which of the following lines are parallel to $y = 2 - x$?

a) $y + x = 3$
b) $y = x - 1$
c) $y = -x - 2$

Answers – 4.3

1 **a)** gradient = 3, y-intercept = 7
b) gradient = 0.5, y-intercept = 2
c) gradient = −1, y-intercept = 4
d) gradient = −2, y-intercept = 11

2 **a)** and **c)**

Function notation

Function notation is an alternative way of writing equations. Using function notation you write $y = 2x + 3$ as $f(x) = 2x + 3$. Using function notation is like replacing the y with $f(x)$. f(3) is the result of substituting 3 into the right-hand side and finding the value.

Example 4.5

For the function $f(x) = 3x + 4$, find:

a) f(2)
b) f(−4).

Solution

a) To find f(2), replace x with 2 in $3x + 4$.
$f(2) = 3 \times 2 + 4 = 10$

b) $f(-4) = 3 \times -4 + 4 = -8$

Example 4.6

If $f(x) = 2x^2 - 7$, find:

a) f(3) **b)** f(−2)

Solution

When substituting numbers into $2x^2$, remember BODMAS or BIDMAS, which tells you to square x before you multiply by 2.

Using your calculator: If x is negative, put it in brackets before you square it.

a) $f(3) = 2 \times 3^2 - 7 = 11$

b) $f(-2) = 2 \times (-2)^2 - 7 = 1$

Exercise 4.4

1 If $f(x) = 2 - 5x$, find:
  a) $f(4)$
  b) $f(0)$
  c) $f(-3)$

2 If $f(x) = 3x^2 - 4$, find:
  a) $f(2)$
  b) $f(-1)$
  c) $f(-4)$

Answers – 4.4

1 **a)** -18 **b)** 2 **c)** 17
2 **a)** 8
  b) $3 \times (-1)^2 - 4 = 3 \times 1 - 4 = 3 - 4 = -1$
  c) $3 \times (-4)^2 - 4 = 3 \times 16 - 4 = 44$

Finding the equation of a line

Example 4.7

From the graphs below, find the equations of the lines.

a)

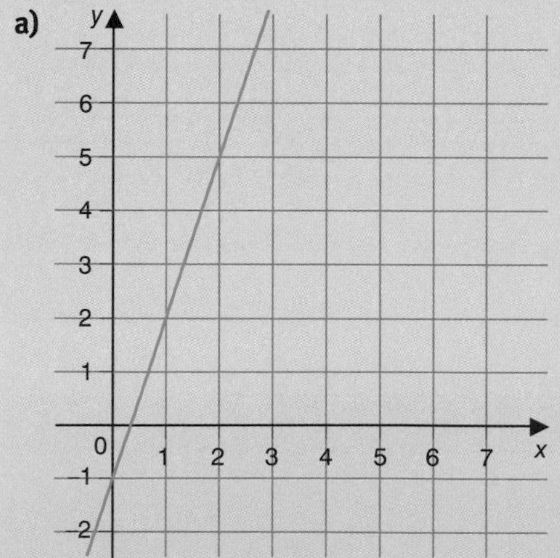

b)

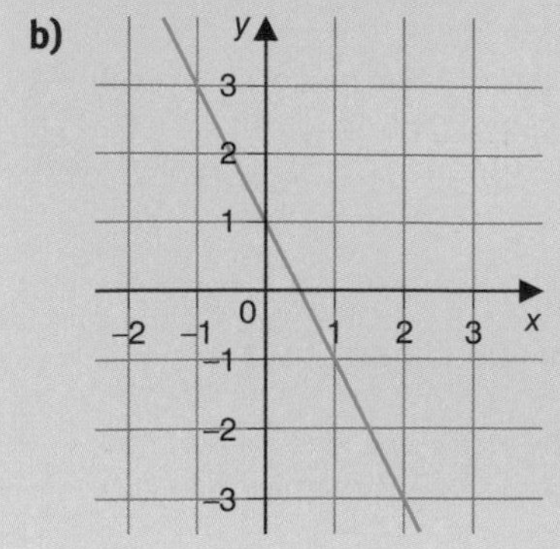

Solution

a) The gradient is $\frac{6}{2} = 3$.

The y intercept is at -1, so the equation is $y = 3x - 1$.

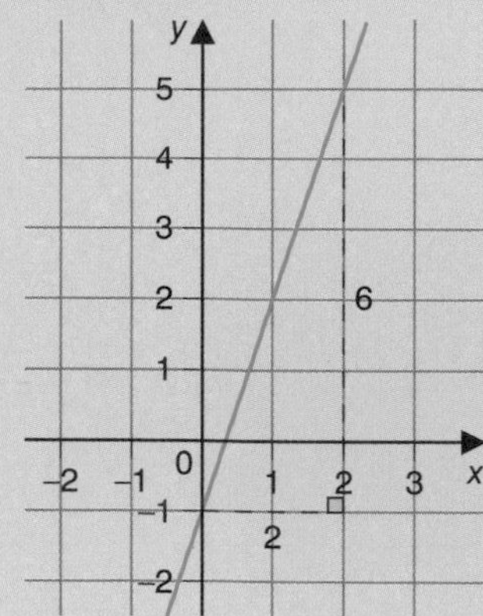

b) The gradient is $-\frac{4}{2} = -2$.

The intercept is at 1, so the equation is $y = 1 - 2x$, or $y = -2x + 1$.

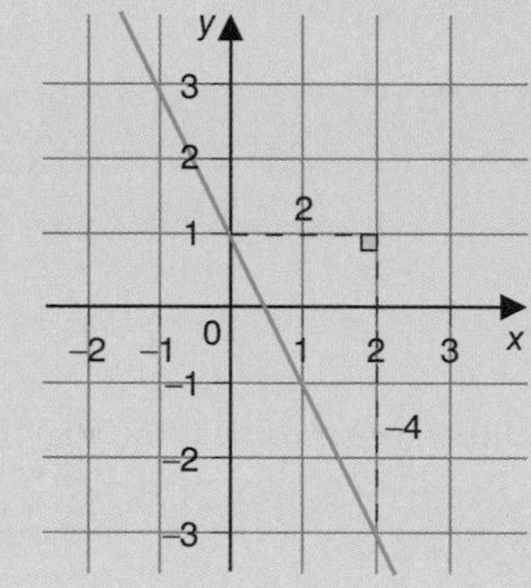

Interpreting the gradient and *y*-intercept

Sometimes you will be presented with a straight-line graph, and asked for the meaning of the gradient or the *y*-intercept.

Look at the labels on the axes, and imagine the word 'per' between them, as shown on either of the diagrams below.

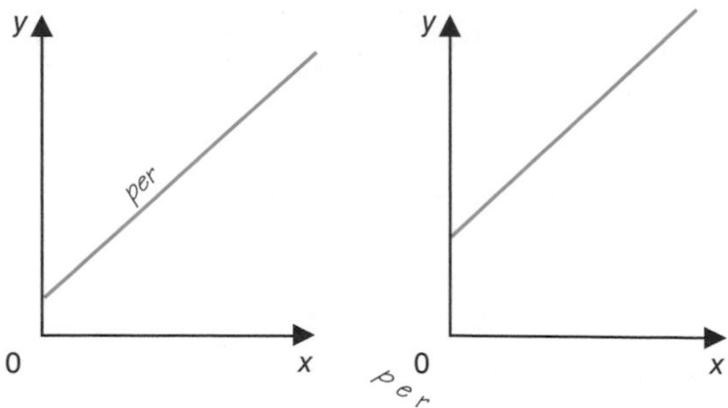

Graph 1 shows the number of pounds per dollar.

Graph 2 shows the cost in pounds (£) per unit.

Graph 3 shows the speed in km per hour because Distance ÷ Time = Speed.

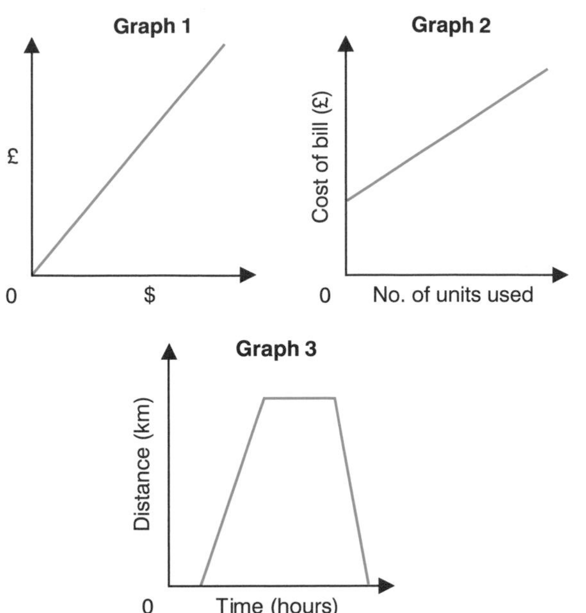

'Per' means 'divided by'. It is the same as the gradient.

The y-intercept is the point where the graph crosses the y-axis. It is also the point where $x = 0$. It usually represents something like the fixed or standing charge that you have to pay, regardless of the quantity used. You generally need the y-intercept when calculating household bills, or hire charges.

To recap ...

The gradient of a line measures its slope.

If the gradient is 0, the line is horizontal.

The bigger the gradient, the steeper the line.

If the line slopes up (i.e. ╱), the gradient is positive.

If the line slopes down (i.e. ╲), the gradient is negative.

Do you get 'horizontal' and 'vertical' mixed up? Remember that the horizontal goes in the same direction as the horizon.

Graphical solutions to simultaneous equations

To solve simultaneous equations graphically, you simply need the values of x and y at the crossing points of the two graphs.

Sometimes the graphs are already drawn, and sometimes you need to construct them using a table of values. If there is no table given, you need to make your own. Take four values of x, such as $x = 0, 1, 2, 3$. Find the corresponding values of y.

Plot the resulting points on the given graph, and confirm that your graph is correct. If the points are not in a straight line, or a smooth curve, there is an error in either your calculations or your plotting, or both.

When drawing the line, extend it to the edge of the graph – don't just connect the first and last points.

Example 4.8

Below is the graph of $2x + y = 6$

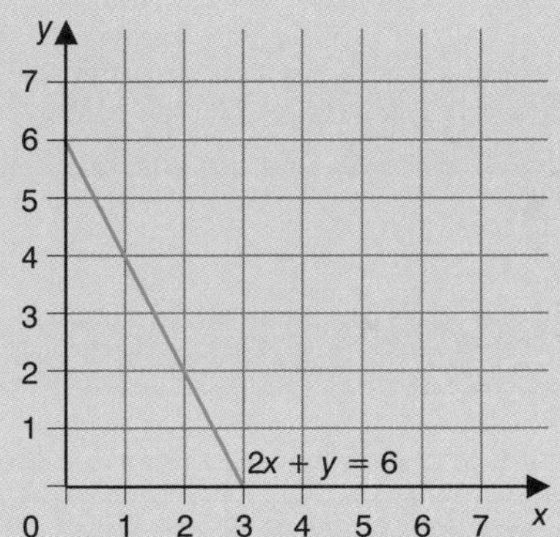

By adding a suitable line, solve the given simultaneous equations.

$2x + y = 6$
$y = 3x + 1$

Solution

Complete a table of values for $y = 3x + 1$ like this.

x	0	1	2	3
y	1	4	7	10

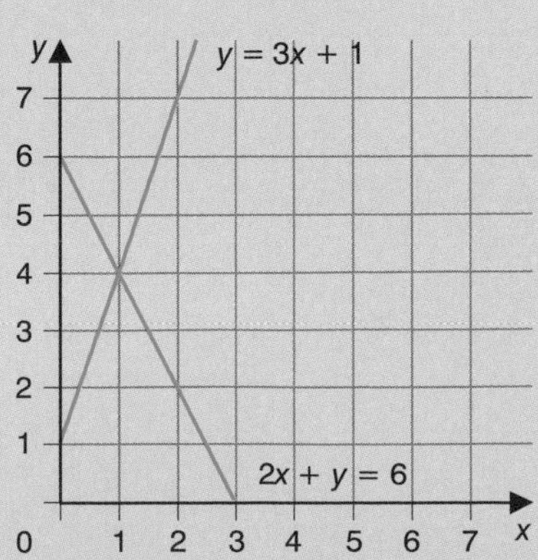

The solution is the point where the lines cross. This is $x = 1$, $y = 4$.

Exercise 4.5

Below is a graph of $2x + y = 8$. By adding a suitable line, solve the given simultaneous equations.

$2x + y = 8$
$y = 2x + 2$

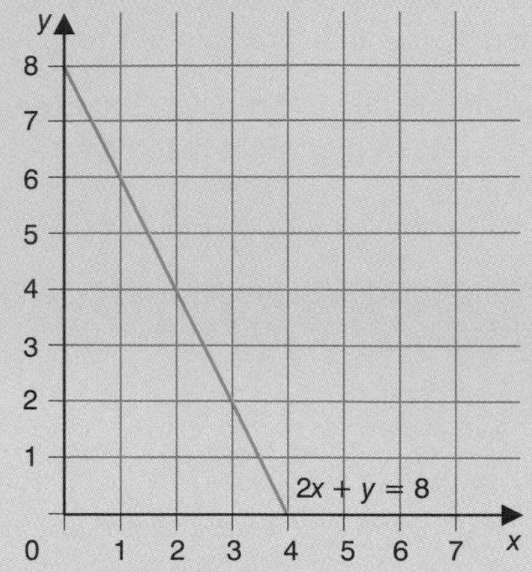

Answers – 4.5

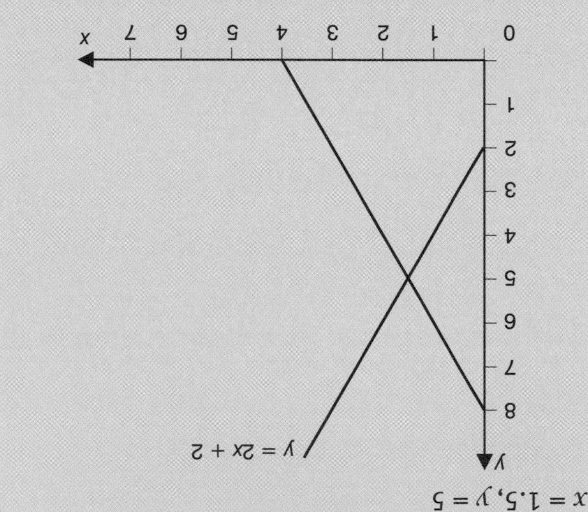

$x = 1.5, y = 5$

Curved graphs

Sketching quadratics

Example 4.9

a) Complete the table for $y = x^2 + x$

x	−3	−2	−1	0	1	2	3
y		2		0			

b) Using the table, draw $y = x^2 + x$ on the graph below.

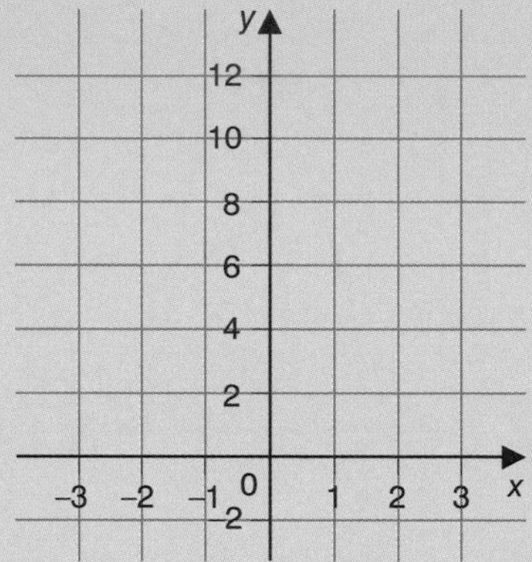

c) From your graph, find the values of x for which $x^2 + x = 3$, giving your answer correct to 1 d.p.

Solution

a) Complete the table of values.

x	−3	−2	−1	0	1	2	3
y	6	2	0	0	2	6	12

Note: *The values at $x = -1$ and $x = 0$ are the same. To find out what happens between these points, find the y-value when $x = -0.5$.*

If $x = -0.5$ then
$y = (-0.5)^2 - 0.5 = 0.25 - 0.5 = -0.25$

b) Use the table to draw the graph.

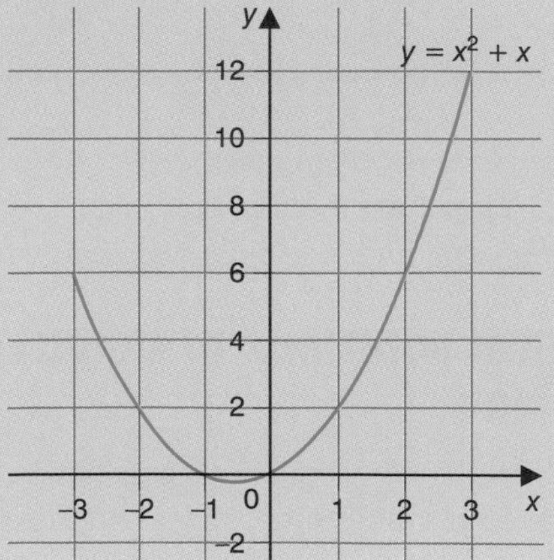

c) Now, to find the point where $x^2 + x = 3$, find where the graph of $y = x^2 + x$ cuts the graph of $y = 3$

On the same graph as before, draw the line $y = 3$

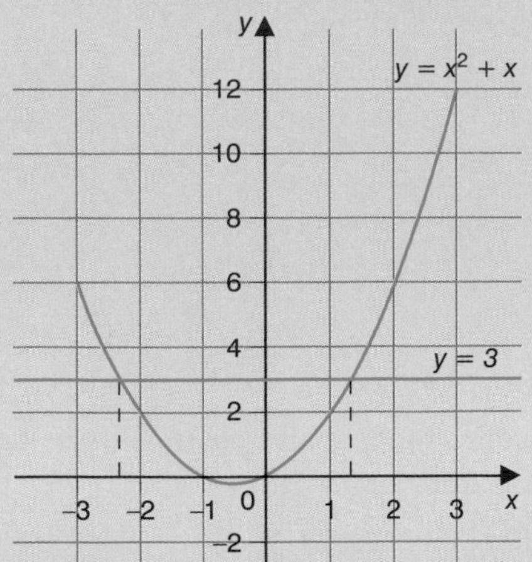

Remember: *$y = 3$ is horizontal, $x = 3$ is vertical.*

At the points where the two lines cross, $x = -2.3$, or $x = 1.3$

Always join the points on a curved graph with a smooth line. Never join the points with a ruler.

Exercise 4.6

$y = x^2 - 5x + 3$

1 Complete the table of values.

x	−1	0	1	2	3	4	5	6
y		3		−3				9

2 Sketch the graph of $y = x^2 - 5x + 3$ on the graph below.

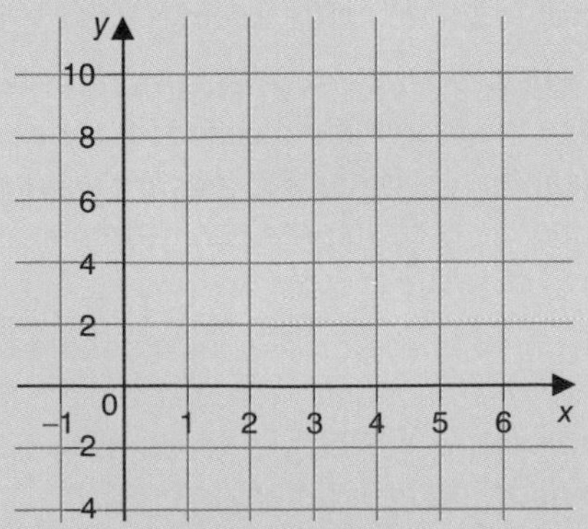

3 From your graph solve $x^2 - 5x + 3 = 0$, giving your answers correct to 1 d.p.

Answers – 4.6

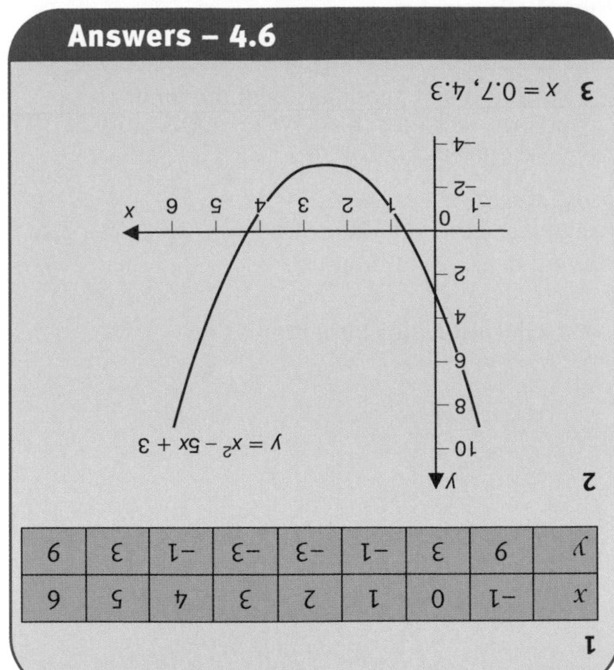

1

x	−1	0	1	2	3	4	5	6
y	9	3	−1	−3	−3	−1	3	9

2

3 $x = 0.7, 4.3$

Identifying mathematical graphs

If you find these difficult to remember, try plotting a few points of the equation to see where the graph appears to be going.

Linear graphs

The equations of these straight-line graphs can be written in the form $y = mx + c$, where m is the gradient and c is the y-intercept. If the gradient is positive, then the line slopes upwards from left to right:

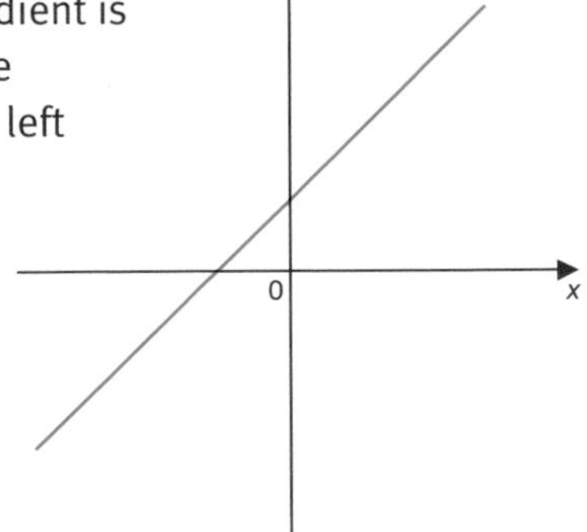

If the gradient is negative, then the line slopes downwards.

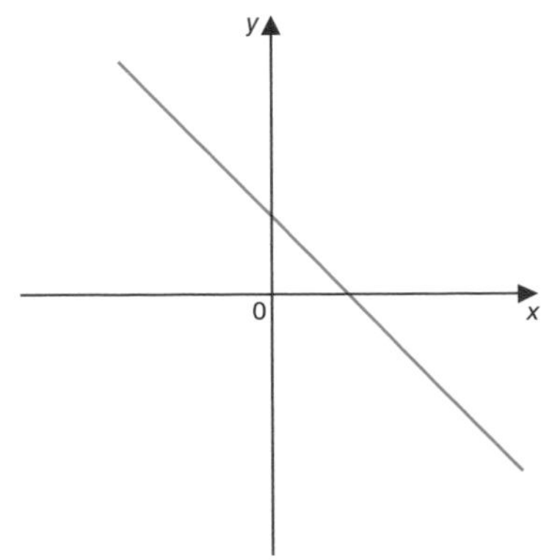

Hyperbolic graphs

Don't be put off by their name! These are curved graphs and their equations are of the form

$y = \frac{k}{x}$ where k is a constant.

Examples of the equations are $y = \frac{1}{x}$ which can also be written as $xy = 1$, and

$y = \frac{3}{x}$ which can also be written as $xy = 3$.

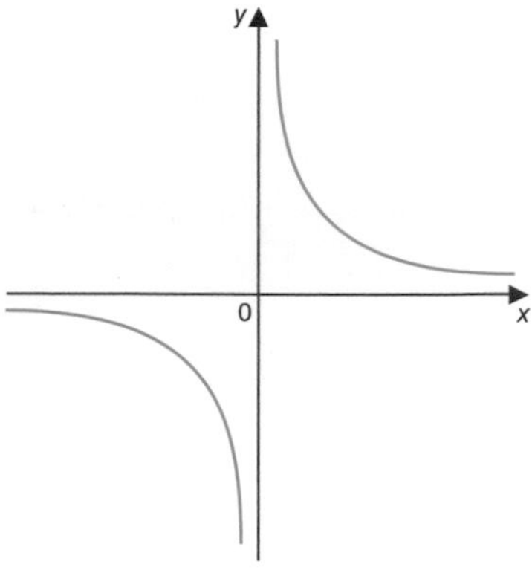

Quadratic graphs

These are also curved graphs. They are like some of the graphs you have already been drawing. Their equations are written in the form $y = ax^2 + bx + c$. For example, the equation $y = 3x^2 - 2x + 5$ will produce a quadratic graph with $a = 3$, $b = -2$ and $c = 5$.

a is the coefficient of x^2.

If a, is positive, then the graph looks like a smile.

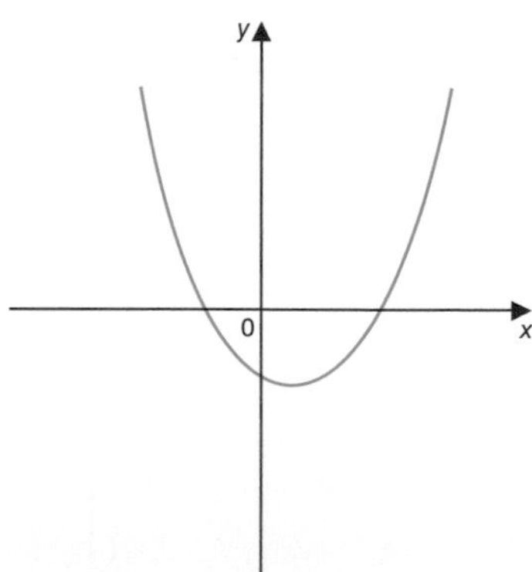

If a is negative, then it looks like a sad mouth.

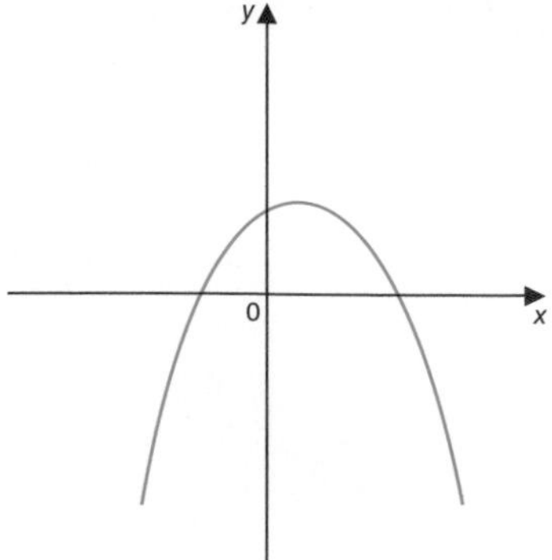

Cubic graphs

These curved graphs have equations that can be written in the form $y = ax^3 + bx^2 + cx + d$.
An example is $y = 3x^3 + 4x^2 - 2x - 1$.

If a (the coefficient of x^3) is positive then, apart from a bump, the graph goes upwards from left to right.

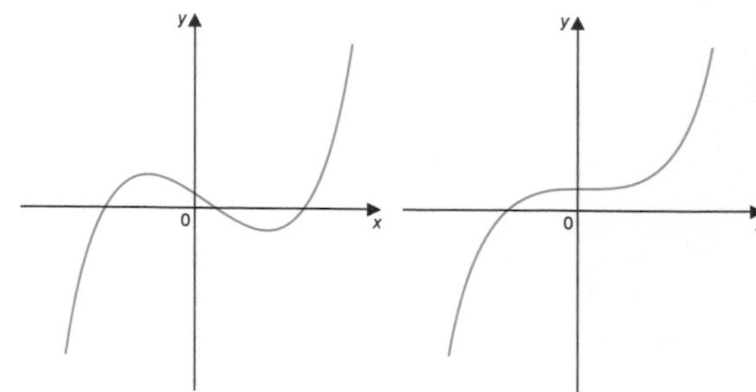

If a is negative then, apart from the bump, it goes downwards from left to right.

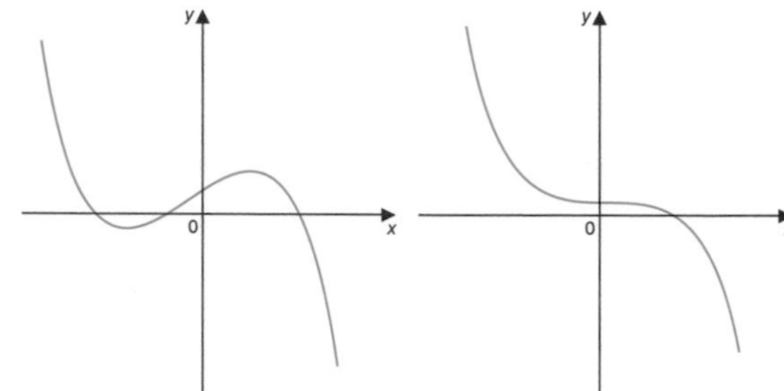

Linear inequalities and regions

Linear inequalities

○ means not including ● means including

$-2 \leqslant x < 5$ means x is between (B ≤ TW ≤≤ N) -2 and 5, and includes -2 but not 5. Another way of expressing this is: x is at least -2 and less than 5.

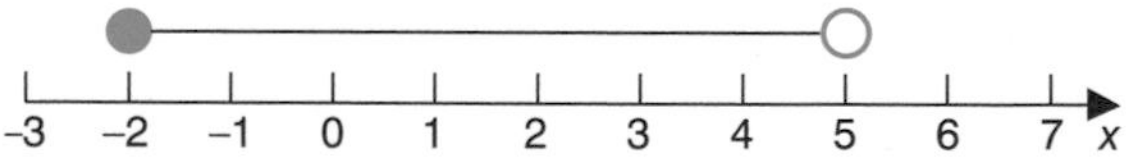

On a number line

Inequalities are very similar to equations, but with two important differences.

Rule 1 *If you swap the entire left and right-hand sides then the inequality reverses. For example, if an elephant (e) is heavier than a mouse (m), then a mouse is lighter than an elephant. In symbols, $e > m$ or $m < e$.*

Rule 2 *If you multiply or divide by a negative number, then the inequality sign is reversed. Below, for example, $5 > 2$ but $-5 < -2$. Also, $5 > -2$ but multiplying by -1 gives $-5 < 2$.*

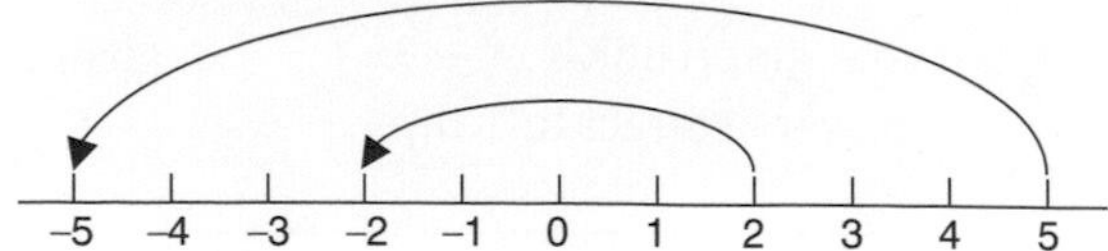

Exercise 4.7

Draw number lines to show the following inequalities.

1 $-5 \leqslant x \leqslant 6$ **2** $-5 < x \leqslant 6$

3 $-5 \leqslant x < 6$ **4** $-5 < x < 6$

Answers – 4.7

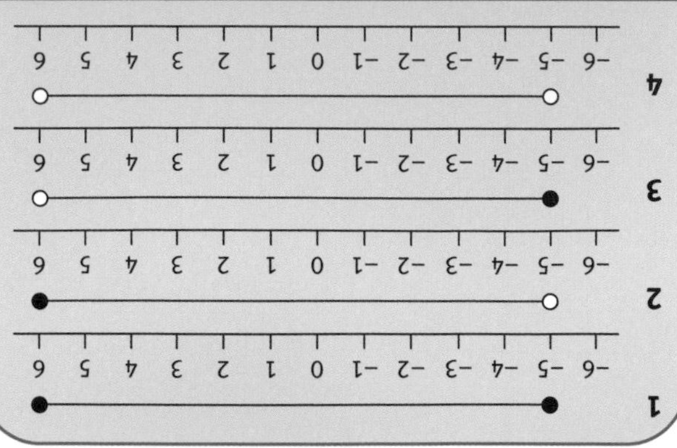

Example 4.10

Find the range of values of x for which $3 - 2x < 7$.

Solution

Method 1:

$3 - 2x < 7$

$3 < 2x + 7$ Taking the $2x$ over to make the coefficient positive.

$2x + 7 > 3$ Swapping the sides and reversing the inequality (rule 1).

$2x > -4$

$x > -2$

Method 2:

$3 - 2x < 7$

$-2x < 4$ Taking the 3 over to get the x term on its own.

$x > -2$ Dividing by -2, the inequality reverses when dividing by a negative number (rule 2).

Method 1 usually takes longer but it is safer. Whichever method you use, the conclusion is the same $3 - 2x < 7$ when $x > -2$.

Example 4.11

Find the largest integer for which $7x + 1 < 46$.

Solution

Solving the inequality gives $x < 6.43$.

The largest integer (whole number) that satisfies this inequality is 6.

Example 4.12

Find the range of values of x for which $2x + 5 < 3x + 7 < 2x + 16$.

Solution

Solving $2x + 5 < 3x + 7$ gives $x > -2$.

Solving $3x + 7 < 2x + 16$ gives $x < 9$.

To satisfy both inequalities, x must be B≤TW≤≤N −2 and 9, but not exactly −2 or 9.

i.e. $-2 < x < 9$

The most common examples of 'between' and 'outside'

Example 4.13

Find the range of values for x for which $x^2 \leqslant 16$.

Solution

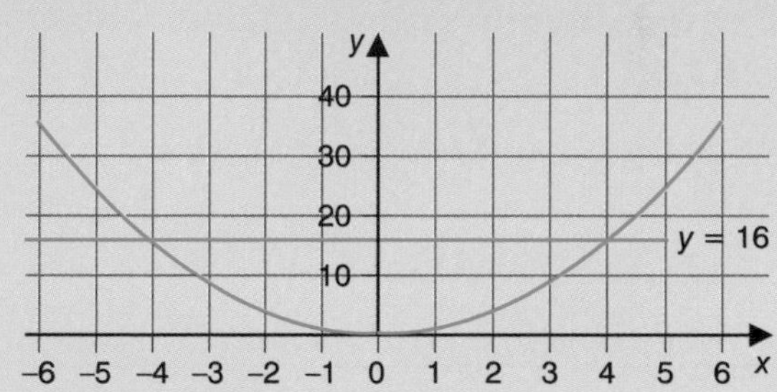

The diagram shows the graph $y = x^2$ and the line $y = 16$.

The curve is below, or less than $y = 16$ for values of x B≤TW≤≤N −4 and 4.

Therefore $-4 \leqslant x \leqslant 4$.

So if the question has an x^2 with an $\leqslant$ (or $<$) sign, use B≤TW≤≤N.

For example $x^2 \leqslant 16$ gives $-4 \leqslant x \leqslant 4$

$x^2 < 25$ gives $-5 < x < 5$

Hence B≤TW≤≤N (or B<TW<<N).

If the question has an x^2 with an $\geqslant$ (or $>$) sign, use ≤≥UTSI|≥E.

For example if $x^2 \geqslant 4$ then x will be ≤≥UTSI|≥E −2 and +2.

So $x^2 \geqslant 4$ gives $x \leqslant -2, x \geqslant 2$

$x^2 > 1$ gives $x < -1, x > 1$

Hence ≤≥UTSI|≥E (or <>UTSI|>E).

Examples of this kind are very common in exam papers.

Example 4.14

Find the range of values for x such that $x^2 \geqslant 16$.

Solution

From the previous graph, it can be seen that for y to be greater than 16, x must be less than −4, or greater than +4. Therefore $x \leqslant -4$, and $x \geqslant 4$.

TYPE 1 B≤TW≤≤N

$x^2 \leqslant 16$

B≤TW≤≤N

$-4 \leqslant x \leqslant 4$

TYPE 2 ≤≥UTSI⊵E

$x^2 \geqslant 16$

$x \leqslant -4$ ≤≥UTSI⊵E $x \geqslant 4$

In other words, x is ≤≥UTSI|≥E the boundaries of −4 and 4.

Exercise 4.8

1 Find the integers such that $-2 \leqslant x < 4$.

2 Find the range of values of x for which:

a) $1 < 3 - 2x$

b) $x^2 \leqslant 36$

c) $x^2 > 25$

Answers – 4.8

1 −2, −1, 0, 1, 2, 3

2 a) $x < 1$ b) $-6 \leqslant x \leqslant 6$ c) $x < -5, x > 5$

Choosing the region

As long as y is positive and on the left-hand side of the inequality, use AI≧OVE/B≤LOW.

For example, the region $x + y \leqslant 6$ will be the region B≤LOW $x + y = 6$.

The region $x + y \geqslant 6$ will be the region AI≧OVE $x + y = 6$.

Drawing the region

If the lines are not already drawn, change the inequality sign to an = sign, and draw the graph in the usual way.

You usually shade the region which you *don't* want, but always **read the instructions** very carefully in case you are asked to shade the required region.

For inequalities involving $>$ or $<$, use a broken line.

Example 4.15

On the graph below, leave unshaded the region which satisfies the following inequalities.

$x + y \leqslant 5$

$x \leqslant 1$

$y \geqslant x$

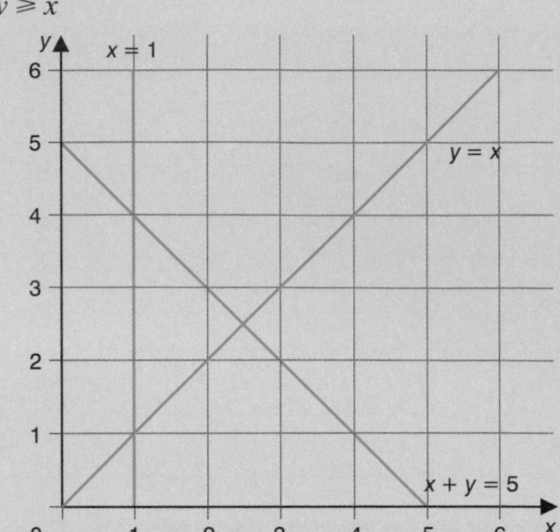

Solution

$x + y \leqslant 5$ the required region is B≤LOW $x + y = 5$.

$x \leqslant 1$ the required region is B≤LOW (i.e. to the L≤FT of) $x = 1$.

$y \geqslant x$ the required region is AI≧OVE $y = x$.

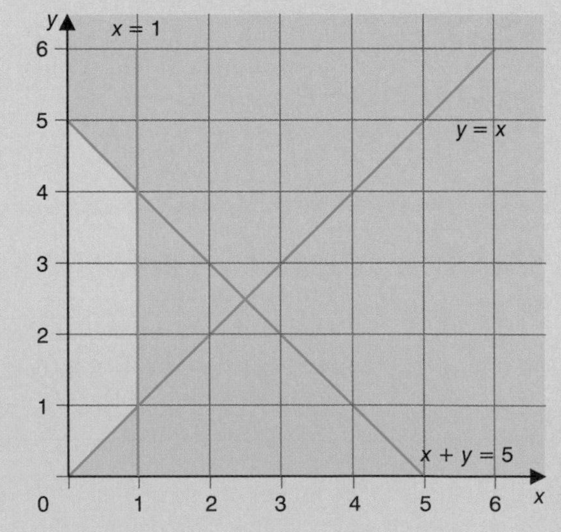

Distance–time graphs

***Remember:** The horizontal goes the same way as the horizon! That leaves vertical as meaning the up-and-down direction.*

The distance is read from the vertical axis, the time from the horizontal axis. The speed is the gradient: the steeper the slope, the higher the gradient, the faster the speed.

Remember: *To calculate gradients, use GRADUAL or GROTty.*

$$\text{Gradient} = \frac{\text{Up}}{\text{ALong}} \quad \text{or} \quad \text{Gradient} = \frac{\text{Rise}}{\text{Tread}}$$

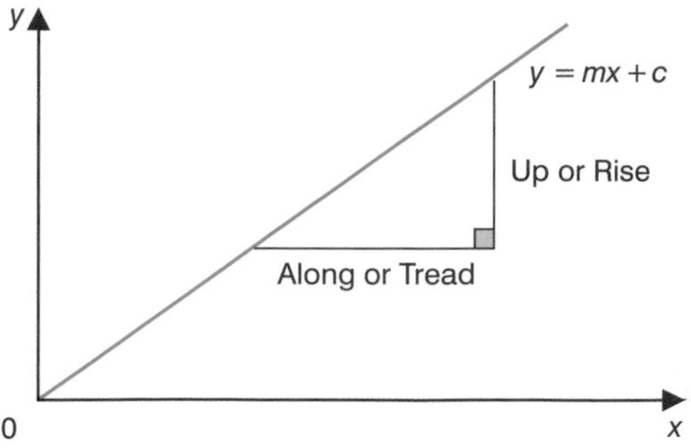

The graph below shows km per hour.

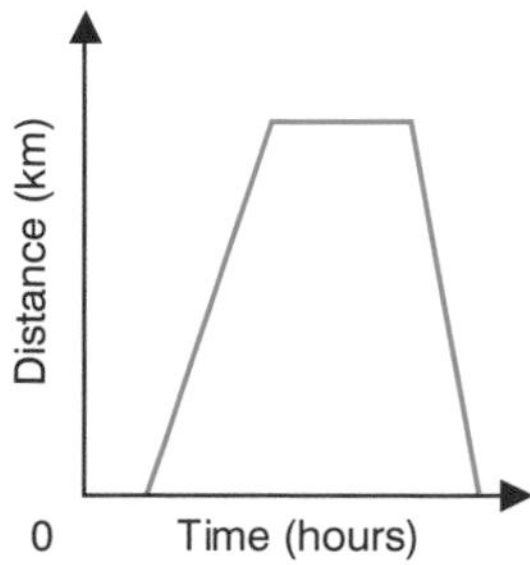

If the graph is horizontal, the object has stopped.

If there are two objects travelling, they meet when the graphs cross.

Example 4.16

Kazim visited his brother's house and then went on to his aunt's house before returning home.
The distance–time graph for his journey is shown below.

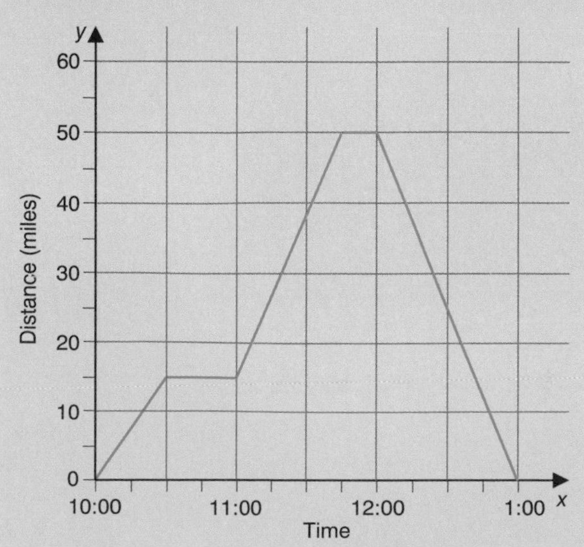

1 Write down:

a) how far it is from his home to his brother's house

b) how long he stayed at his brother's house

c) how far it is from his brother's house to his aunt's house

d) how long he stayed at his aunt's house

2 Calculate the speed at which he drove from:

a) home to his brother's house

b) his brother's house to his aunt's house

c) his aunt's house to his home

Solution

1 a) It is 15 miles to his brother's house.

b) He stopped at his brother's house. This is shown by the first horizontal section of the graph. He stayed for half an hour (30 minutes).

c) It is 50 miles from his home to his aunt's house, so it is 50 – 15 = 35 miles from his brother's to his aunt's house.

d) His time at his aunt's house is shown by the second horizontal section. He stayed for 15 minutes (a quarter of an hour).

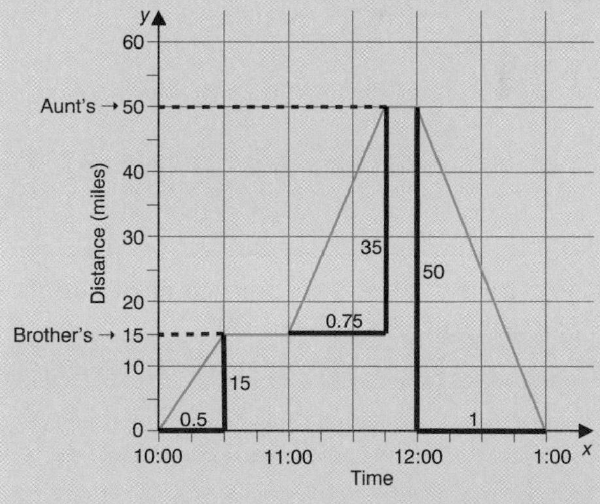

2 To calculate the speeds, draw the triangles as shown on the diagram.

a) Gradient = 15 ÷ 0.5 = 30 miles per hour

b) Gradient = 35 ÷ 0.75 = 47 miles per hour to 2 s.f.

c) Gradient = 50 ÷ 1 = 50 miles per hour

Exercise 4.9

Will left home to drive to Kenny's house. Will's brother Noel left half an hour later. Will returned home later. The distance–time graph showing their journeys is given below.

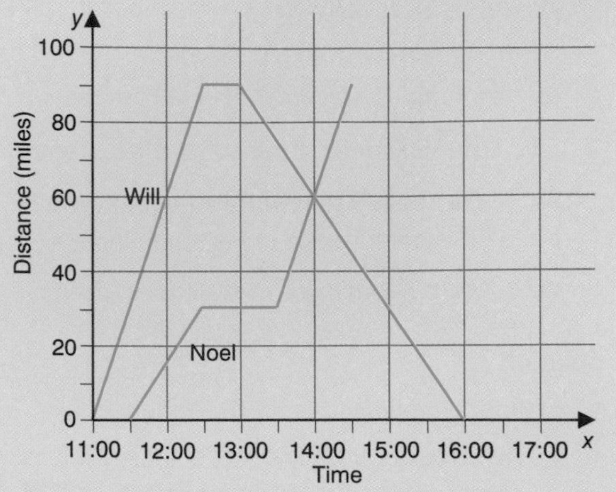

1 Find:

a) how long it took Will to get to Kenny's house,

b) how long Will stayed there

c) at what time Will left Kenny's house.

2 Noel stopped for a time on the way to Kenny's house.

a) At what time did he stop?

b) How long did he stop for?

3 Calculate:

a) the speed at which Will travelled to Kenny's house

b) the speed at which he travelled home.

4 At what time did they pass each other?

Answers – 4.9

1 **a)** $1\frac{1}{2}$ hours or 90 minutes

b) $\frac{1}{2}$ hour or 30 minutes

c) 13:00

2 **a)** 12:30

b) 1 hour or 60 minutes

3 **a)** $90 \div 1.5 = 60$ miles per hour

b) $90 \div 3 = 30$ miles per hour

4 14:00 (where the graphs meet)

REVIEW

How much have you learnt?
Tick off each topic in the list when you are confident that you can cope with it.

- ☐ **Solve simultaneous equations graphically.**
- ☐ **Interpret a straight-line graph involving two variables.**
- ☐ **Calculate and interpret the gradient of a straight-line graph.**
- ☐ **Calculate and interpret the y-intercept on a straight-line graph.**
- ☐ **Find a set of values to satisfy an inequality.**
- ☐ **Show regions on a graph that satisfy a set of inequalities.**
- ☐ **Match simple graphs and their equations.**
- ☐ **Match rates of flow in containers with their graphs.**

If you feel the need, go back and try the questions at the beginning of the chapter. If you are feeling confident, try the Algebra review which follows.

1 Solve the following pair of simultaneous equations.

$x + y = 6$
$x + 2y = 8.5$

2 In the following sequences find:

a) the next two terms
b) the difference
c) the nth term.

i) 8, 11, 14, 17, ...
ii) 2, 6, 10, 14, ...
iii) 1, 4, 9, 16, ...

3 Factorise these expressions completely.

a) $3ab + 6b^2$
b) $10y^2 - 2y$
c) $16xy^2 + 7x^2y$

4 A boy's sister is three years older than he is, and his mother is three times as old as his sister.

a) If his age is given as n years, write down in terms of n the ages of:
i) his sister
ii) his mother.

b) If the total of their ages is 67 years, form an equation in n, and simplify it.

c) Solve the equation to find the ages of the three people.

5 $C = ab + v^2$

a) Using the above formula, find C when $a = 0.7$, $b = 0.1$ and $v = 0.03$, giving your answer correct to 3 d.p.

b) Give your answer to **a)** in standard form correct to 2 sig. figs.

c) Make v the subject of the formula.

d) Hence or otherwise find v to the nearest integer when $C = 10.3$, $a = 2.1$ and $b = 0.6$.

6 On the graph below shade the region which satisfies all these inequalities.

$1 \leqslant x \leqslant 3$
$y \geqslant 1$
$x + y \leqslant 5$

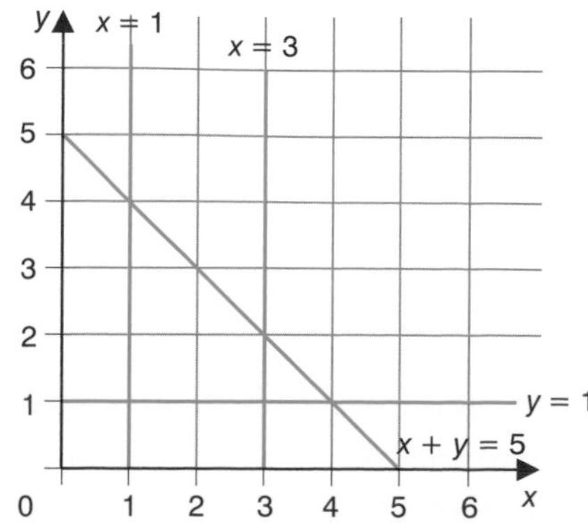

7 Write down the gradient and y-intercept of the graphs of the following equations.

a) $y = 1 - 2x$
b) $y + x = 3$
c) $y = \frac{x}{2} - 1$

8 The length of a rectangle is three times its width.

a) If its width is x cm, write in terms of x:
i) its length
ii) its area.

b) If its area is 75 cm^2, write an equation in x and solve it to find x.

9 Factorise and hence solve the following quadratic equations.

a) $x^2 + 7x + 10 = 0$
b) $x^2 + 4x - 5 = 0$
c) $x^2 - 10x - 11 = 0$
d) $x^2 - 5x + 6 = 0$
e) $x^2 - 5x - 6 = 0$

10 $c = a(m - v)^2$

Find c when $a = 0.3$, $m = 0.1$ and $v = 0.6$.

11 $V = \frac{1}{3}\pi h^3$

a) Rearrange the formula to give h in terms of V and π.

b) Hence or otherwise find h when $V = 10.7$.

12 By drawing suitable lines on the graph below, solve the given simultaneous equations.

$y = x + 1$
$y = 5 - x$

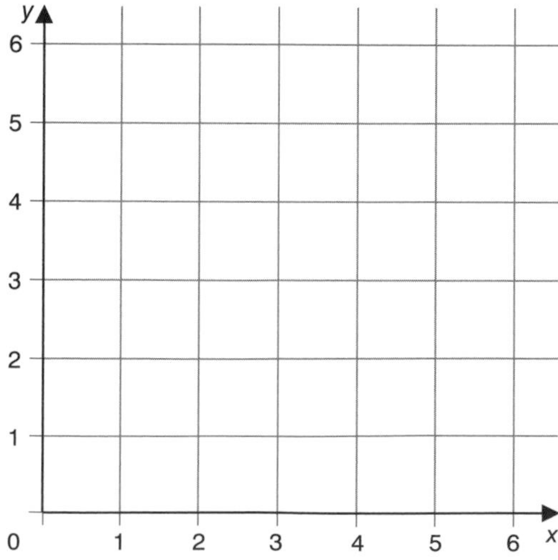

13 Find the range of values of x which satisfies each inequality.

a) $1 - 4x < 4 - 3x$
b) $x^2 \leqslant 25$
c) $x^2 > 9$

14 At a theatre, two adults' tickets and four children's tickets cost £37.00 and five adults' tickets and three children's tickets cost £64.50. Using x to represent the cost for an adult's ticket in pounds, and y to represent the cost of a child's ticket in pounds, form two equations and solve them to find the cost of three adults' tickets and seven children's tickets. Do not use a trial and improvement method.

15 Solve for x.
$5(x + 3) = 2(x - 6)$

16 Solve these simultaneous equations.
$x + 3y = -2$
$y = x + 6$

17 The graph below represents the daily hire charge for renting a car.

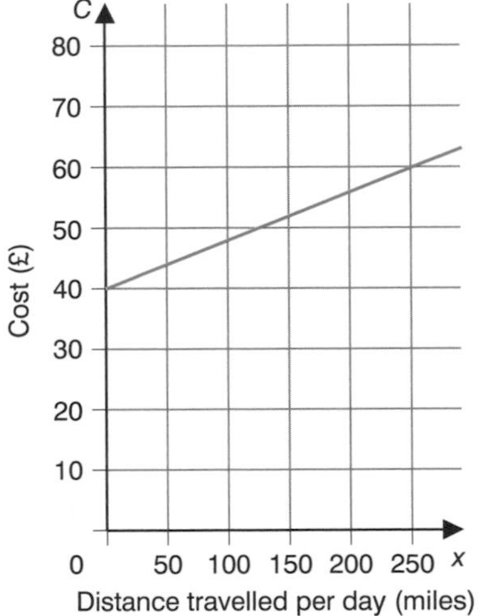

a) What is the gradient of the line?
b) What does the gradient represent?
c) Express the equation of the line in the form $C = ax + b$

18 On the graph below, shade the area which satisfies the following inequalities.
$y \leq 4$ $0 \leq x \leq 3$ $x + y \leq 5$

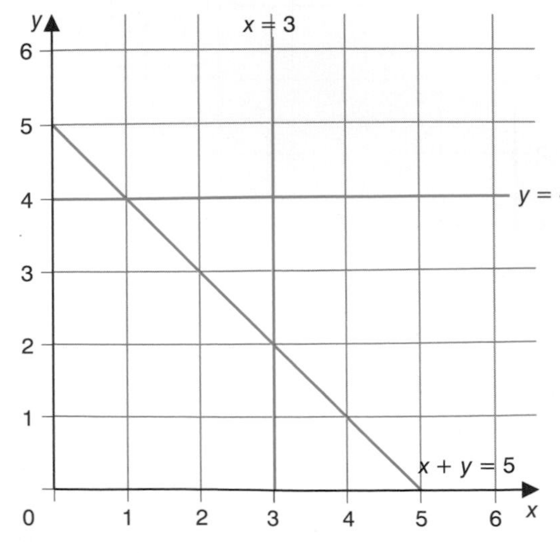

19 Match the following equations to the graphs below.

a) $y = x^3$ **b)** $y = x + 1$

c) $y = \frac{1}{x}$ **d)** $y = x^2$

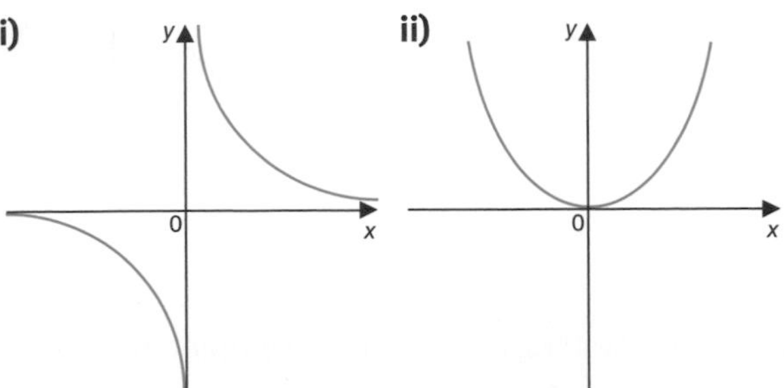

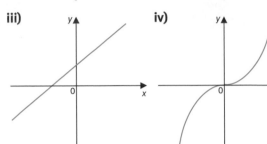

20 Complete the following table of values for $h = t^2 - 2t$.

t	−2	−1	0	1	2	3	4
h		3	0				8

Hence draw the graph of $h = t^2 - 2t$ on the axes below. Use your graph to solve the equation $t^2 - 2t = 2$, giving your answers correct to 1 d.p.

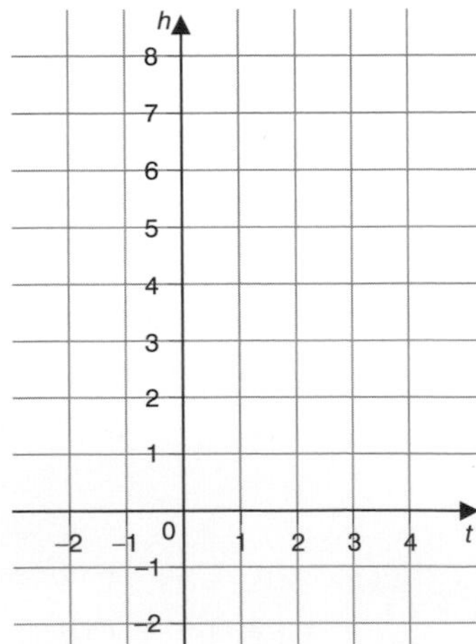

21 The cost (c), in pounds, of a function is given as £80 to hire the hall plus £22 per guest.

a) If the number of guests is x, write an equation in c and x.
b) Use your equation to find the cost of a function for 50 guests.
c) Make x the subject of your equation.
d) If a function cost £2060, how many guests were present?

Answers – Algebra review

1 $x = 3.5, y = 2.5$

2 **i)** **a)** 20, 23 **b)** +3 **c)** $3n + 5$

ii) **a)** 18, 22 **b)** +4 **c)** $4n - 2$

iii) **a)** 25, 36

b) The difference between the numbers increases by 2 each time.

c) n^2

3 **a)** $3b(a + 2b)$ **b)** $2y(5y - 1)$

c) $xy(16y + 7x)$

4 **a)** **i)** $n + 3$

ii) $3(n + 3)$ or $3n + 9$, but not $3n + 3$

b) $n + n + 3 + 3n + 9 = 5n + 12 = 67$

c) $n = 11, n + 3 = 14, 3(n + 3) = 42$

5 **a)** 0.071 **b)** 7.1×10^{-2} **c)** $v = \sqrt{C - ab}$

d) 3

6

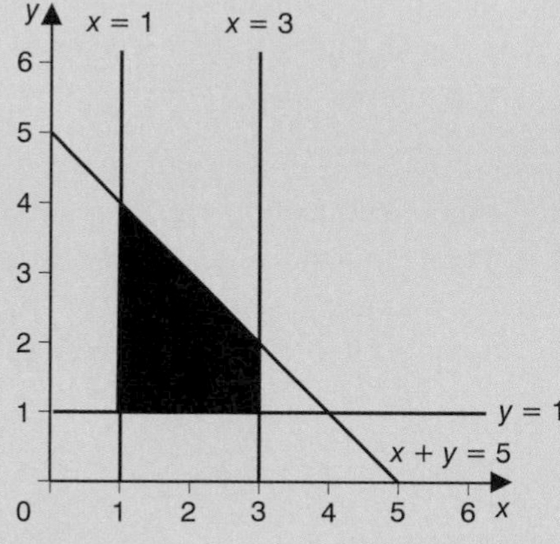

7 **a)** gradient = −2, y-intercept = 1

b) gradient = −1, y-intercept = 3

c) gradient = $\frac{1}{2}$, y-intercept = −1

8 **a)** **i)** $3x$ **ii)** $3x^2$

b) $3x^2 = 75, x^2 = 25, x = 5$

9 **a)** $(x + 5)(x + 2); x = -5, x = -2$

b) $(x + 5)(x - 1); x = -5, x = 1$

c) $(x - 11)(x + 1); x = 11, x = -1$

d) $(x - 3)(x - 2); x = 3, x = 2$

e) $(x - 6)(x + 1); x = 6, x = -1$

10 0.075

11 **a)** $h = \sqrt[3]{\frac{3V}{\pi}}$

b) 2.2 (1 d.p.) or 2.17 (2 d.p.)

12 $x = 2, y = 3$

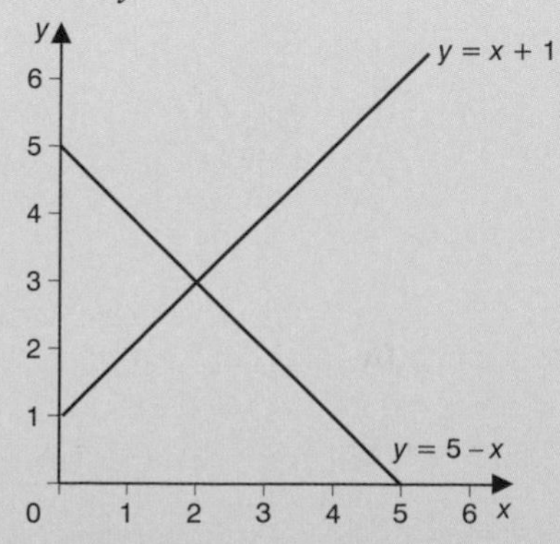

13 **a)** $x > -3$ **b)** $-5 \leqslant x \leqslant 5$ **c)** $x < -3, x > 3$

14 $2x + 4y = 37.00$

$5x + 3y = 64.50$

An adult's ticket costs £10.50 and a child's ticket costs £4.00. 3 adults' and 7 children's tickets cost 3 × £10.50 + 7 × £4.00 = £59.50.

15 Using FaBuLouS, there are no fractions, so you can start by expanding (working out) the brackets, to give $5x + 15 = 2x - 12$
Collecting together like terms, with all the x-terms on one side of the equation and all the integers (whole numbers) on the other, gives $3x = -27$. You can Sort this out by dividing both sides by 3.

$x = -9$

16 $x = -5, y = 1$

17 **a)** 0.08 **b)** The charge (in £) per mile

c) $C = 0.08x + 40$

18

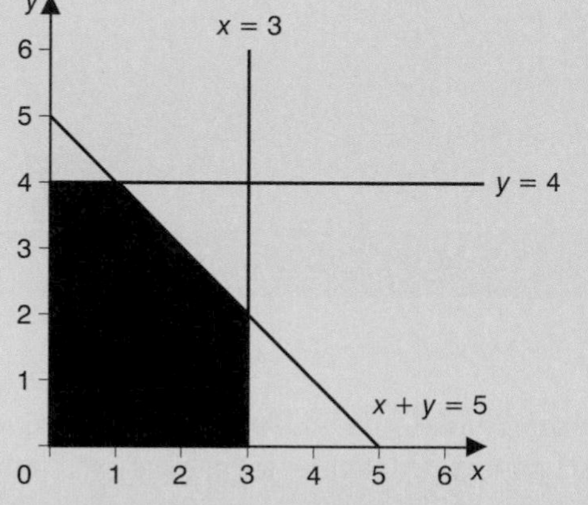

19 **a)** (iv) **b)** (iii) **c)** (i) **d)** (ii)

20

t	−2	−1	0	1	2	3	4
h	8	3	0	−1	0	3	8

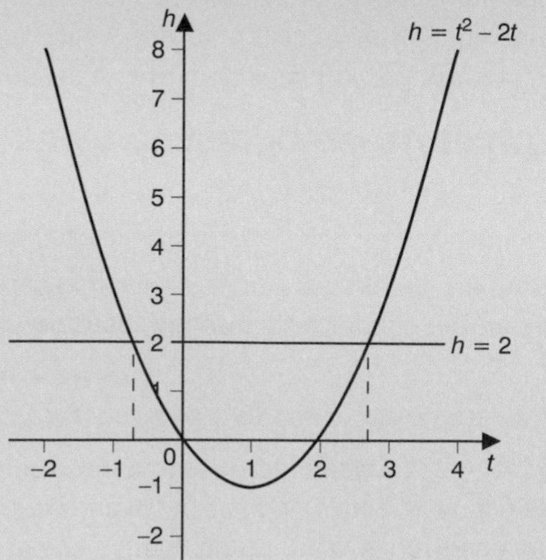

$t = -0.7, t = 2.7$

21 **a)** $c = 22x + 80$ **b)** £1180

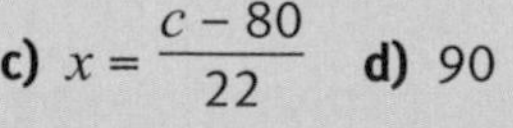

c) $x = \frac{c - 80}{22}$ **d)** 90

PREVIEW

By the end of this chapter you will be able to:

- **use Pythagoras' theorem or trigonometry to calculate the side or angle of any right-angled triangle**
- **recognise when to use Pythagoras' theorem and when to use trigonometry**
- **calculate and use angles of elevation and depression**
- **understand and use bearings in conjunction with trigonometry or Pythagoras' theorem.**

How much do you know already?

Questions in this section will often ask you to find lengths. If the question does not specify the number of **decimal places** or **significant figures** required in the answer, use the degree of accuracy that was used in the question. For example, if the question uses one decimal place, you should give your answer correct to one decimal place (1 d.p.).

If the question asks for an angle, you should give the answer to the nearest degree, unless the question asks otherwise.

Exercise 5.1

In questions 1–8, find the length of the side, or the size of the angle, marked x. All the lengths are in centimetres.

1

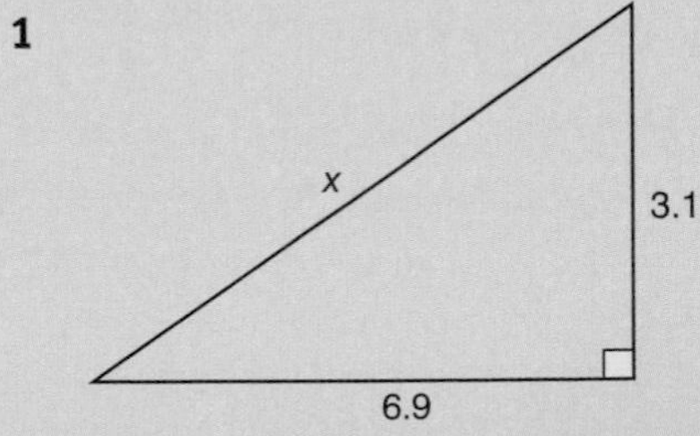

2

3

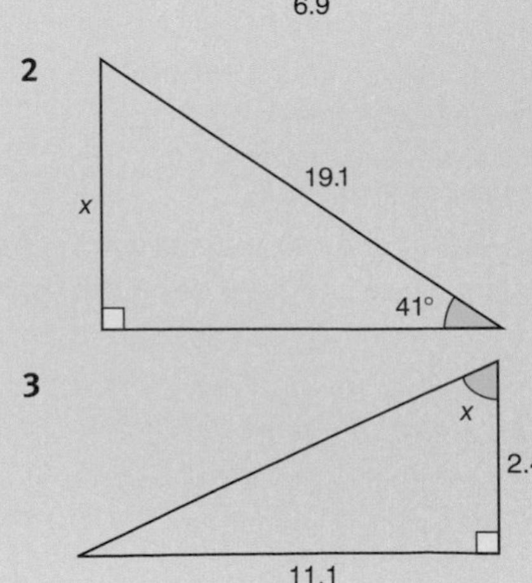

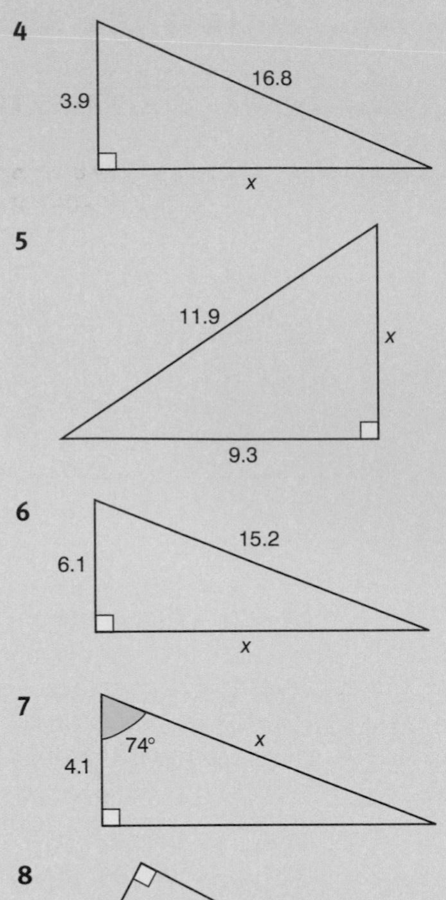

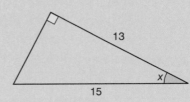

9 Miriam is at the top of a climbing frame. Her friend Avril, who is 1.6 m tall, is 20 m away on the ground. If the angle of elevation of Miriam from Avril is 10°, how high above the ground is the top of Miriam's head?

10 Monika plans to live nearer her school. At present she lives 8 km due south of her school, but is moving to a house 3 km due east of it. What is the bearing of her new home from her old?

11 A boat is due south of a lighthouse. It moves 5.3 km on a bearing of 073°. If it is now due east of the lighthouse, how far is the boat from the lighthouse?

12 Standing in the playground, Jamie notices a mark on the ground. If Jamie is 1.8 m tall and the angle of depression is 65°, how far is the mark from his feet?

Answers – 5.1

1 7.6 cm
2 12.5 cm
3 78°
4 16.3 cm
5 7.4 cm
6 13.9 cm
7 14.9 cm
8 30°
9 4.8 m
10 021°
11 5.1 km
12 0.84 m or 84 cm

How did you get on?

All or most questions right?

Well done! You probably don't need to do the next few exercises. Turn to the examination-type questions in Exercise 5.7 at the end of the chapter and see how you well you do. If you have any problems, turn back to the examples and exercises which you hoped to avoid, and work through some of them to sort out the difficulty.

Numbers 1, 4, 5, 6 right?

Fine! Pythagoras' theorem is no problem to you, but your trigonometry needs some help.

Numbers 2, 3, 7–12 right?

You are brilliant at trigonometry, but somewhere along the line you have forgotten how to use Pythagoras' theorem.

Don't even ask?

Never mind. It's better to find out the worst now.

Pythagoras' theorem

When c is the hypotenuse, and a and b are the other two sides, $c^2 = a^2 + b^2$

Identifying the hypotenuse

The **hypotenuse** is the name given to the longest side of a right-angled triangle. You will always find it opposite the right angle.

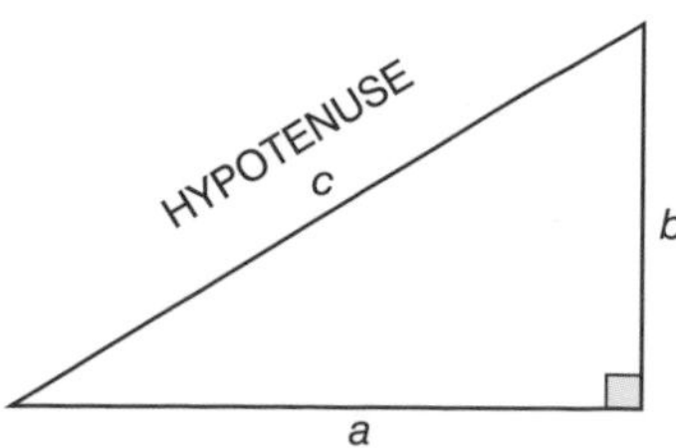

Sometimes they try to confuse you by turning the triangle round, but as long as you always **start by locating the right angle**, you can correctly identify the hypotenuse as being the side opposite it.

If you have an **isosceles** triangle (a triangle with two equal sides), you will probably not have a right angle. Don't worry! Just turn it on to its odd side and imagine a line downwards. (The line is the perpendicular bisector.)

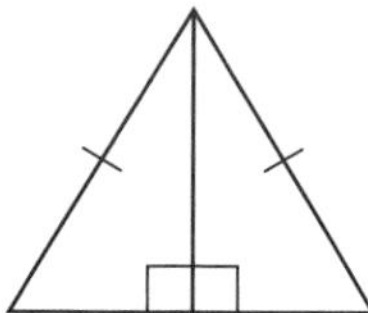

Calculating the hypotenuse

Once you have located the hypotenuse, it's plain sailing. Using your calculator, square the other two sides, add the results and then find the square root of the answer.

'When finding the longest side called the hypot,
Add the squares of the sides and square root the lot.'

So if c is the hypotenuse, then $c^2 = a^2 + b^2$ and $c = \sqrt{a^2 + b^2}$

Example 5.1

In the triangle below, calculate the length of the side marked x. Give your answer correct to 1 d.p.

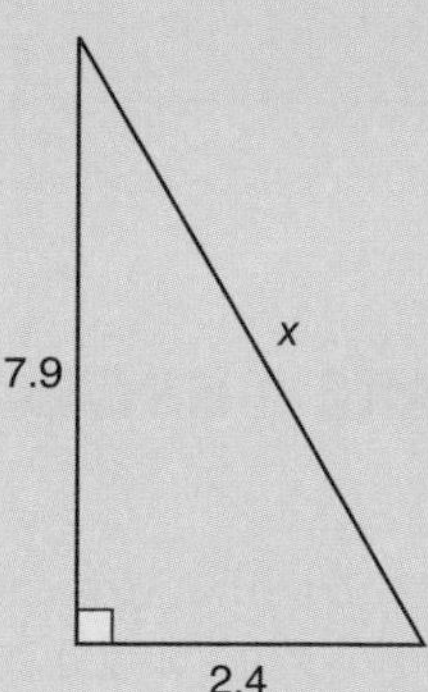

Solution

$7.9^2 + 2.4^2 = 68.17$

$\sqrt{68.17} = 8.3$

You have to be careful not to get carried away and write all the calculations in one long string, e.g.

$7.9^2 + 2.4^2 = 68.17 = \sqrt{68.17} = 8.3$

because 68.17 cannot possibly equal $\sqrt{68.17}$, and you may lose marks.

Exercise 5.2

In each triangle below, calculate the length of the side marked x. Give your answers correct to 1 d.p.

1

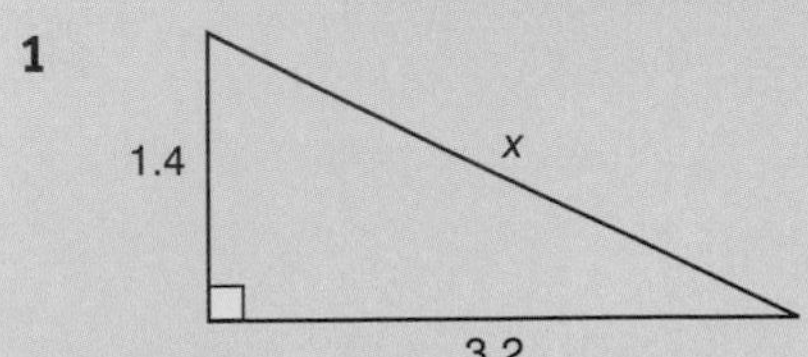

2

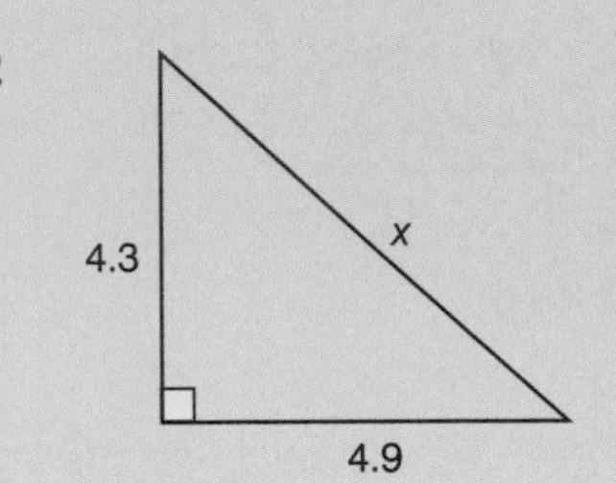

3

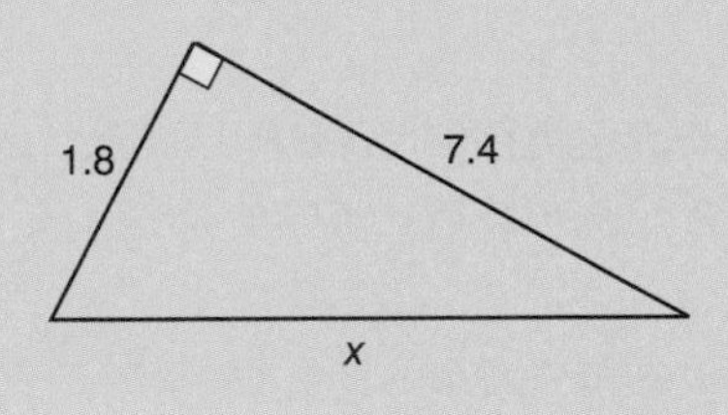

Answers – 5.2

1 3.5
2 6.5
3 7.6

TAKE A BREAK

If you were successful in that exercise, you're ready to tackle the shorter sides. If you are still making mistakes, don't worry. It should become clear shortly. Either way, take a short break now.

Calculating a shorter side – i.e. one that is not the hypotenuse

$c^2 = a^2 + b^2 \quad \Rightarrow \quad c = \sqrt{a^2 + b^2}$

$a^2 = c^2 - b^2 \quad \Rightarrow \quad a = \sqrt{c^2 - b^2}$

$b^2 = c^2 - a^2 \quad \Rightarrow \quad b = \sqrt{c^2 - a^2}$

or simply remember:
*for **S**horter **S**ides **S**ubtract.*

Example 5.2

In the triangle below, calculate the length of the side marked x. Give your answer correct to 1 d.p.

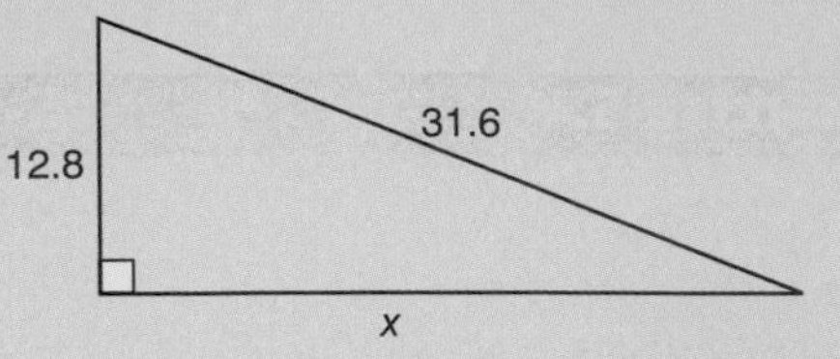

Solution

$31.6^2 - 12.8^2 = 834.72$

$\sqrt{834.72} = 28.9$ to 1 d.p.

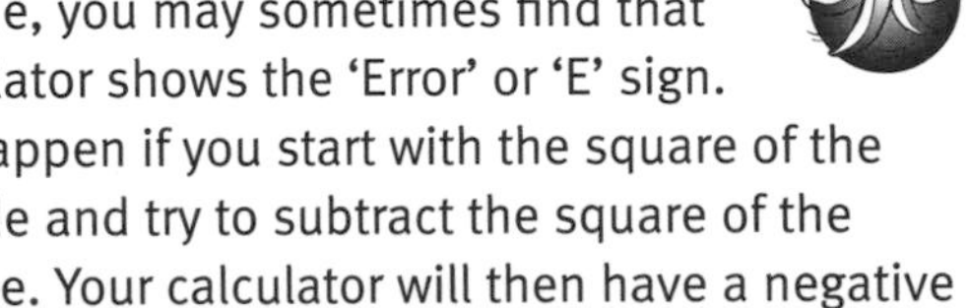

When you are trying to find the length of a shorter side, you may sometimes find that your calculator shows the 'Error' or 'E' sign. This will happen if you start with the square of the shorter side and try to subtract the square of the hypotenuse. Your calculator will then have a negative number, for which it can't find the square root.

Safety first! Always start with the larger number.

Exercise 5.3

In each triangle below, calculate the length of the side marked x. Give your answers correct to 1 d.p. where appropriate.

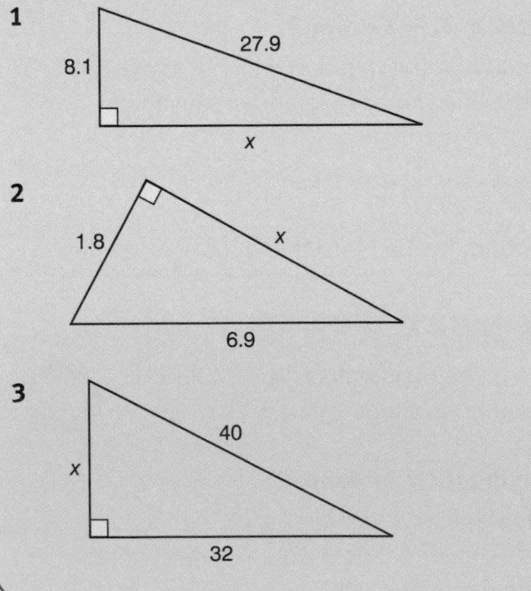

Answers – 5.3

1 26.7
2 6.7
3 24

By now you should be feeling much more confident about using Pythagoras' theorem. The next exercise reinforces what you have just learnt, and gives you a chance to show off your new skill.

Exercise 5.4

1 In the school playground, there is a slide for the children to play on. They slide down from the top, a height of 4 m, and land on cushions on the ground. If the cushions are at a distance of 7.2 m from the base of the slide, find the length of the slide.

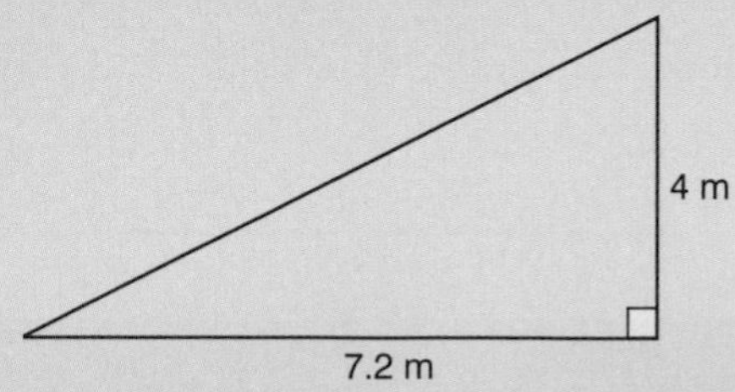

2 A folding ladder is 16 m long, and can be bent in half to form an upside-down V. The ladder extends to a width of 2.5 m when fully open. If someone stands at the highest point, how high are they above the ground?

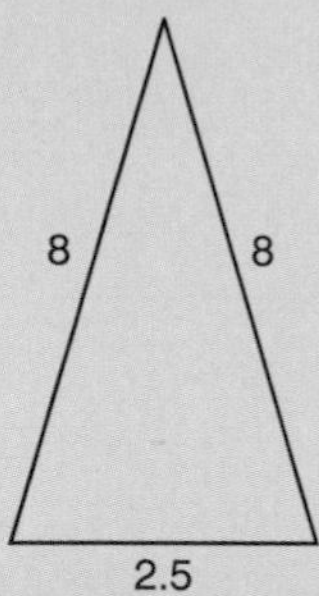

3 The hypotenuse of a triangle is 10 cm. If one of the shorter sides is 6 cm, find the length of the third side.

Answers – 5.4

1 8.2 m

2 7.9 m

3 $10^2 - 6^2 = 64$

$\sqrt{64} = 8$ cm

TAKE A BREAK

Now is probably a good time for another short break.

Trigonometry

Always make sure your calculator is set on 'deg' before you start your work in trig.

Some calculators require you to press the sin, cos or tan key before the number, e.g. sin 23, whereas others work the other way round and would require 23 sin. Make sure you know how yours works.

Pythagoras' theorem or trigonometry?

Whereas Pythagoras' theorem gives a relationship between **three sides** of a right-angled triangle, trigonometry involves **two sides and an angle**.

You may have learnt the trigonometry rules by using SOH CAH TOA. If you find this hard to remember, say to yourself,

'Some Old Hags Can't Always Hide Their Old Age.'

Here are these formulae in action.

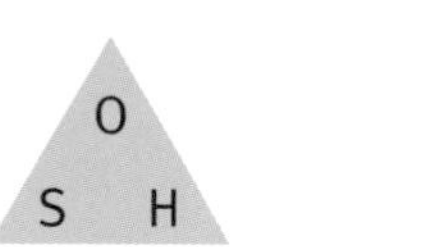

S: $\sin x = \dfrac{\text{opp}}{\text{hyp}}$

O: $\text{opp} = \sin x \times \text{hyp}$

H: $\text{hyp} = \dfrac{\text{opp}}{\sin x}$

A
C H

C: $\cos x = \dfrac{\text{adj}}{\text{hyp}}$

A: $\text{adj} = \cos x \times \text{hyp}$

H: $\text{hyp} = \dfrac{\text{adj}}{\cos x}$

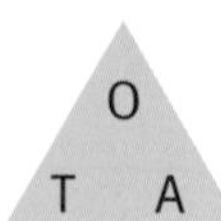

T: $\tan x = \dfrac{\text{opp}}{\text{adj}}$

O: $\text{opp} = \tan x \times \text{adj}$

A: $\text{adj} = \dfrac{\text{opp}}{\tan x}$

Remember: Put the middle letters of SOH, CAH and TOA at the top of the triplets.

To recap ...

- The hypotenuse is the longest side of a right-angled triangle.
- The opposite is the side that is opposite (or does not touch) the angle you are using.
- The adjacent (which means 'next to') is the other side.

Using trigonometry to find sides

1 Write out the triplets for SOH CAH TOA.

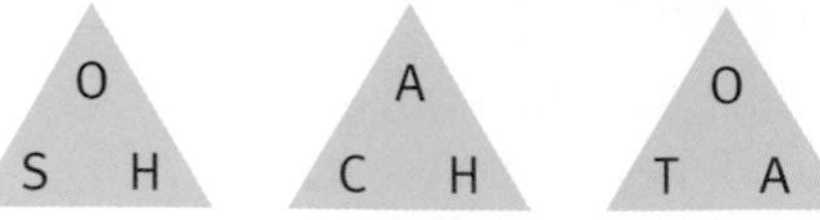

2 Look for the side which the question ignores, and cross out the triplets which contain it. The remaining triplet is the one to use.

3 Cover or cross out the letter representing the side or angle which you need to find. As usual, if the remaining letters are on the same level, you multiply them, and if one is on top of the other, you divide the top by the bottom.

Example 5.3

In the triangle below, calculate the length of the side marked x. Give your answer correct to 1 d.p.

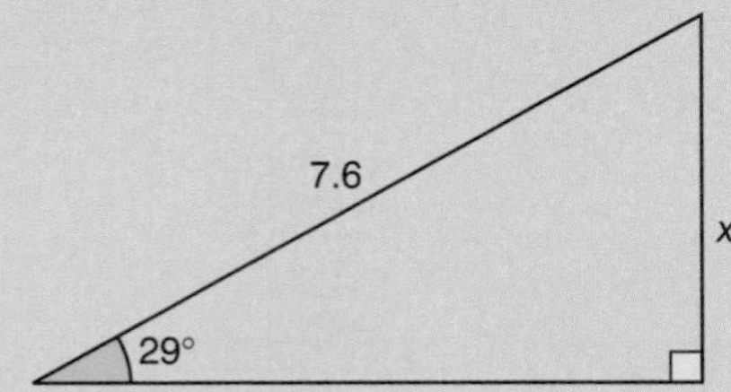

Method

1 Label the triangle in the usual way. The side of length 7.6 is H and the side marked x is O.

2 The side not mentioned is A, so cross out the triplets containing A and keep

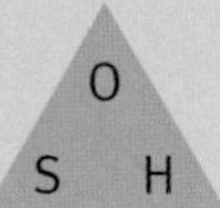

3 You need to find O, so cover or cross it out, and you will be left with S H. Multiply these.

Solution

sin 29° × 7.6 = 3.7

Example 5.4

In the triangle below, calculate the length of the side marked x. Give your answer correct to 1 d.p.

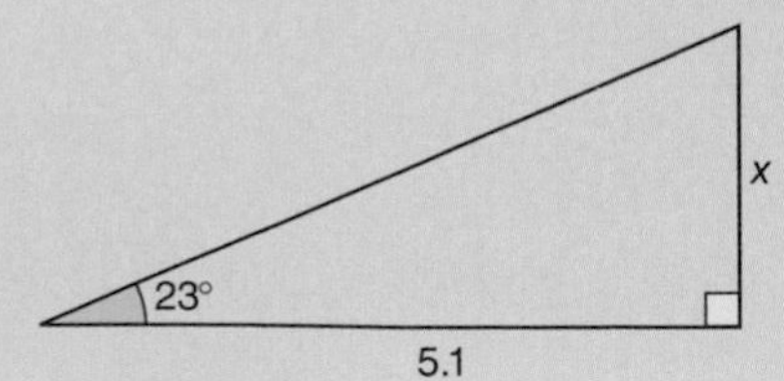

Method

1 Label the triangle in the usual way. The side marked x is O and the side of length 5.1 is A.

2 H is not mentioned, so cross out the two triplets containing it and you will be left with

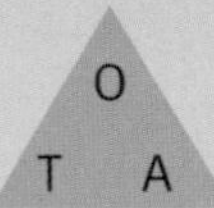

3 You are looking for O so cover or cross it out. T and A are on the same level, so you multiply them.

Solution

tan 23° × 5.1 = 2.2

Example 5.5

In the triangle below, calculate the length of the side marked x. Give your answer correct to 1 d.p.

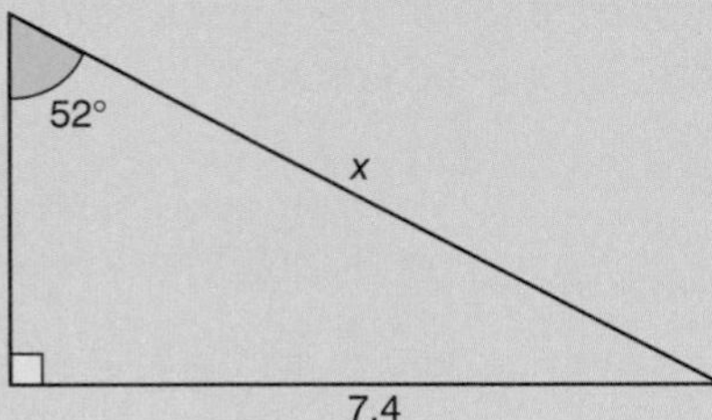

Method

When you have labelled the triangle, you should find that the unwanted side is A. Crossing out the unwanted triplets leaves

This time, however, the required side is H, and covering or crossing this out leaves

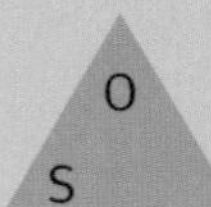

You need to divide O by S.

Solution

7.4 ÷ sin 52° = 9.4

Check that you know how to get these answers on your calculator.

Example 5.6

In the triangle below, calculate the length of the side marked x. Give your answer correct to 1 d.p.

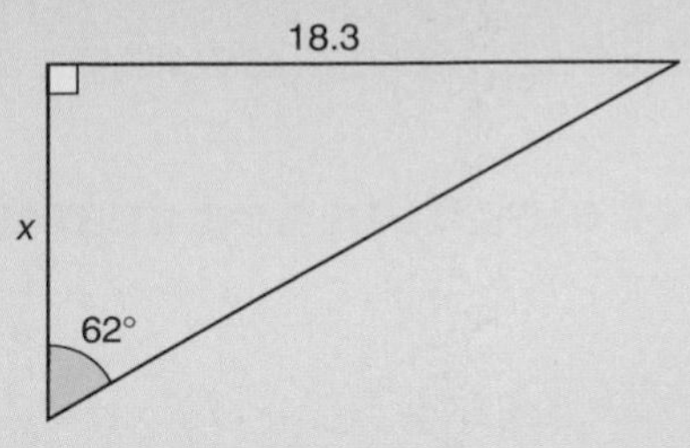

Method

When you have labelled the triangle, and crossed out the triplets in the usual way, you should have

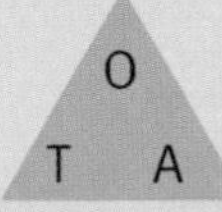

As you are looking for A, you will have to divide.

Solution

$18.3 \div \tan 62° = 9.7$

Exercise 5.5

In each triangle below, calculate the length of the side marked x. Give your answers correct to 1 d.p.

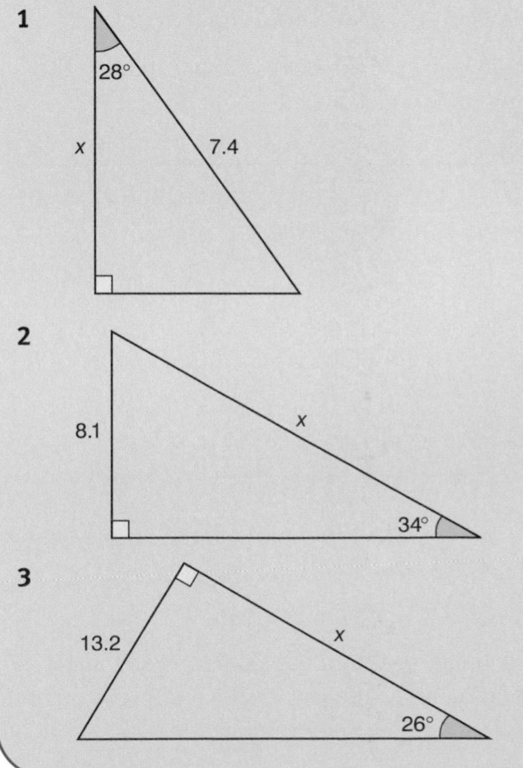

Answers – 5.5

1 6.5
2 14.5
3 27.1

Using trigonometry to find angles

To find the value of an angle, you must always start by finding its sin, cos or tan. Then you need to find the **inverse** sin, cos or tan, which some books write as **$\sin^{-1}$**, **$\cos^{-1}$** or **$\tan^{-1}$**. To do this, you press the key which is probably in the top left-hand corner of your calculator, and labelled inv, shift or 2nd f.

If you are getting an 'Error' or 'E' sign, or a ridiculous answer, you are probably not pressing = before you press inv sin, cos or tan. Some calculators require you to press = at the end. Another possibility is that you need to insert brackets. It's a good idea to make sure that you know how your calculator works, well ahead of the examination. If you still can't find where you went wrong, check again that your calculator is set to degrees.

Example 5.7

In the following triangle, find, to the nearest degree, the angle marked x.

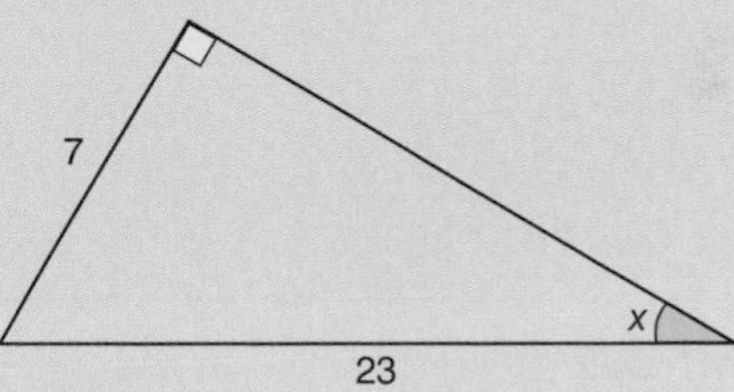

Method

1 Label the triangle in the usual way.
2 You do not know anything about A, so cross out the two triangles containing this letter. You should have

Solution

$$\sin x = \frac{O}{H} = \frac{7}{23} = 0.304$$

Angle $x = \sin^{-1} 0.304 = 18°$ to the nearest degree.

Example 5.8

In the following triangle find, to the nearest degree, the angle marked x.

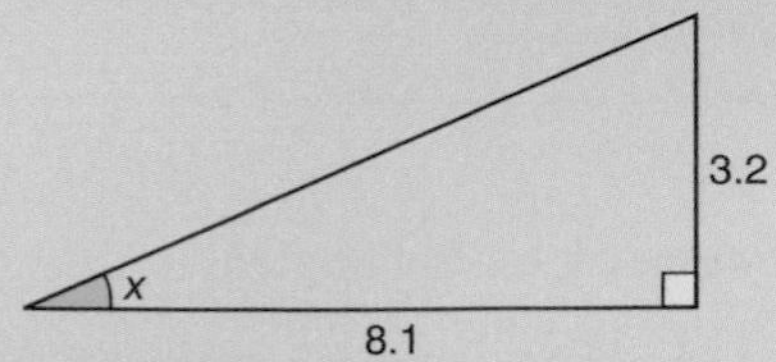

Labelling the triangle in the usual way should eliminate H.

Solution

$\tan x = \frac{O}{A} = \frac{3.2}{8.1} = 0.395$

Angle $x = \tan^{-1} 0.395 = 22°$

Example 5.9

In the following triangle find, to the nearest degree, the angle marked x.

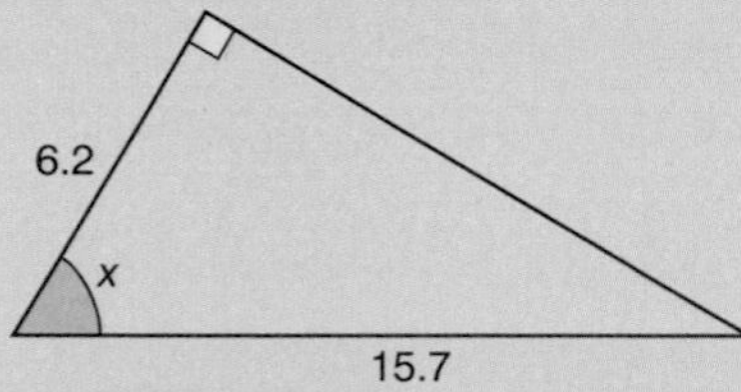

The required triplet this time is

Solution

$\cos x = \frac{6.2}{15.7} = 0.3949$

Angle $x = \cos^{-1} 0.3949 = 67°$

Exercise 5.6

In each of the following triangles find, to the nearest degree, the angle marked x.

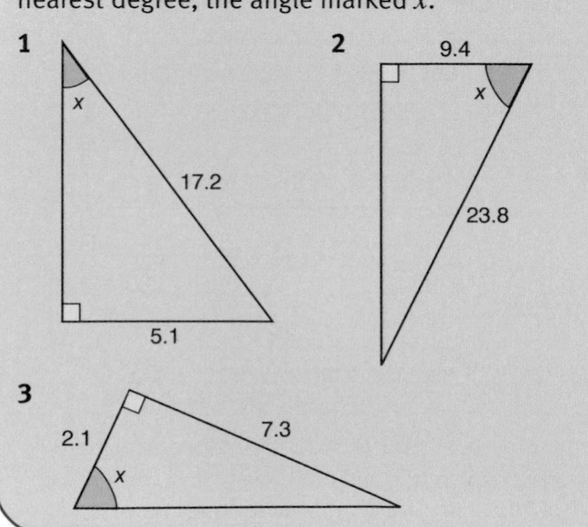

Answers – 5.6

1 17°
2 67°
3 74°

Angles of elevation and depression

Angles of elevation and depression are always measured **from the horizontal**. Look at the horizon, and go **up for an angle of elevation** or **down for an angle of depression**.

Example 5.10

Suki is sitting 3 m away from the base of a trampoline. Her friend Tamsin is showing off – as usual – on the trampoline. Suki's eyes are level with the trampoline and the angle of elevation when Suki looks at Tamsin is 53°.

a) How high is Tamsin above the trampoline?

b) When Tamsin looks down at Suki, what is the angle of depression?

Solution

a) Sketch a triangle of the situation, and label the triangle in the usual way.

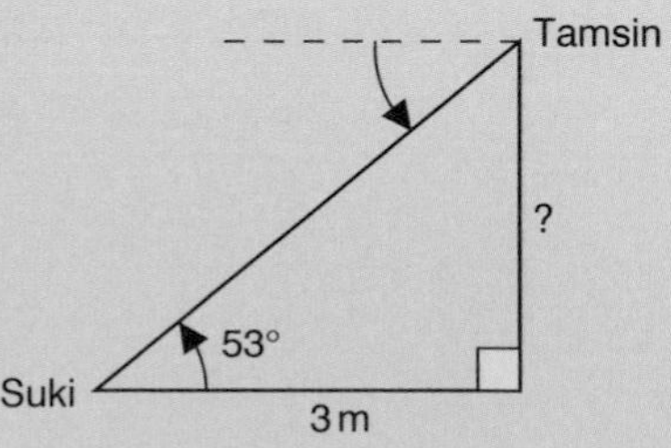

You are not interested in H, so the necessary calculation is

$\tan 53° \times 3 = 3.98$ m or 4.0 m

b) As you can see from the sketch, Suki's angle of elevation and Tamsin's angle of depression are the same. (They are alternate angles.)

Tamsin's angle of depression = 53°.

Bearings

Bearings are three-figure numbers which represent directions. They are always measured as the **clockwise angle from the north.**

Here are some examples showing bearings of 010°, 135° and 315° are shown below.

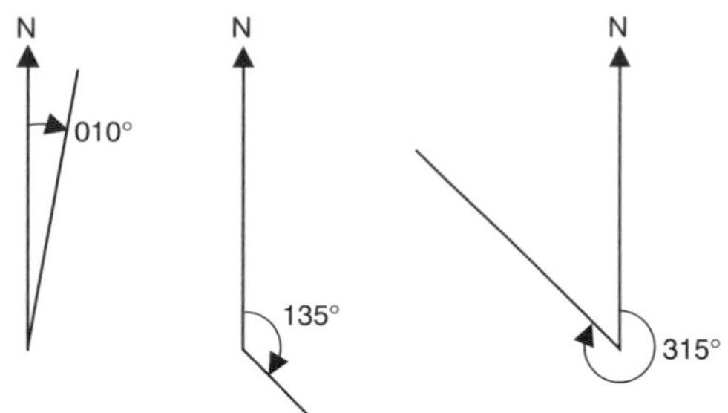

The bearings clock

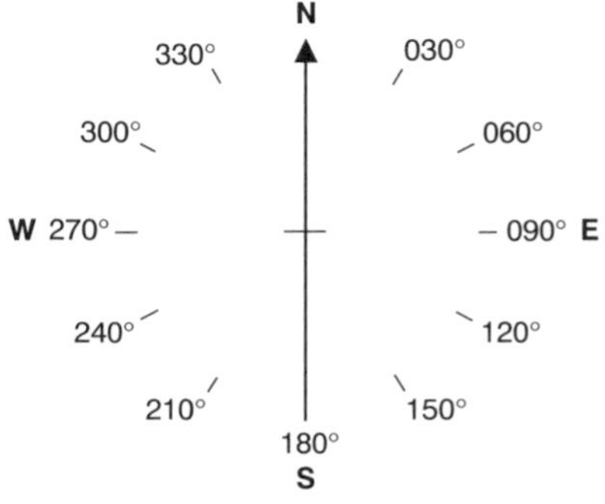

Summary – the four points of bearings

- Always start at 'from'.
- Then look north.
- Always turn clockwise.
- Always use three figures to write the bearings.

Example 5.11

If Connor is standing on a bearing of 024° from Danny, what is the bearing of Danny from Connor?

Solution

'From' gives the clue as to where you start.

Start by sketching the two men **from** the position of Danny.

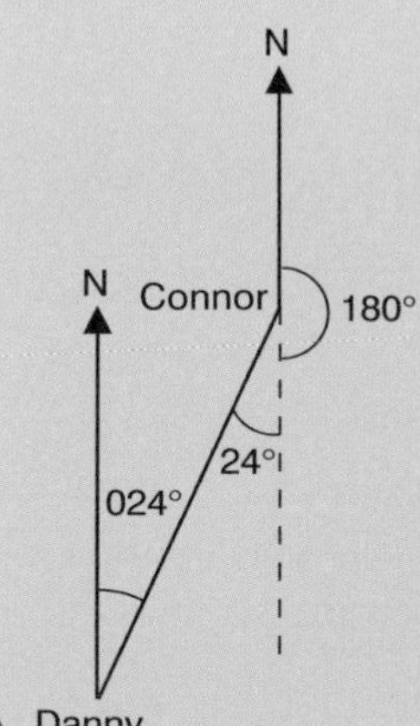

As you then have to calculate the bearing from Connor, draw a short line in the northerly direction and mark the required angle (24°) as indicated on the diagram. As both north lines are parallel, you have a pair of 'Z' or alternate angles. From north to south measures 180°, so the answer is 180° + 24° = 204°

Trigonometry or Pythagoras' theorem?

- You must have two sides to use Pythagoras' theorem.
- You must involve an angle for trigonometry.

Sometimes you can choose whichever you prefer, but remember:

TRig **IN**volves **A**ngles (TRINA)

Exercise 5.7

1 A ship is at S, 5 km south of a lighthouse at L. It needs to sail to a port P which is due east of L. If the bearing of P from S is 035°, find the distance that it needs to travel.

2 From the top of a cliff a man sees a rock jutting up from the sea. If the angle of depression of the rock from the top of the cliff is 15°, and the rock is 76 m from the base of the cliff, how high is the cliff?

3 An isosceles triangle has a base of 10cm and two equal sides of 17 cm.
   a) Find its perpendicular height.
   (**Hint:** draw a line perpendicular to the odd side, i.e. the base.)
   b) Find its area.

4 A ladder 8 m long reaches up a wall to a window 6.5 m up from the ground.
   a) What is the furthest possible distance between the building and the base of the ladder?
   b) What angle would the ladder make with the building?

5 Imagine two right-angled triangles. Triangle A has shorter sides 5 and 12 cm. Triangle B has shorter sides 3 and 13 cm. Which has the longer hypotenuse and by how much? Give your answer to 2 d.p.

6 Use trigonometry or Pythagoras' theorem.

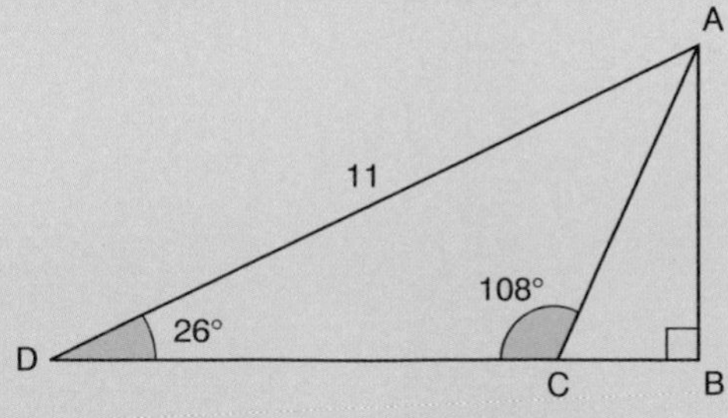

   a) Find AB. **b)** Find BD.
   c) Write down the size of angle ACB.
   d) Find AC. **e)** Find CD.
   (**Remember:** As triangle ACD is not right-angled, you cannot use SOH CAH TOA.)

7 The lengths of the two shorter sides of a right-angled triangle are x cm and $x + 3$ cm. Find a formula for the hypotenuse in terms of x.

Answers – 5.7

1 6.1 km

2 20 m

3 **a)** $17^2 - 5^2 = 264$

$\sqrt{264} = 16.2$ cm

b) Area $= 5 \times 16.2 = 81$ cm^2

(You will get the same answer if you use $\frac{1}{2} \times 10 \times 16.2$)

4 **a)** 4.7 m

b) 36°

(If you have 54°, you have found the angle between the ladder and the ground, not the wall.)

5 Hypotenuse of Triangle A is 13 cm.

Hypotenuse of Triangle B is 13.34 cm.

Triangle B's hypotenuse is longer by 0.34 cm.

6 **a)** 4.8 m

b) 9.9 m

c) 72° (180° − 108°)

d) 5.0 m

(Use triangle ABC, the angle ACB which you have just found and the length AB.)

e) 8.5m

7 Hypotenuse $= \sqrt{x^2 + (x + 3)^2}$

REVIEW

How much have you learnt?
Tick off each topic in the list when you are confident that you can cope with it.

- ☐ **Use Pythagoras' theorem or trigonometry to calculate the side or angle of any right-angled triangle.**
- ☐ **Recognise when to use Pythagoras' theorem and when to use trigonometry.**
- ☐ **Calculate and use angles of elevation and depression.**
- ☐ **Understand and use bearings in conjunction with trigonometry or Pythagoras' theorem.**

PREVIEW

By the end of this chapter you will be able to:

- **identify the centre, radius and circumference of a circle**
- **calculate the circumference and area of a circle, given the radius or diameter**
- **calculate the area of a rectangle, square, triangle, parallelogram**
- **calculate the surface area of a cuboid**
- **calculate areas of shapes made up of rectangles, triangles and semicircles**
- **identify the cross-section of a prism and calculate its volume**
- **recognise formulae for lengths, areas and volumes from their dimensions**
- **calculate distances travelled by wheels and the number of revolutions made by a wheel in covering a given distance**
- **compare depths of liquids in various containers**
- **compare base areas of containers according to their volume or capacity.**

How much do you know already?

Exercise 6.1

1 Find the area of a circle of radius 2.8 cm.

2 Find the volume of a cuboid 12 cm by 30 cm by 5 cm.

3 A circle has a diameter of 16.2 cm. What is its circumference?

4 A rectangle is twice as long as it is wide.

a) If its width is x cm, state its length in terms of x.

b) Give its perimeter in terms of x.

c) What is its area in terms of x?

d) If its area is 98 cm^2, write an equation in x and solve it to find the width of the rectangle.

5 Find the area of the following shape.

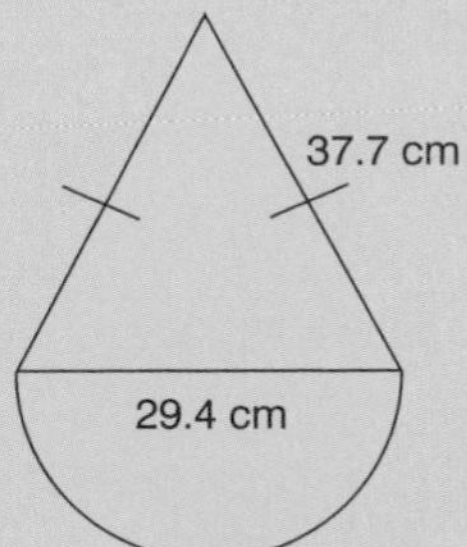

6 The letters h, l, and r, refer to lengths. State, with reference to dimensions, whether each of the following is a formula for length, area, volume or none of these.

a) $\pi r + 2h$ **b)** $3r^3 - r$

c) $2l(r + h)$ **d)** $\pi r^2 + h^2 - (l + h)$

7 A cylinder containing 2.25 litres of a liquid has a radius of 5.5 cm. How deep is the liquid? Give your answer to the nearest cm. (1 litre = 1000 cm^3)

8 A wheel has a circumference of 1 m. What is its diameter, in cm?

9 How many complete revolutions would a wheel of radius 18 cm make in travelling 50 m?

10 Find the area of a circle radius 1.8 cm.

11 Find the area of the shape below.

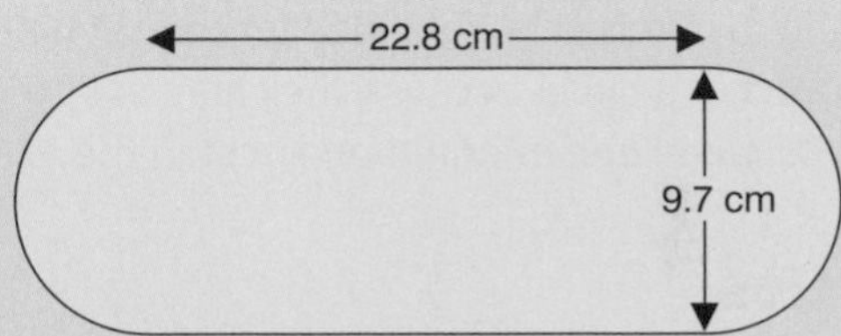

12 Compost is to be spread on a rectangular garden measuring 10 m by 6 m. If the depth of the compost is to be 10 cm, what will be the required volume of compost? Express your answer in m^3.

13 A picture frame is 32 cm wide and 45 cm long. What is its area? Give your answer in square metres.

14 A cuboid is 1 m long, 1.5 m high and 2.2 m wide. Find its volume in cubic centimetres.

Answers – 6.1

1 24.6 cm^2 **2** 1800 cm^3

3 50.9 cm

4 a) length = $2x$ **b)** perimeter = $6x$

c) area = $2x^2$ **d)** $2x^2 = 98$ so $x = 7$ cm

5 850 cm^2 to 3 sig figs.

6 a) length **b)** none of them

c) area **d)** none of them

7 24 cm **8** 31.8 cm

9 44 **10** 10.2 cm^2

11 295 cm^2. This shape is the equivalent of a rectangle and a circle.

12 6 m^3 **13** 0.14 m^2

14 3 300 000 cm^3

How did you get on?

All or most of them right?

You only need to glance through this chapter to make sure that there is nothing in it which will catch you out.

Six or more right?

Look on the bright side! Six or more right means that you already know at least half of this chapter.

Don't even ask?

Keep going, and you'll make it!

Perimeter

The perimeter is the distance all round a shape. The perimeter of a circle is called the circumference. You should memorise the formulae for the **circumference** and area of a circle because they may not be given on the *Formulae and information* sheet in the exam.

Circles

These are the principal parts of a circle.

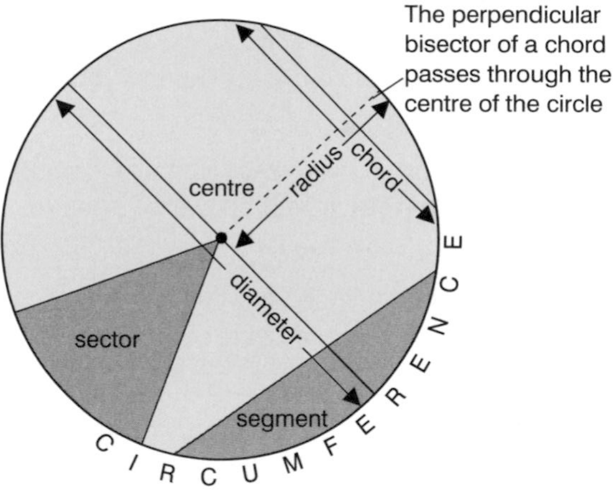

The area and circumference of a circle

The area of a circle is $A = \pi r^2$.

The circumference of a circle is $C = 2\pi r$ or πd.

The formula for the area of a circle

Remember '*πr squarea gives you the area*'.

When calculating πr^2, it's safer to put r into your calculator, then square it, then multiply by π.

The formula for the circumference of a circle

From the formula for the area, πr^2, imagine the 2 running around the circumference to the front to give $2\pi r$. This is totally non-mathematical, but may help!

As $d = 2r$. we can also write $2\pi r$ in terms of d, i.e. πd.

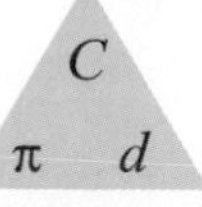

Thus $d = \dfrac{C}{\pi}$ or $C = \pi d$

This is sometimes useful if you are given the circumference and are asked for the diameter.

Example 6.1

A circle has a radius of 4.6 cm. Find:

a) its area
b) its circumference.

Solution

a) Area = πr^2

$\pi \times 4.6^2 = 66.5\ \text{cm}^2$ correct to 1 d.p.

b) If the radius is 4.6, the diameter $= 4.6 \times 2$
$= 9.2$

$C = \pi d$ or $C = 2\pi r$

Circumference = 28.9 cm correct to 1 d.p.

Example 6.2 – Finding the radius when given the area

A circle has area $124.7\ \text{cm}^2$. Find its radius.

Solution

Use the formula.

$A = \pi r^2$

$124.7 = \pi r^2$

Divide both sides by π. It's probably easier, too, if you swap the equation round, like this.

$r^2 = 124.7 \div \pi$ Divide 124.7 by π.

$r^2 = 39.7$

Take the square root on both sides.

$r = \sqrt{39.7}$

$r = 6.3$ cm

Example 6.3

The area of a circle is $85\ \text{cm}^2$. Find the diameter.

Solution

$A = \pi r^2$

$85 = \pi r^2$

$r^2 = 85 \div \pi$

$r^2 = 27.06$ Take the square root on both sides.

$r = 5.2$

$d = 5.2 \times 2 = 10.4$ cm

Exercise 6.2

1. The area of a circle is $175\ cm^2$. Find the length of its radius, correct to 2 significant figures.
2. Find the area of a circle with radius 3.5 cm. Give your answer correct to 3 significant figures.
3. The area of a circle is $38.6\ cm^2$ correct to 3 significant figures. What is its diameter, correct to 2 significant figures?

Answers – 6.2

1. $\pi r^2 = 175$
   $r^2 = 175 \div \pi = 55.704$
   Taking square roots on both sides gives
   $r = 7.5$ cm to 2 sig. figs.
2. $38.5\ cm^2$ to 3 sig. figs.
3. $\pi r^2 = 38.6$
   $r^2 = 38.6 \div \pi = 12.287$
   Taking square roots on both sides gives
   $r = 3.505$ cm. So $d = 7.0$ cm to 2 sig. figs. (As the question asks for 2 sig. figs. you will lose marks if you write 7 and not 7.0.)

Distance, circumference and revolutions (turns)

Examination questions often feature revolving wheels.

Distances are often written in metres and the radius of the wheel is usually given in centimetres. Be very careful to work in the same units for both.

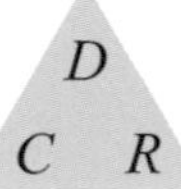

*Remember **D**odgem **C**a**R**s.*

Example 6.4

Miguel rolls a wheel down a chute. If the wheel has a radius of 2.5 cm, and it revolves six times from the top to the bottom of the chute, how long is the chute? Give your answer to a sensible degree of accuracy.

Solution

One revolution is the same measurement as the circumference. You need to find the distance D travelled, i.e. six complete turns.

$D = CR \qquad R = 6$

$C = \pi d = \pi \times 5 = 15.7$ cm

$D = 15.7 \times 6 = 94.2$ cm.

Example 6.5

How many complete revolutions would a wheel of radius 20 cm make in travelling 500 m?

Solution

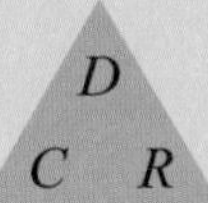

First find the circumference.

$C = \pi d$ or $C = 2\pi r$ which both give

$C = \pi \times 2 \times 20 = 125.66$ cm.

Be very careful at this point, because the radius is given in centimetres and the distance in metres. It doesn't matter which units you choose, but you must work in one or the other.

$C = 125.66\text{ cm} = 1.2566\text{ m}$

The number of revolutions is $\frac{50\,000}{125.66}$ or $\frac{500}{1.2566}$

The number of complete revolutions is 397.

Exercise 6.3

1. A circular brooch has a radius of 27 mm. Calculate its area.
2. A circular table has a circumference of 408 cm.
   a) Find its radius to the nearest centimetre.
   b) Find its area, in square centimetres, correct to two significant figures.
3. A bicycle wheel has a radius of 35 cm. How far will it travel in 40 revolutions? Give your answer, in metres, to the nearest 10 m.
4. A circular tablecloth has an area of $17\,955\ cm^2$. What is its diameter?

Answers – 6.3

1. $2290\ mm^2$
2. **a)** 65 cm **b)** $13\,000\ cm^2$
3. 90 m
4. 151.2 cm (If your answer was 75.6, you found the radius.)

Area of shapes other than circles

By now you probably know that the area of a rectangle is length × width. Since the length and width of a square are the same, you can find the area by multiplying one side by itself, or squaring it.

Sometimes, however, you are given the area and have to work back to find a side. If you are given the area of a square, you find the length of each side by finding the square root ($\sqrt{}$) of the area. If you start with a rectangle, you divide the area by the side which you are given.

If the area of a square is $100\,\text{cm}^2$, each side is $\sqrt{100} = 10\,\text{cm}$.

If the area of a rectangle with a length of 6 cm is $18\,\text{cm}^2$, then the width is

$18 \div 6 = 3\,\text{cm}$.

Area of a triangle

$$\text{Area} = \frac{\text{base} \times \text{height}}{2}$$

or you may have learnt it as

area = $\frac{1}{2}$ base × height.

Be very careful to use the perpendicular height! The lengths you multiply must be at right angles.

Area of a parallelogram

Area = base × perpendicular height.

Remember that the perpendicular height is the perpendicular from the base to the opposite side.

Area of a trapezium

$$\text{Area of a trapezium} = \frac{(a+b)}{2} \times \text{height}$$

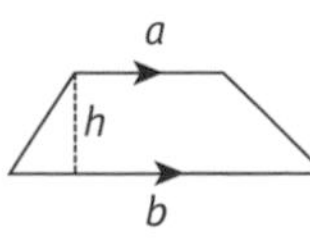

Areas of other shapes

Somewhere on the examination paper, or as a loose insert, you will probably find the formula for the area of a trapezium, but you have to remember the other formulae yourself. This is not as daunting as it sounds, as you can usually split these up into rectangles, triangles, circles or semicircles. Then it is simply a matter of adding together all the separate parts.

Example 6.6

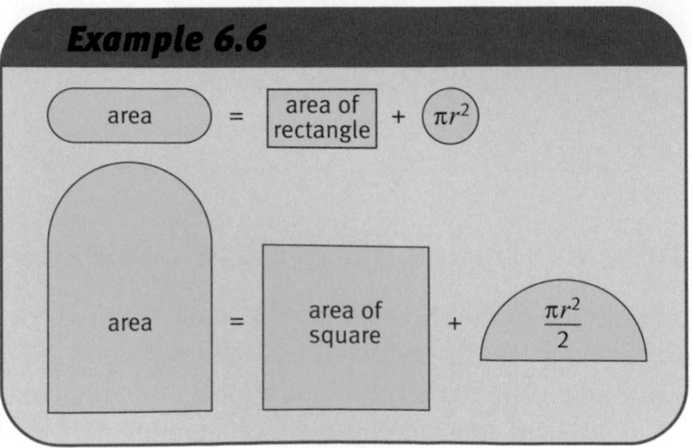

Exercise 6.4

Find the area of the following shapes.

1

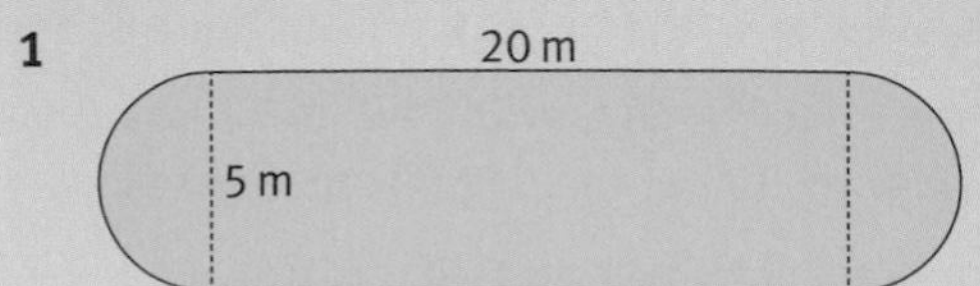

2

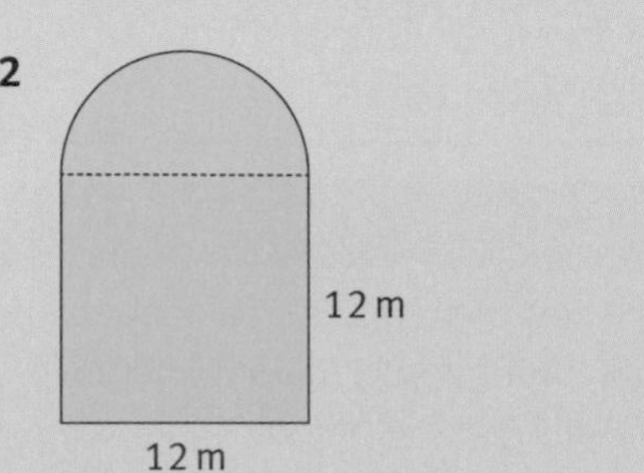

3 A garden consists of a rectangular lawn 12 m by 5 m surrounded by a path 1m wide. Find
  a) the length and width of the garden
  b) the area of the garden
  c) the area of the lawn
  d) the area of the path.

4 A circular pond of radius 3 m is dug in the middle of a rectangular lawn 8 m by 5 m. What area of the lawn remains?

Answers – 6.4

1 $20 \times 5 + \pi \times 2.5^2 = 119.6\,\text{m}^2$

2 $12 \times 12 + \frac{\pi \times 6^2}{2} = 200.5\,\text{m}^2$

3 **a)** 14 m and 7 m
  b) $98\,\text{m}^2$
  c) $60\,\text{m}^2$
  d) $98 - 60 = 38\,\text{m}^2$

4 $40 - \pi \times 3^2 = 11.7\,\text{m}^2$

Surface area

Imagine that you can take the shape apart and lay each piece flat. This is also what you do when you make a net (see Chapter 7, Shapes, loci and construction). It often helps to sketch the pieces and calculate their separate areas.

A closed cylinder, when taken apart, is made up of two circles and a rectangle. The surface area of a cylinder = $2\pi r^2 + 2\pi r \times h = 2\pi r(r + h)$.

The shape of a triangular prism is quite easy to remember if you think of a well-known brand of Swiss chocolate. The net is made up of three rectangles, with two triangles, one at each end.

Volume of a prism

A prism is a 3D shape which can be cut into identical slices. The shape of each slice is called its **cross-section**. For example, if you slice a cylinder, each piece is a circle. A prism with a rectangular 'slice' is called a cuboid.

The volume of a prism is found by multiplying its area of cross-section by its length.

Volume of a prism = area of cross-section × length

This is easy when the question involves an obvious length. Sometimes, however, the question asks for a depth or a thickness and you may not immediately spot that this is equivalent to asking for the length. If you recognise yourself in this situation, do not despair. Here is a method which just might work!

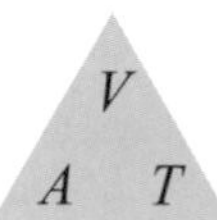

V stands for volume. The word 'volume' is usually used, although occasionally you may be asked for the capacity.

A stands for the area of the cross-section.

T stands for The Other One. In place of T put the dimension you have not already used. This may be length, width, depth, height or thickness.

Example 6.7

a) A cylindrical glass has a base radius 3.5 cm. If the glass is filled to a depth of 7.2 cm, find the volume of liquid in the glass.

b) The liquid is then poured into a vase in the shape of a cuboid with base dimensions 14.1 cm by 12.2 cm. How deep is the liquid?

c) The same liquid is poured into a cylindrical glass of height 9.7 cm. If the glass is completely filled, what is its radius?

Solution

a) Volume $= \pi r^2 h = \pi \times 3.5^2 \times 7.2 = 277\ \text{cm}^3$
or $V = A \times T$

b) $A = 14.1 \times 12.2 = 172.02\ \text{cm}^2$
$T = V \div A = 277 \div 172.02 = 1.6\ \text{cm}$

c) $\pi r^2 h = V$

$r^2 = \dfrac{V}{\pi h}$

$r^2 = \dfrac{277}{\pi \times 9.7} = 9.09$

$r = 3.0\ \text{cm}$

or

$A = \dfrac{V}{T} = \dfrac{277}{9.7}$

$A = 28.56$

$\pi r^2 = 28.56$

$r^2 = 9.09$

$r = 3.0\ \text{cm}$

Calculating area and volume

Example 6.8

A rectangle measures 84 cm by 96 cm. Find its area in square metres (m^2).

Solution

It is probably easier to convert the centimetres to metres before you start.

$0.84\ \text{m} \times 0.96\ \text{m} = 0.8064\ \text{m}^2$

Changing metric units

Length

mm
÷ 10 ↓↑ × 10 — 10 mm = 1 cm
cm
÷ 100 ↓↑ × 100 — 100 cm = 1 m
m
÷ 1000 ↓↑ × 1000 — 1000 m = 1 km
km

Weight

g
÷ 1000 ↓↑ × 1000 — 1000 g = 1 kg
kg
÷ 1000 ↓↑ × 1000 — 1000 kg = 1 tonne
tonne

Capacity/volume

ml
÷ 1000 ↓↑ × 1000 — (1 ml = 1 cm^3)
l — 1000 ml = 1 l

Example 6.9

A cuboid is 96 cm long, 55 cm wide and 75 cm high. Find its volume in cubic metres (m^3).

Solution

Change all the lengths to metres first.

$0.96 \times 0.55 \times 0.75 = 0.396\ \text{m}^3$

Example 6.10

Express:

a) $4500\ \text{cm}^2$ in m^2 **b)** $1.2\ \text{m}^3$ in cm^3

Solution

a) The area of a square of sides 1 m is $1\ \text{m}^2$. Think of the square as having sides of length 100 cm.

The area becomes $100 \times 100\ \text{cm}^2 = 10\,000\ \text{cm}^2$.

$1\ \text{m}^2 = 10\,000\ \text{cm}^2$
$4500\ \text{cm}^2 = 4500 \div 10\,000 = 0.45\ \text{m}^2$

b) A cube with each side of length 1 m could also be described as having sides of length 100 cm.

The volume is 1 m^3 or $100 \times 100 \times 100\text{ cm}^3 = 1\,000\,000\text{ cm}^3$.

$1\text{ m}^3 = 1\,000\,000\text{ cm}^3$
$1.2\text{ m}^3 = 1\,200\,000\text{ cm}^3$

Example 6.11

A solid cylinder has a length of 3.2 m, and a cross-sectional area of approximately 275 cm^2. Find its volume in:

a) m^3 **b)** cm^3.

Solution

a) Change the area of 275 cm^2 to 0.0275 m^2.

If you can't remember how many cm^2 there are in $1\ m^2$, remember that area has two dimensions, so divide by 100 and then divide by 100 again.

$3.2 \times 0.0275 = 0.088\text{m}^3$

b) Change the 3.2 m to 320 cm.

$320 \times 275 = 88\,000\text{ cm}^3$

Exercise 6.5

1 A cuboid container measures 1.8 m by 0.7 m by 90 cm. Find its volume in m^3.

2 A rectangle is 1.4 m long and 90 cm wide. Find its area in:
a) cm^2 **b)** m^2

3 The area of a piece of card is 1.2 m^2. What is this in square centimetres?

4 A book is 15 mm thick. How many of these books would fit on a shelf 1 m in length?

Answers – 6.5

1 $1.8 \times 0.7 \times 0.9 = 1.134\text{ m}^3$

2 **a)** $140 \times 90 = 12\,600\text{ cm}^2$
b) $1.4 \times 0.9 = 1.26\text{ m}^2$ or $12\,600 \div 10\,000 = 1.26\text{ m}^2$

3 $1\text{ m}^2 = 1\text{ m}$ by $1\text{ m} = 100\text{ cm}$ by $100\text{ cm} = 10\,000\text{ cm}^2$
$1.2\text{ m}^2 = 1.2 \times 10\,000 = 12\,000\text{ cm}^2$

4 Change one of the measurements so that you are working in the same unit throughout. Using millimetres, the calculation would be $1000 \div 15 = 66.\dot{6}$. Using metres, the calculation would be $1 \div 0.015 = 66.\dot{6}$. Note that although you would usually round up, the number of books is 66, as you couldn't have two thirds of a book on the shelf.

Mass, volume and density

M stands for mass. The question may refer either to weight or mass.

V stands for volume or capacity.

D stands for density.

Remember: Maths can be **V**ery **D**ifficult if you are **V**ery **D**ense!

Example 6.12

An object has mass of 7.2 kg and volume of 20 m^3. Calculate its density, stating the units used.

Solution

$$D = \frac{M}{V} = \frac{7.2}{20} = 0.36\text{ kg per m}^3$$

Exercise 6.6

1 The base of a cuboid box measures 20 cm by 13.5 cm. If its volume is 1215 cm^3, find its depth.

2 Find the volume of the triangular prism sketched here.

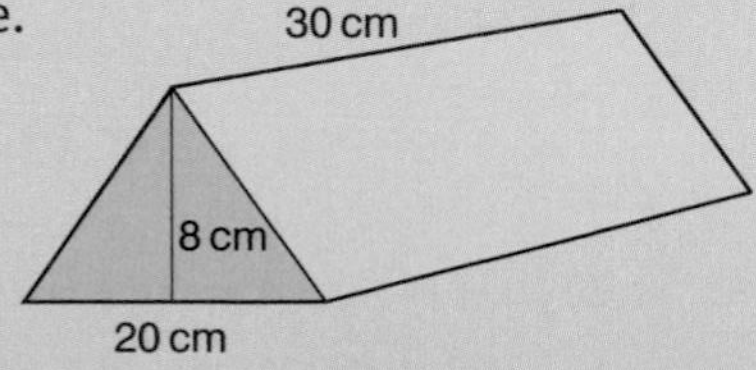

3 A cylinder holds 1 litre of water. If the radius of the cylinder is 4.5 cm, how deep is the water?

4 1 litre of fertiliser is to be spread over a garden to a depth of 4 cm. What area will it cover?

Answers – 6.6

1 4.5 cm
2 2400 cm^3
3 15.7 cm
4 250 cm^2

Imperial and metric units

Length — **Conversion**

cm/inches

30 cm ≈ 12 in or 1 ft

m/inches

1 m ≈ 39 in

km/miles

1 km ≈ $\frac{5}{8}$ mile

'Journey's end is full of smiles
8 km make 5 miles.'

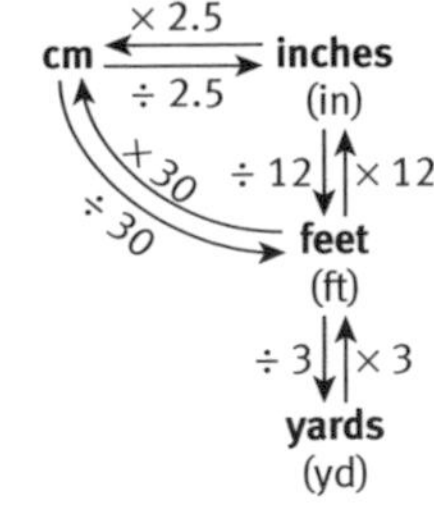

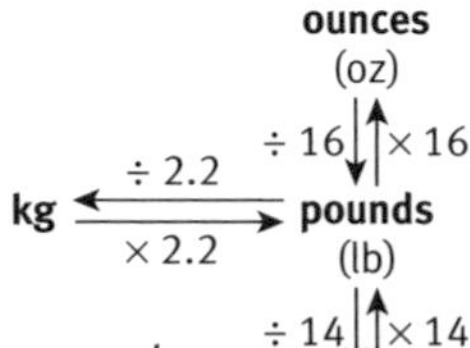

Mass/weight — **Conversion**

1 kg ≈ 2.2 lb

'To change to pounds,
here's what to do:
kilograms times 2.2.'

ounces (oz)
÷ 16 × 16
kg ÷ 2.2 / × 2.2 pounds (lb)
÷ 14 × 14
stones (st)

(In questions where calculators are not allowed take 1 kg = 2 lb.)

Capacity/volume — **Conversion**

1 *l* ≈ 1.8 pt

4.5 *l* ≈ 1 gal

litre × 4.5 / ÷ 4.5 gal

Roughly, a litre of water is a pint and three-quarters.

TAKE A BREAK

This is a good point to take a short break. When you come back, look quickly over this section once again and then have a go at the last topic in this chapter.

Dimensions

In questions on dimensions you will be given expressions and asked whether they relate to length, area, or volume, or are impossibilities. These questions are easier to understand if you work in a basic unit. For convenience, we shall use cm, cm^2 or cm^3 in the following way.

Length	cm	1 dimension
Area	cm^2	2 dimensions
Volume	cm^3	3 dimensions

Remember: *Any measurement of length, area or volume follows the same pattern.*

Rule 1: Adding or subtracting like with like

- length + length = length
  Example, perimeter of a rectangle
  cm + cm = cm
- area + area = area
  cm^2 + cm^2 = cm^2
- volume + volume = volume
  cm^3 + cm^3 = cm^3

Rule 2: Multiplication of dimensions

- length × length = area
  Example, area of a square
  cm × cm = cm^2
- length × length × length = volume
  Example, volume of a cube
  cm × cm × cm = cm^3
- area × length = volume
  cm^2 × cm = cm^3

Rule 3: Division of dimensions

- volume ÷ area = length
  Example, height of liquid in a container
  cm^3 ÷ cm^2 = cm
- volume ÷ length = area
  Example, finding cross-sectional area of a prism
  cm^3 ÷ cm = cm^2
- area ÷ length = length
  Example, finding length of one side

Rule 4: Adding or subtracting different dimensions gives a nonsense result

For example, length + area = nonsense!
volume + area = nonsense!

If you can, work with the expressions alone. The diagrams are often confusing and unnecessary.

1 Cross out all the numbers, including fractions and πs. These have no effect on the dimensions. For example, whether an area is 1000 km^2 or 10 mm^2, it is still an area, regardless of size.

2 Change all the letters that are left into their usual units of measurement, leaving the power.

   For example, h would become cm
   r^2 would become cm^2
   l^3 would become cm^3

3 Then use the four rules above to find whether the formula is one for length, area, volume or none of them.

Example 6.13

In these examples l, r and h represent lengths. State, with a reason, whether the following formulae are for perimeter, area, volume or none of these.

1 $4\pi r + 2h + l$

Cross out the 2, 4 and π.

This leaves $r + h + l$.

cm + cm + cm = cm

The formula is one for a length or perimeter.

2 $6r(l + h)$

Cross out the 6.

This leaves $r(l + h)$.

cm(cm + cm)

but (cm + cm) = cm which leads to

cm(cm) = cm × cm = cm^2 = area

The formula is one for an area.

3 $\frac{3}{4}lh - 2\pi r^2$

Cross out the $\frac{3}{4}$ and the 2π.

This leaves $lh - r^2$

cm × cm − cm^2

cm^2 − cm^2 = cm^2 = area

The formula is one for an area.

4 $r^2h + 3rh^2 + 3.5hlr$

Cross out the 3 and the 3.5.

This leaves $r^2h + rh^2 + hlr$

$r^2h = r \times r \times h$ = cm^3

$rh^2 = r \times h \times h$ = cm^3

$hlr = h \times l \times r$ = cm^3

cm^3 + cm^3 + cm^3 = cm^3 = volume

5 $\dfrac{6\pi r^3}{r}$

Cross out 6π.

This leaves $r^3 \div r = r^2$ = area

The formula is one for an area.

6 $2r^3 + 4lh^2 + 2h$

Cross out the 2, 4 and the final 2.

This leaves $r^3 + lh^2 + h$

$lh^2 = l \times h \times h$ = cm^3

$r^3 + lh^2 + h$ = cm^3 + cm^3 + cm = nonsense

7 r^2l^2

cm^2 × cm^2 = cm^4

This is to the power of 4, so it cannot be length, area or volume.

Chapter 2, Number, may help you to understand the principles behind the calculation of dimensions.

TIP: Times ⇒ Indices Plus
DIM: Divide ⇒ Indices Minus

For example:

length × area = volume

cm^1 × cm^2 = cm^3

volume ÷ area = length

cm^3 ÷ cm^2 = cm^1

volume ÷ length = area

cm^3 ÷ cm^1 = cm^2

But, as was shown in Chapter 2, Number, you cannot add or subtract different powers of numbers – or units.

Now look back at those rules on page 87. We hope they make more sense now. Don't worry, though, if they still seem confusing. Just keep trying and things should become clearer.

Exercise 6.7

The letters p, q and r represent lengths. State whether the following are lengths, areas, volumes or none of these.

1 $4\pi r^2 + q^2$

2 $6pr^2 - \pi q^2r$

3 $2pq + 3r$

4 $2pr + q^2 + qr$

5 $\pi pq^2 \div 6r^2$

Answers – 6.7

1 area
2 volume
3 none
4 area
5 length

REVIEW

How much have you learnt?
Tick off each topic in the list when you are confident that you can cope with it.

- ☐ **Identify the parts of a circle.**
- ☐ **Identify the circumference of a circle.**
- ☐ **Calculate the circumference of a circle, given the radius or diameter.**
- ☐ **Calculate the area of a circle, given its radius or diameter.**
- ☐ **Calculate the area of**
  - ☐ **a rectangle**
  - ☐ **a square**
  - ☐ **a triangle**
  - ☐ **a parallelogram.**
- ☐ **Calculate the surface area of a cuboid.**
- ☐ **Calculate areas of shapes made up of rectangles, triangles and semicircles.**
- ☐ **Identify the cross-section of a prism.**
- ☐ **Calculate the volume of a prism.**
- ☐ **Recognise formulae for lengths, areas and volumes from their dimensions.**
- ☐ **Calculate distances travelled by wheels.**
- ☐ **Calculate the number of revolutions made by a wheel in covering a given distance.**
- ☐ **Compare depths of liquids in various containers.**
- ☐ **Compare base areas of containers according to the volume or capacity of liquid in them.**

Chapter 7 Shapes, loci and constructions

PREVIEW

By the end of this chapter you will be able to:

- **name the different types of triangle (isosceles and equilateral)**
- **identify special angles formed by intersecting lines**
- **name and identify different types of quadrilaterals**
- **list the properties of different quadrilaterals**
- **recognise congruent shapes**
- **identify regular and irregular polygons**
- **find the interior and exterior angles of polygons**
- **state whether a polygon will tessellate**
- **understand and use circle theorems to find angles**
- **construct perpendicular bisectors of lines**
- **construct bisectors of angles**
- **construct equilateral triangles**
- **construct angles of 90°, 60°, 30° and 45°**
- **draw simple loci**
- **make scale drawings.**

How much do you know already?

Exercise 7.1

1 What is the difference between isosceles and equilateral triangles?

2 Mark the angles in the diagram below which are equal to x. Give a reason in each case.

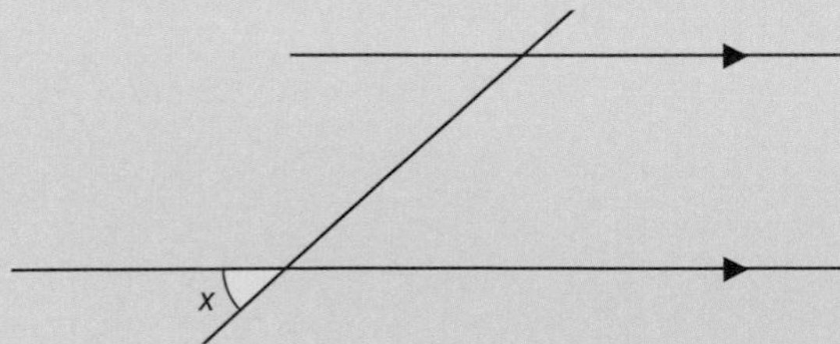

3 How many sides does a quadrilateral have?

4 Mark angle AXD.

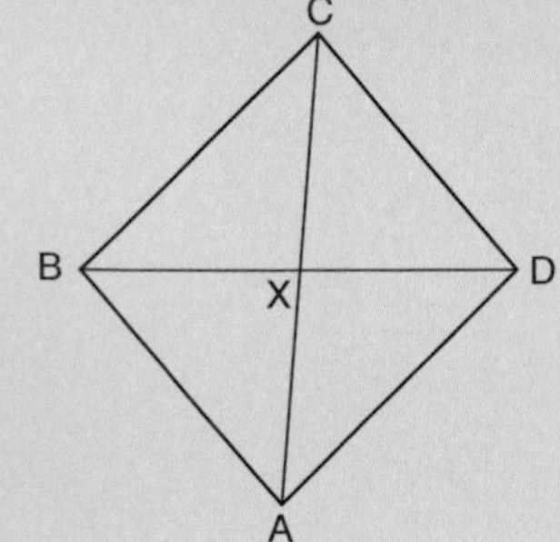

5 What is the difference between congruent and similar shapes?

6 Name the following shapes.

a)

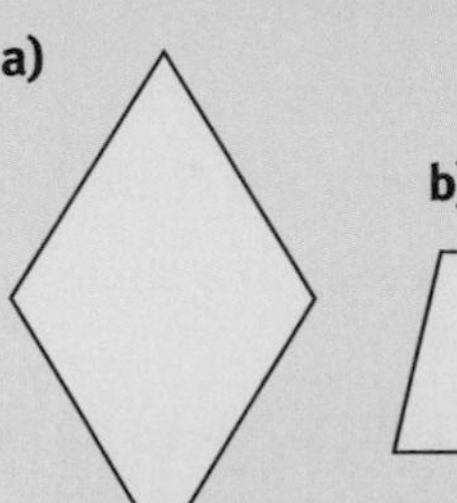

b)

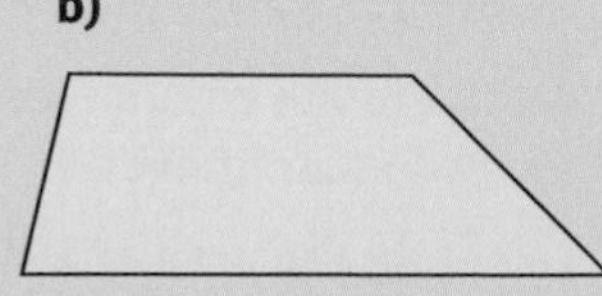

c)

d)

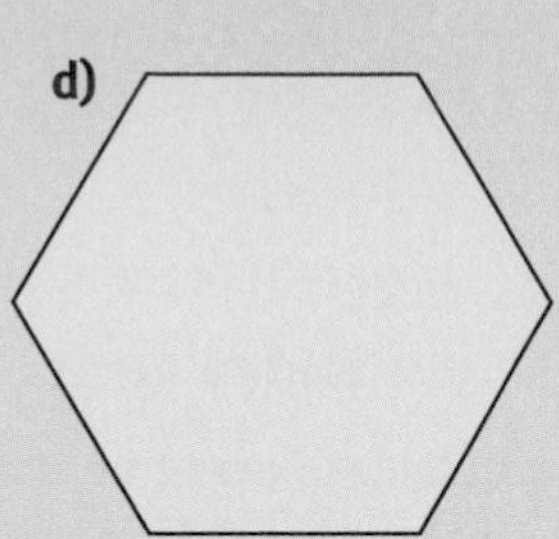

7 What is the difference between a polygon and a pentagon?

8 How do you know if a regular polygon will tessellate?

9 What is the difference between a regular and an irregular polygon?

10 Calculate the interior angle of a regular octagon.

11 From the diagram below, calculate the angles labelled x, y and z.

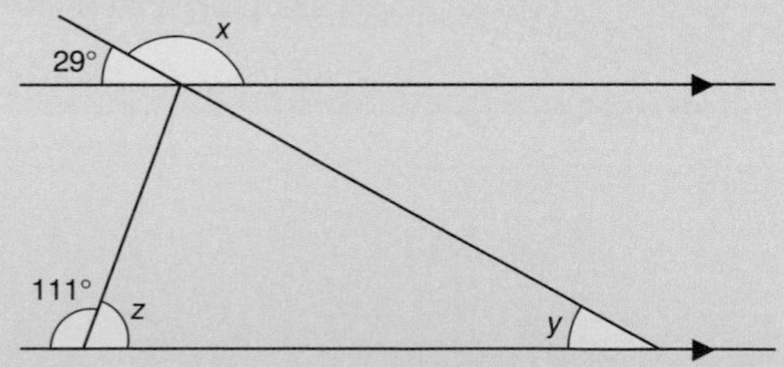

12 The diagram below represents a cage. If a monkey inside the cage can reach 60cm through the bars, draw the locus of the points which the monkey can reach, using a scale of 1 : 40.

Answers – 7.1

1 An isosceles triangle has two equal sides and two equal angles. An equilateral triangle has all three sides equal and each angle is 60°.

2 Opposite angles and alternate angles.

3 4

4

5 Congruent shapes are identical, although you may have to flip one of them over or turn it round to make both of them match. Similar shapes are the same shape but different sizes, so their angles are the same, but one is an enlargement of the other.

6 **a)** rhombus **b)** trapezium **c)** parallelogram **d)** hexagon

7 A polygon is any straight-sided two-dimensional (2D) shape. A pentagon is a five-sided shape.

8 The interior angles of the polygon divide exactly into 360°.

9 All the sides and angles of a regular polygon are the same, whereas the sides and angles of an irregular polygon are not all the same.

10 135°

11 $x = 151°$, $y = 29°$, $z = 69°$

12

How did you get on?

All or most of them right?

You probably don't need to work through this chapter. There are more shape and construction questions in the Shape and space review on page 109. If you have any problems with them you can come back to this chapter for help.

Five or more right?

You know most of what you need to know for the exam, but there are still some gaps. You should be able to skim through this chapter, leaving out the parts you know and concentrating on where you went wrong.

Don't even ask?

This chapter is one of the easiest to learn, and once again we have provided easy ways of jogging your memory.

Angles and triangles

Types of triangles

Scalene All three sides and all three angles different

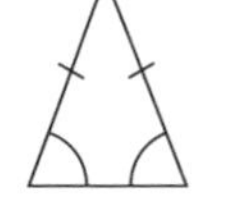

Isosceles Two sides and two angles the same

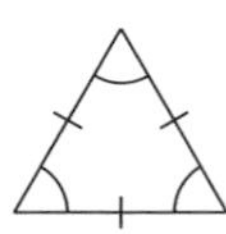

Equilateral All three sides the same and each angle is 60°

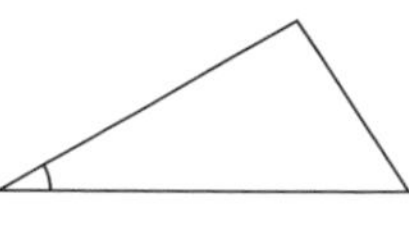

Acute angles are $< 90°$

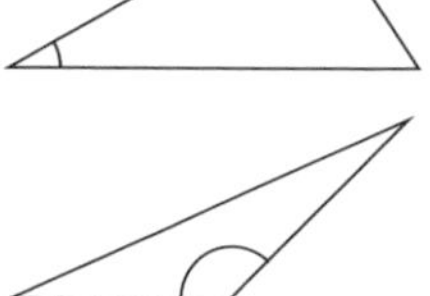

Obtuse angles are $> 90°$ but $< 180°$

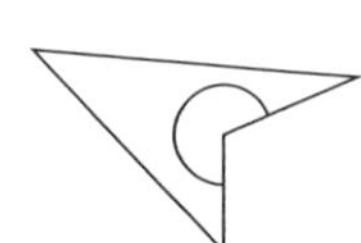

Reflex angles are $> 180°$ but $< 360°$

Triangle area

Area of a triangle $= \frac{1}{2}$ base $\times$ **perpendicular** height
(perpendicular means at right angles)

or $\frac{\text{base} \times \textbf{perpendicular}\text{ height}}{2}$

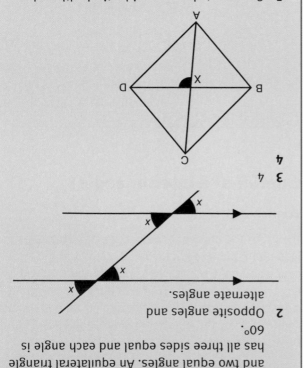

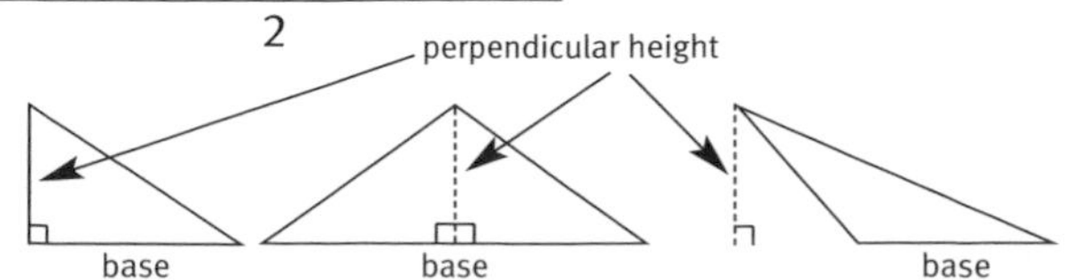

Labelling angles

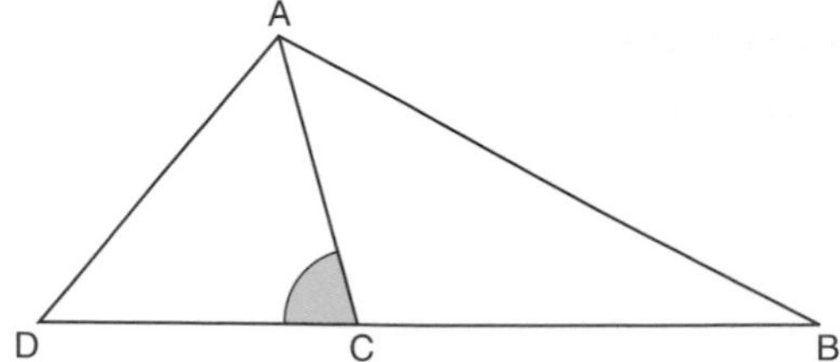

The angle marked at C may be called angle ACD or angle DCA. In some books this is written ∠ACD, ∠DCA, $A\hat{C}D$ or $D\hat{C}A$.

The marked angle at C consists of two lines AC and CD. To name the angle, you would follow the line from A to C to D or vice versa. This is to avoid confusion with the other angle at C running from A to C to B, or vice versa – which is called ∠ACB or ∠BCA. The angle is located at the point indicated by the middle letter.

Intersecting and parallel lines

Intersecting lines are lines which cross each other.

Hints & Tips

*Remember **FXZ**.*

Corresponding: you correspond with a F riend.

Opposite: 

Alternate: know your angles from A to 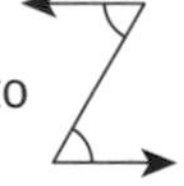

Straight line: 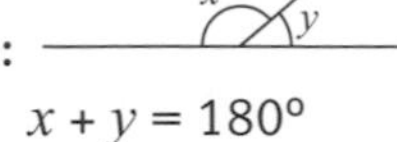

$x + y = 180°$

Triangles: 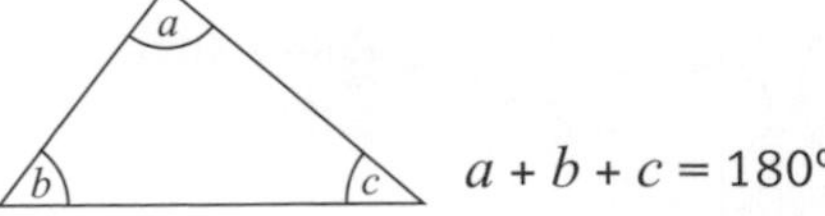

$a + b + c = 180°$

Hints & Tips

*As you can see, the letters 'F', 'X' and 'Z' are particularly helpful in reminding you of the difference between corresponding, opposite and alternate angles. In addition, you can see that the letters at the beginning of each line form the word **COAST**.*

Exercise 7.2

Find the following angles by calculation giving reasons for your answers. None of the diagrams in this exercise is drawn accurately, so do not attempt to answer the questions by measuring the angles.

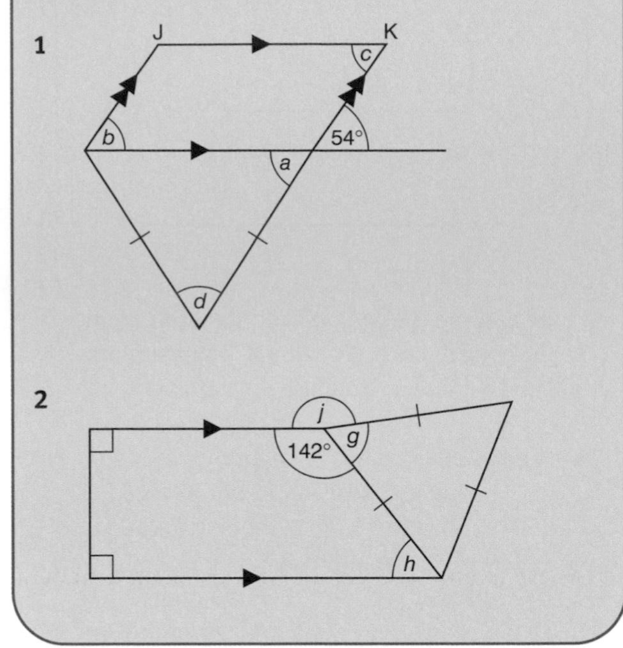

Answers – 7.2

1 $a = 54°$ (opposite angles)
$b = 54°$ (corresponding angles)
$c = 54°$ (alternate angles)
$d = 72°$ (isosceles triangle.
Angle $d = 180° - 2 \times 54° = 72°$.)

2 $g = 60°$ (equilateral triangle)
$h = 38°$ (angles of a quadrilateral total 360°)
$j = 158°$ (angles round a point total 360°)

Exterior and interior angles

Exterior angles

These are the angles at the outside of a shape, as illustrated on page 93. If you travel right round a shape and get back to where you started, you will have travelled through 360°. For a regular polygon (all sides are equal and all interior angles are equal), just divide 360° by the number of sides, and you will find the exterior angle.

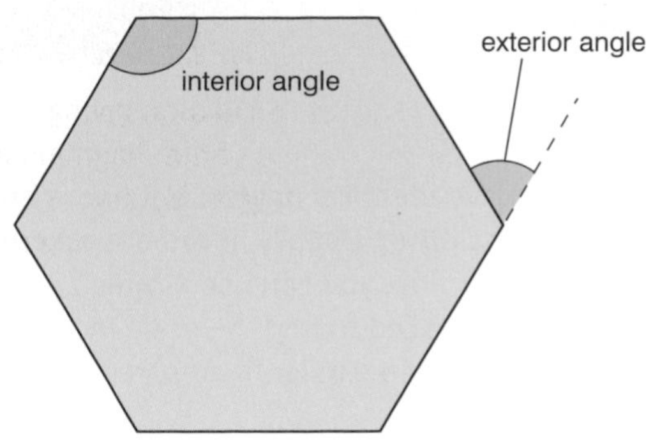

The exterior angle of an n-sided regular polygon is $\frac{360°}{n}$

The number of sides of a regular polygon is $\frac{360°}{\text{exterior angle}}$

Interior angles

1 Find the exterior angle by calculating $\frac{360°}{n}$

2 As the interior and exterior angles lie on a straight line, they add up to 180°.

interior angle = 180° – exterior angle

The angle at the centre of a regular polygon is the same as the exterior angle.

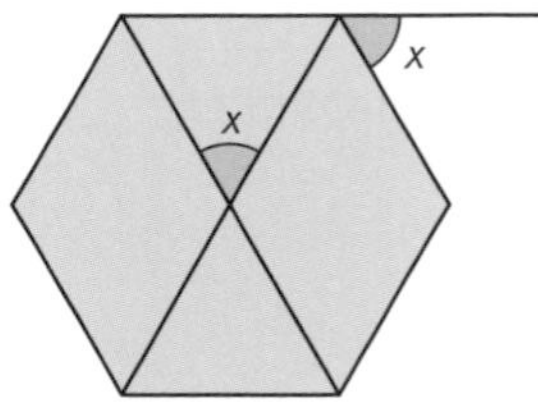

Exterior angle of a triangle

The exterior angle of a triangle is the sum of the two interior angles as shown in the diagram below.

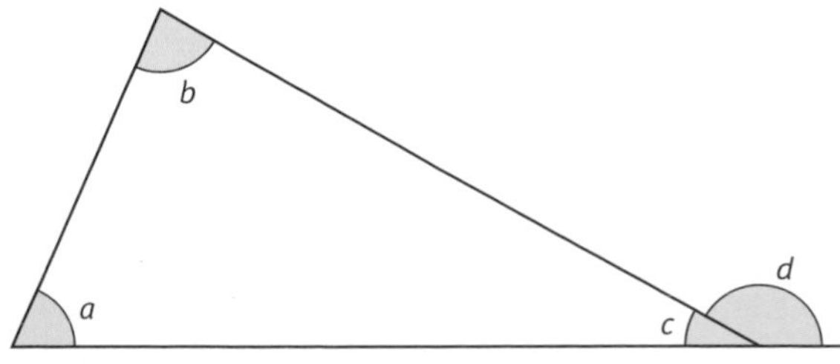

$a + b + c = 180°$ (angles of a triangle)

$c + d = 180°$ (angles on a straight line)

So $a + b = d$

Example 7.1

In the diagram below, AC = BC. Find x.

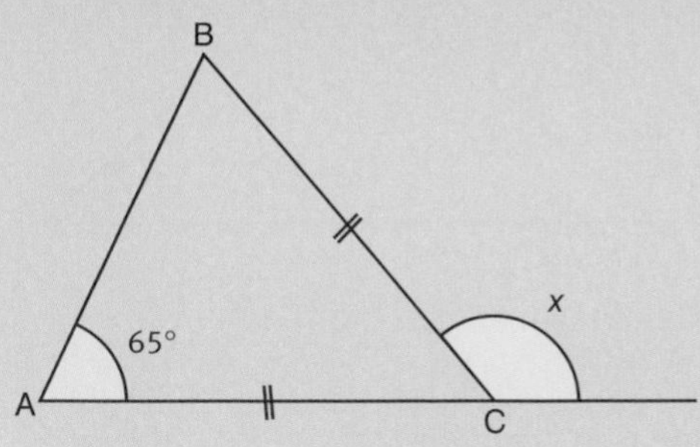

Solution

As the triangle is isosceles, angle CAB = angle ABC = 65°

So $x = 65 + 65 = 130°$

Example 7.2

Study the diagram below.

a) Write down an equation in x.

b) Find x.

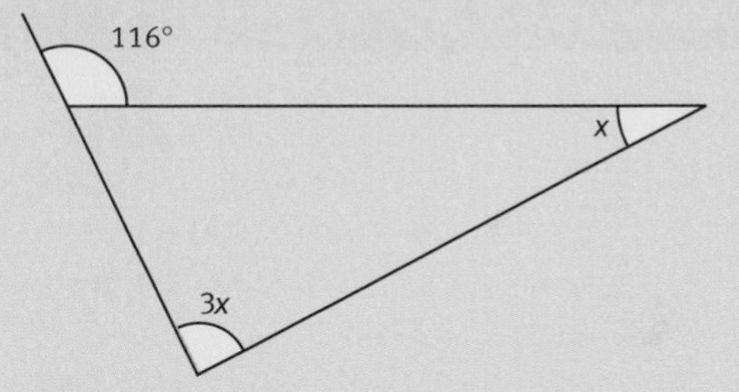

Solution

a) $3x + x = 116°$

$4x = 116°$

b) $x = 29°$

Exercise 7.3

1 Find x in the triangle below:

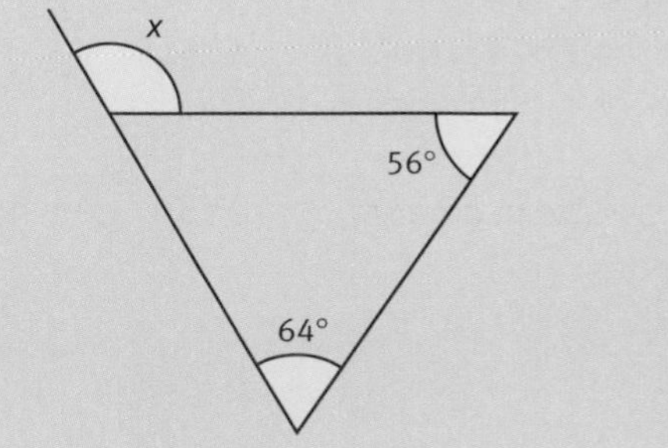

2 For the triangle below:

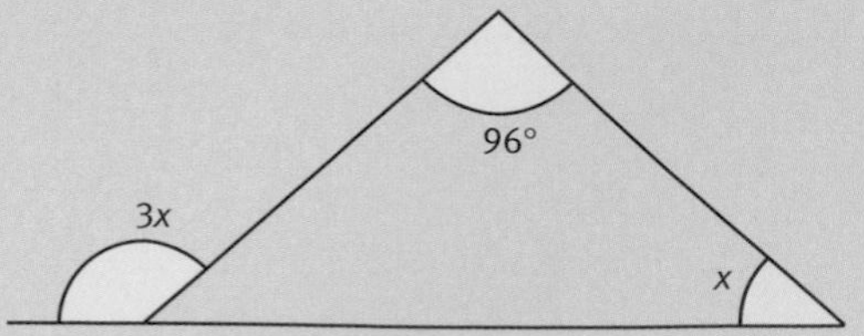

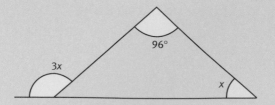

a) Write down an equation in x.
b) Find x.

3 A regular polygon has an interior angle of 120°.
a) Find its exterior angle.
b) How many sides does the polygon have?

4 Find the exterior and interior angles of a regular octagon.

5 A regular polygon has an exterior angle of 36°.
a) Find the interior angle.
b) Find the number of sides of the polygon.
c) Find the sum of the interior angles of the polygon.

Answers – 7.3

1 $x = 56 + 64 = 120°$

2 **a)** $3x = x + 96$
b) $2x = 96$, so $x = 48°$

3 **a)** $180° - 120° = 60°$
b) $360° \div 60° = 6$ sides

4 Exterior angle $= 360° \div 8 = 45°$, interior angle $= 180° - 45° = 135°$

5 **a)** $180° - 36° = 144°$
b) $360° \div 36° = 10$ sides
c) $144° \times 10 = 1440°$

Tessellation

For shapes to tessellate, the angles at any point where they meet must add up to 360°. Designs of kitchen and bathroom flooring are often good examples of shapes that tessellate.

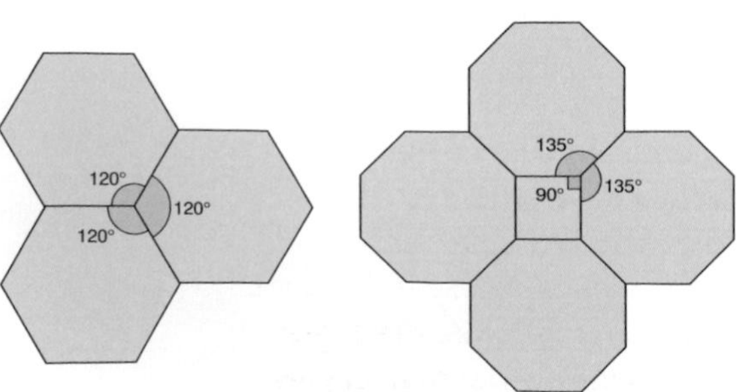

Polygons

Similar shapes

Similar shapes have identical angles, but one is an enlargement of the other. Usually, if you are asked to find the length of a side, you can use X-Direct. However, if you are asked to find the scale factor of an enlargement between similar figures, remember the scale factor equals:

$$\frac{\text{Second length}}{\text{First length}}$$

*or **S**econd **O**ver the **F**irs**T***
and you are SOFT in the head if you forget.

Example 7.3

In the diagram below, BE and CD are vertical poles. Using the lengths given on the diagram, find AD.

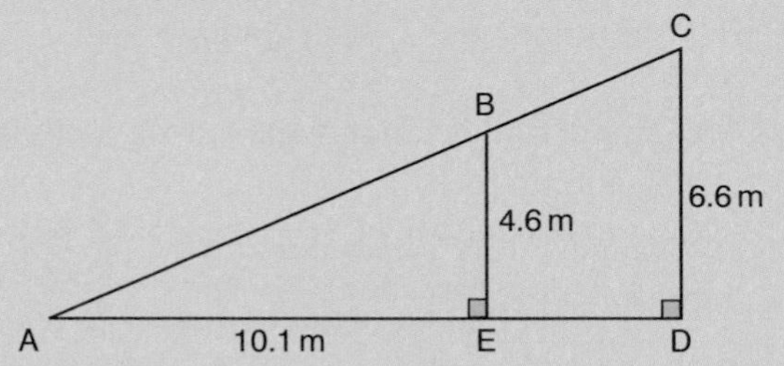

Solution

Draw the triangles separately:

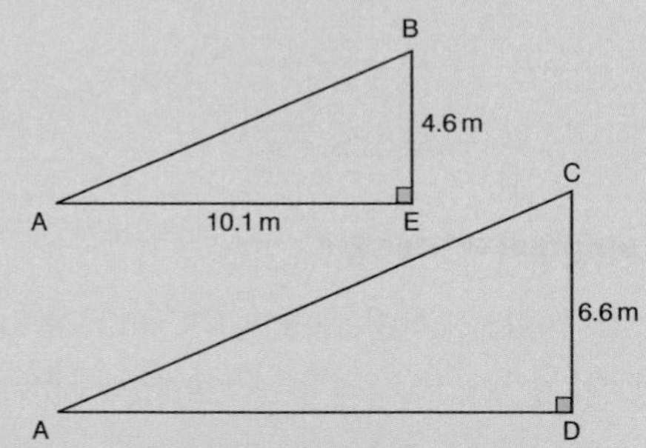

Triangles ABE and ACD are similar.

Using X-Direct:

	ABE	ACD
Pole length	4.6	6.6
Horizontal distance	10.1	?

$\frac{10.1 \times 6.6}{4.6} = 14.5$ The length of AD is 14.5 m.

In some questions like this you could use trigonometry, but this method is much quicker.

Example 7.4

Two pictures are similar. The smaller one has width 5.5 cm and length 7.4 cm. If the width of the larger one is 46.75 cm, find:

a) the scale factor of the enlargement
b) the length of the larger picture.

Solution

a) The scale factor is $\frac{46.75}{5.5} = 8.5$

Take care to choose the width, not the length.

b) The length of the larger picture is $7.4 \times 8.5 = 62.9$ cm

Alternatively you can use X-Direct.

	Smaller	Larger
Width	5.5	46.75
Length	7.4	?

Length of the larger picture $= \frac{7.4 \times 46.75}{5.5}$

$= 62.9$

The length is 62.9 cm.

Just to confuse you, if the scale factor is less than 1, enlargements actually make things smaller!

Recognising polygons

A polygon or a polyhedron?

A polygon is a 2D shape, such as a hexagon. A polyhedron is a 3D shape, such as a pyramid.

Regular polygons are shapes with all sides the same and all angles the same.

Irregular polygons are shapes where the sides and angles are not all the same.

Congruent shapes

Congruent shapes are identical in size and shape, although you may have to flip one over or turn it around for the two to appear to match.

Note: The words 'congruent' and 'similar' can describe any group of shapes. However, 'congruent' is more usually applied to triangles.

The rules for congruency in two triangles are:

1 SAS side, angle, side – two sides and the angle between them are the same

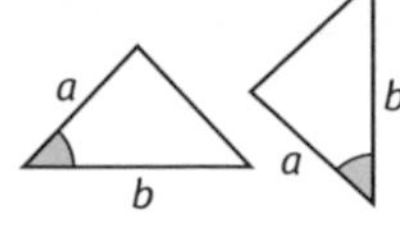

2 AAS – angle, angle, side – two angles and the corresponding side are equal

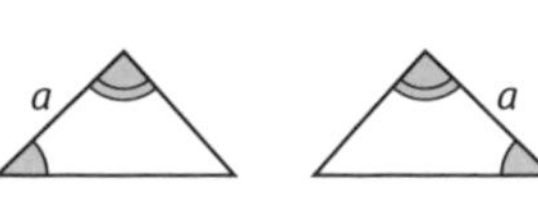

3 SSS – all corresponding sides are equal

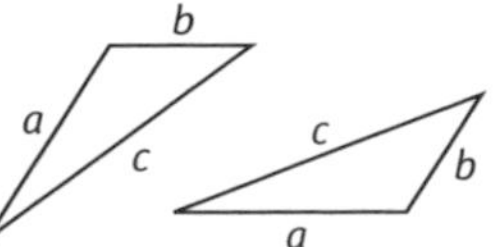

4 HRS – hypotenuse, right angle and corresponding side are equal

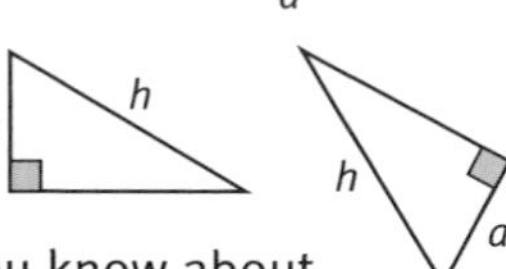

Always go through what else you know about triangles and **RISE** above any problem.
The triangle in the question may be

- **R**ight-angled – you may have a Pythagoras, trigonometry or area question
- **I**sosceles – you may be able to use the fact that 2 sides and 2 angles are equal.
- **S**imilar to another triangle – make sure that you know which sides go together so that you can find the scale factor
- **E**quilateral – all sides are the same length and all angles are 60°.

Quadrilaterals

square → rhombus

rectangle → parallelogram

Square

- 4 right angles
- all sides are equal
- opposite sides are parallel
- diagonals cross at right angles

Rhombus

(like a squashed square or a diamond)
As with a square:

- all sides are equal
- opposite sides are parallel
- diagonals cross at right angles
- opposite angles are equal but angles are not right angles

Rectangle

- 4 right angles
- opposite sides are equal and parallel
- diagonals do not cross at right angles

Parallelogram

(like a squashed rectangle)
As with a rectangle:

- opposite sides are equal
- diagonals do not cross at right angles
- opposite angles are the same but angles are not right angles

Trapezium
- one pair of sides parallel

Kite
- 2 pairs of sides are equal
- diagonals cross at right angles
- 1 set of opposite angles are equal

Summary

Shape	Square	Rectangle	Parallelogram
Area	$l \times w$ (l, w)	$l \times w$ (l, w)	$b \times h$ (height, base)
Lines of symmetry Reflections	4	2	0
Order of symmetry Rotations	4	2	2

Shape	Kite	Rhombus	Trapezium
Lines of symmetry Reflections	1	2	0 or 1
Order of symmetry Rotations	1	2	1 or 1

Area of a trapezium $= \frac{(a + b)}{2} \times$ height

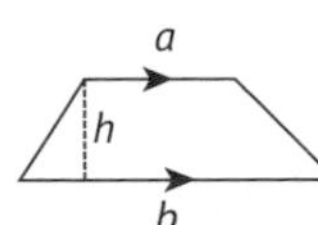

TAKE A BREAK

As you have worked this far, you will probably feel in need of a break.

Nets of solids

Imagine a hollow 3D shape that has been cut along some of its edges so that it can be flattened and opened out. If the shape has curved surfaces, you may have to make extra cuts. The flattened shape is the net of the solid.

Exercise 7.4

Sketch a net for each of the following closed objects.

1

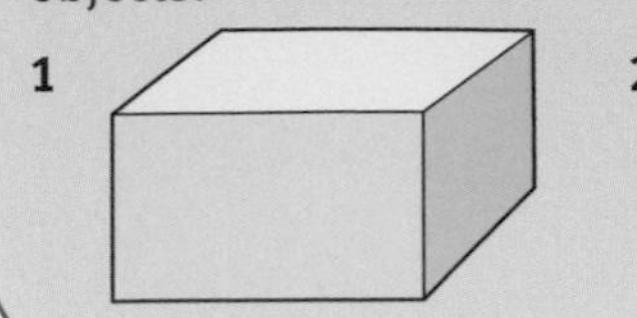

2

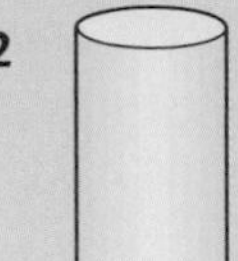

Answers – 7.4

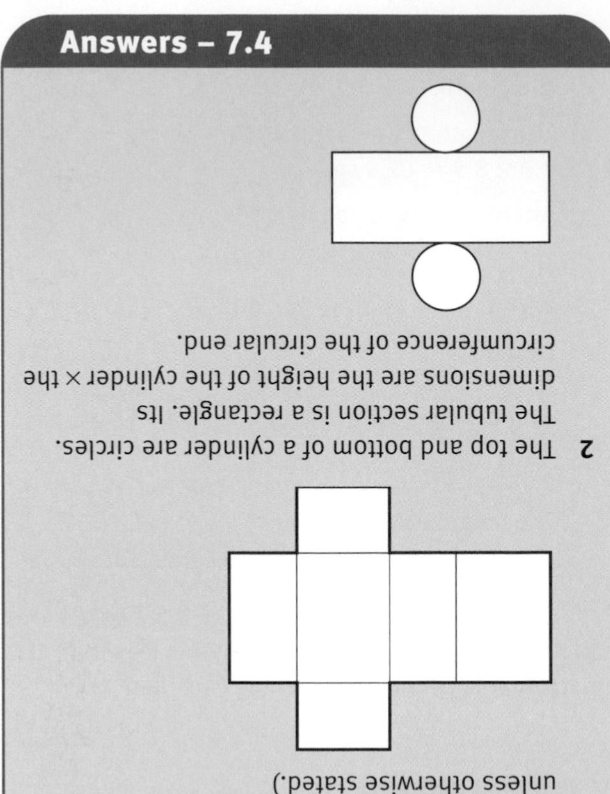

1 A cuboid has six sides which would close to make a cuboid. (Do not allow extra for flaps unless otherwise stated.)
2 The top and bottom of a cylinder are circles. The tubular section is a rectangle. Its dimensions are the height of the cylinder × the circumference of the circular end.

Read questions concerning cylinders and cuboids extra carefully, because sometimes they do not have a lid, e.g. waste bins, fish tanks, etc. There is often more than one right way of drawing the net. Always check at the end that the net you have chosen would fold up into the original shape.

Circle theorems

There are six theorems to learn, and it is as easy as one, two, three.

Cyclic quadrilaterals: one rule

1. Opposite angles of cyclic quadrilaterals sum to 180°. (Conversely if opposite angles of a quadrilateral sum to 180°, the quadrilateral is cyclic.)

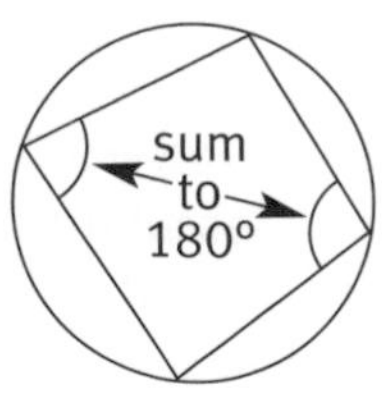

Tangents: two rules

1. The angle between a tangent and the radius at the point of contact is 90°.

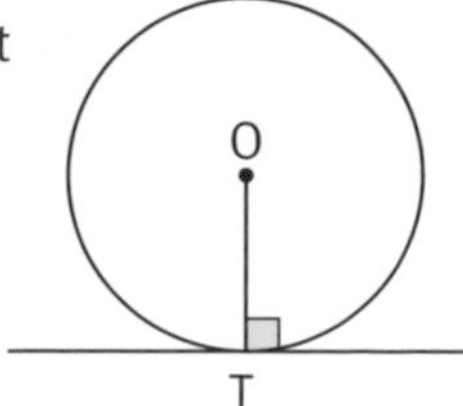

2. Tangents from a common point are equal in length.

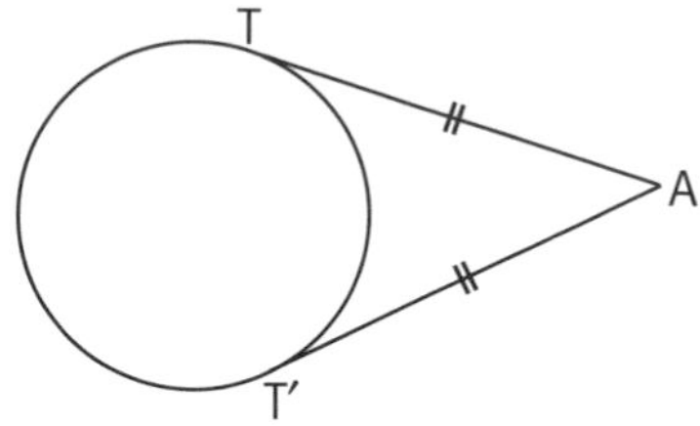

Make sure that you can explain each of these theorems or rules. Questions often ask you to give reasons for your answers.

Look out for isosceles triangles: those having two sides as radii can be difficult to spot.

Fill in on the diagram any angles that you find, even if the question does not ask for them. They may help you find the angles that the question does ask for.

Always use a pencil when labelling angles, just in case you make a mistake. Unless it is absolutely necessary, try not to add any lines to the diagram as they can often make it much more confusing.

Angles: three rules

1. The angle subtended at the circumference by the diameter of a circle is 90°.

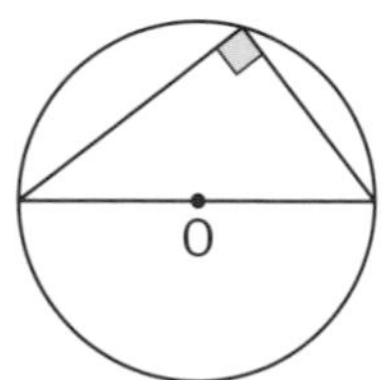

2. The angle subtended at the centre of a circle is twice the angle subtended at the circumference, from the same two points.

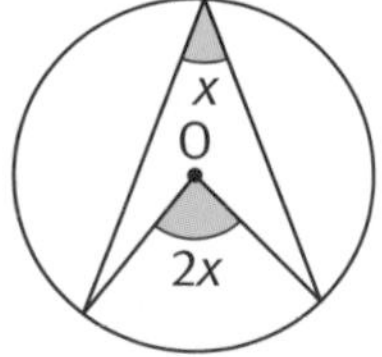

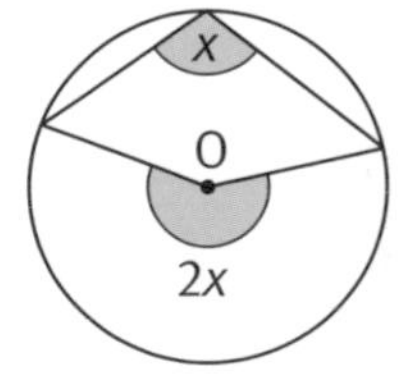

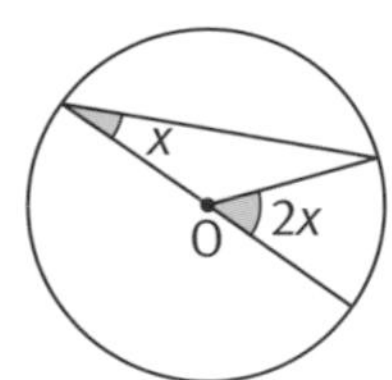

3. The angles subtended anywhere on the circumference, but in the same sector, from the same two points are equal.

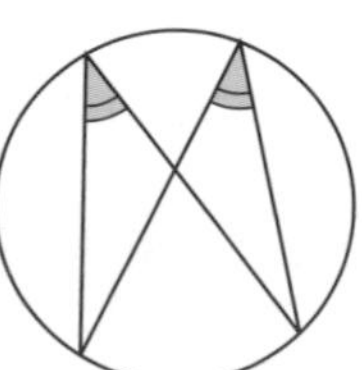

What does 'subtended' mean?

If you choose two points on the circumference of a circle, and draw an angle on the circumference, the angle is **subtended** by the two points. Notice that any two points can subtend more than one angle. Angles can also be subtended at the centre.

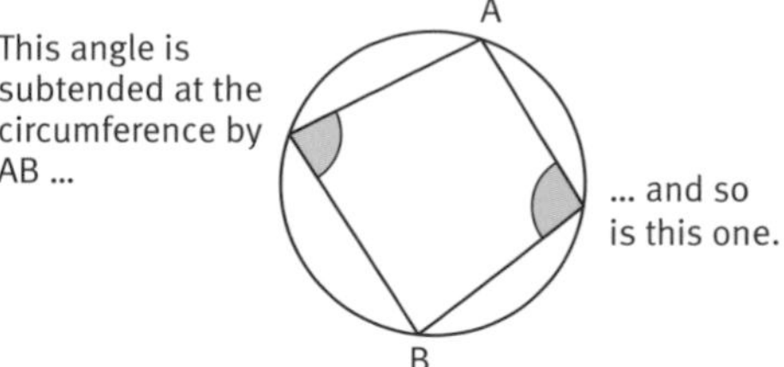

Example 7.5

Find the angles marked x and y in the diagram, giving reasons for your answers.

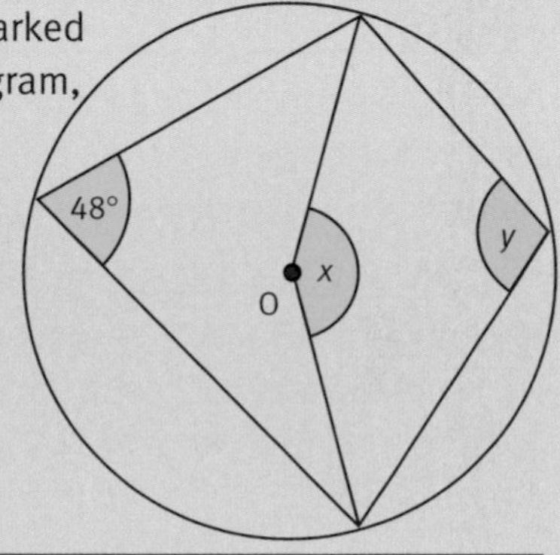

Solution

$x = 96°$, because the angle subtended from two points at the centre is twice that subtended at the circumference.

$y = 132°$, because opposite angles of a cyclic quadrilateral sum to 180°.

Example 7.6

Find the angles marked x, y and z in the diagram, giving reasons for your answers.

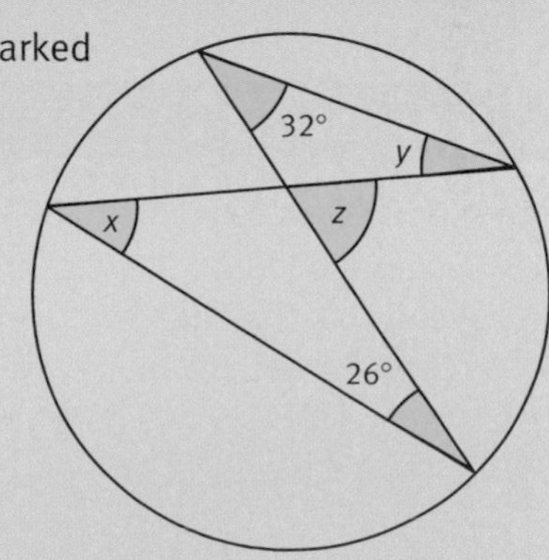

Solution

$x = 32°$, because the angles in the same sector of the circle subtended from common points are equal.

$y = 26°$, because the angles in the same sector of the circle subtended from common points are equal.

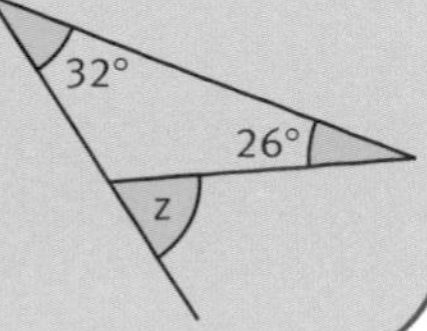

$z = 58°$, because the exterior angle of a triangle is the sum of two interior angles.

Example 7.7

In the diagram below, PT and PS are tangents to the circle centred at O. Find the angles marked e, f, g and h, giving reasons for your answers.

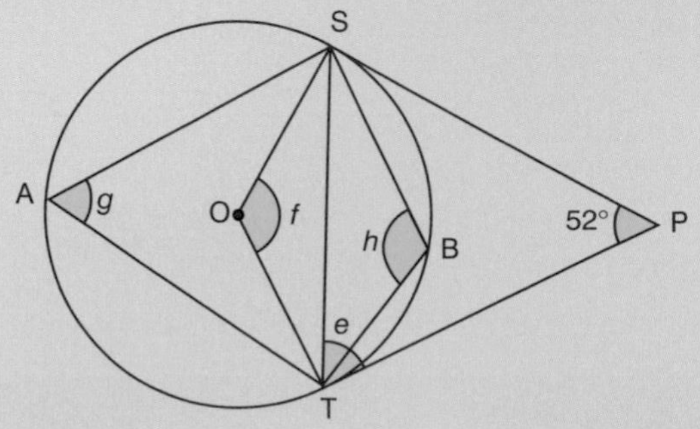

Solution

$e = 64°$, because PT and PS are equal in length as they are tangents from a common point, so triangle PST is isosceles.

$f = 128°$, because OS and OT are perpendicular to the tangents SP and TP respectively, so the angles OTP and OSP are 90°. As the angles of quadrilateral OTPS sum to 360°, angle $f = 360° - 90° - 90° - 52° = 128°$

$g = 64°$, because the angle at the centre of a circle is twice the angle at the circumference subtended from the same two points.

$h = 116°$, because ASBT is a cyclic quadrilateral and the opposite angles add up to 180°.

Exercise 7.5

1 JL and KL are tangents to the circle centred at O. M is a point on the circumference of this circle. Find the angles a, b and c, giving a reason for each of your answers.

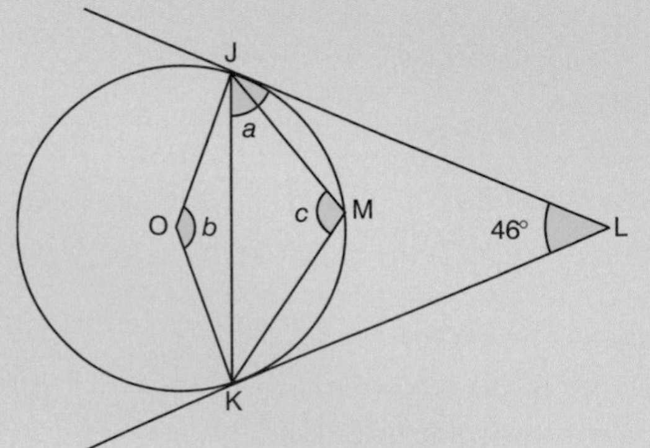

2 PR passes through O, the centre of the circle. Angle PRQ = 55° and angle PQS = 25°.

Find:

a) angle SQR　　**b)** angle QPR

c) angle QSR　　**d)** angle SOR.

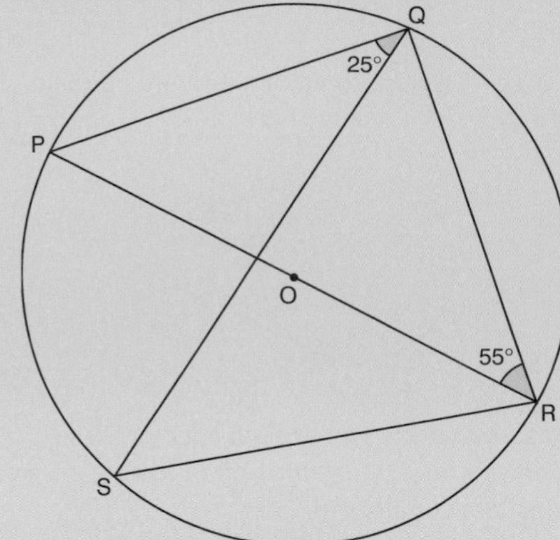

3 The line PT is a tangent to the circle centred at O. Find the angles marked x and y, giving reasons for your answers.

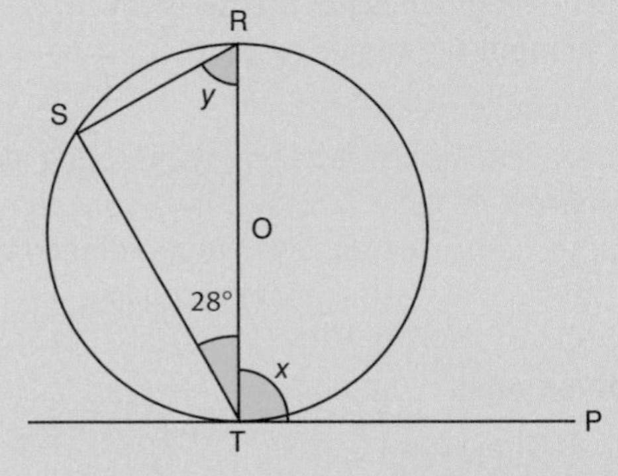

Answers – 7.5

1 $a = 67°$. As JL and KL are equal in length, triangle JKL is isosceles.
$b = 134°$. Angles OJL and OKL are both 90°, so $b = 360° - 2 \times 90° - 46° = 134°$.
$c = 113°$. c is half the size of the reflex angle at O. $(360° - 134° = 226°)$

2 **a)** angle SQR = 65°. As PR is the diameter, PQR = 90°.

b) angle QPR = 35°. As PR is the diameter, PQR = 90° and angle QPR = 180° − 90° − 55°.

c) angle QSR = 35°. As angles in the same segment and from common points are equal, angle QSR = angle QPR.

d) angle SOR = 130° or twice angle SQR. The angle at the centre of the circle is twice the angle at the circumference subtended from the same two points.

3 $x = 90°$, because the angle between the tangent and its radius is 90°.
$y = 62°$, because the angle subtended by the diameter at the circumference is 90°, so $y = 180° - 90° - 28° = 62°$.

Loci and constructions

How much do you know already?

Exercise 7.6

1 Do you know what 'perpendicular' means?
2 Do you know what 'bisect' means?
3 Can you draw a perpendicular bisector?
4 Do you know what a locus is?
5 Can you give the plural of 'locus'?
6 What do you get when you draw the locus of a point a fixed distance from another given point? Can you draw it?
7 What do you get when you draw the locus of a point a fixed distance from a given line? Can you draw it?

Answers – 7.6

1 Two lines are perpendicular when they meet each other at right angles.
2 To 'bisect' something means to cut it in half.
4 The path made by a point following a given rule.
5 Loci.
6 A circle centred at the fixed point.
7 A line parallel to the given line.

How did you get on?

Five right

You deserve the rest of the day off, but perhaps you should finish this chapter first!

Fewer than five right?

It's worth wading through the rest of this chapter, because questions about loci often crop up in the exam, and they are an easy way of acquiring those valuable marks.

Locus (plural loci)

The locus of a point is the path made by a point following a given rule. For instance, the locus of a point P which is always 3cm from a fixed point O is a circle of radius 3 cm centred at O.

Perpendicular bisector

Perpendicular means at right angles.
Bisect means cut in half.

*The **L** reminds you that perpendicu**L**ar **L**ines are at right angles.*

The perpendicular bisector is a line which cuts another line in half and is perpendicular to it. It is also equidistant (i.e. the same distance) from the end points of the line.

If two points A and B are marked on a straight line, the part of the line from A to B is called the line segment AB.

The midpoint of AB is the point that is halfway along, at equal distances from A and B.

How to draw the perpendicular bisector

Whenever you are drawing loci and constructions, always leave your compass marks on so that the examiner can tell that you have used the right method. **Don't** use set squares or protractors.

Example 7.8

Draw a line perpendicular to AB.

A ● ——— ● B

Method

1 Put the point of your compasses on one end of the line, say at B, and open the compasses to a radius which is more than half the length of the line AB.
2 Using only light pressure, draw an arc either side of the line.

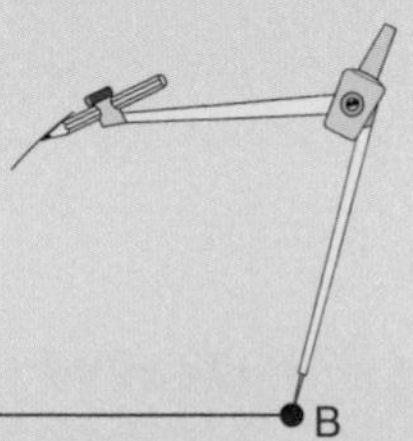

3 Without changing the radius, draw an arc from the other end. Join the two crosses to make the perpendicular bisector.

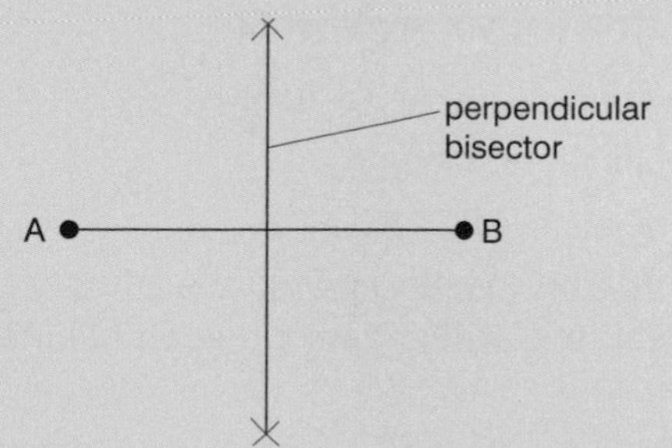

Do not use a pair of compasses with a loose joint. Always hold them from the top, so that the radius is the same for both ends.

Do not rub out the arcs that you draw in constructions. They show the examiner that your method was correct.

Finding the shortest distance from a point to a line, or drawing a perpendicular from a line to a point

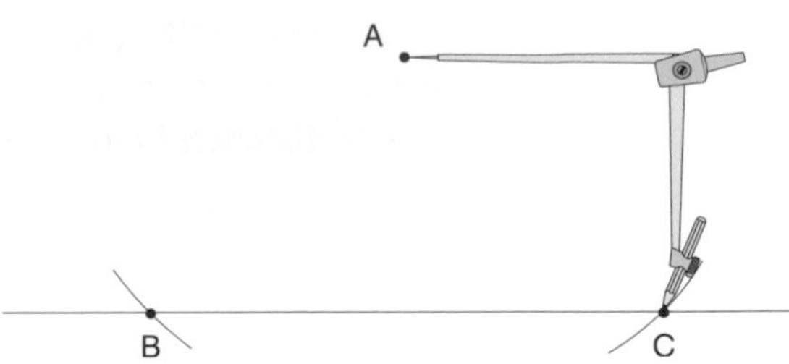

Set your compasses to any suitable length and draw an arc from A, cutting the horizontal line twice. Label the two points of intersection of the arc and line as B and C. Draw the perpendicular bisector of the line BC, making it pass through A. This gives a line, at right angles to BC, and cutting it at X, Then XA is the shortest distance from BC to A.

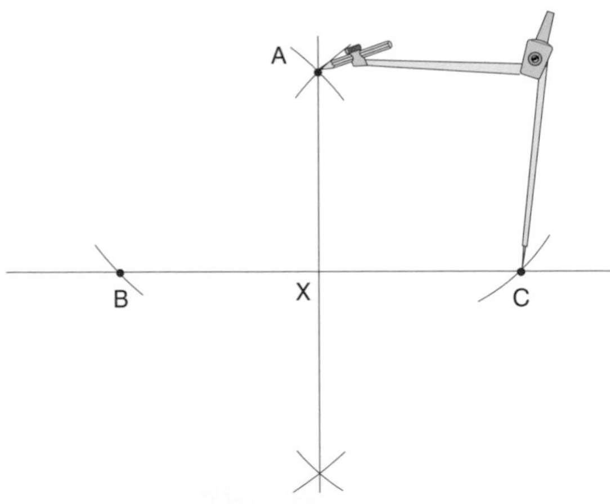

Constructing an angle of 90°

You can do this using the perpendicular bisector method described above.

Constructing an angle of 60°

This is the same as the method used for constructing an equilateral triangle.

Draw any line AB. Set your compasses to the length of AB. Put the compass point on A and draw an arc. Repeat for B. A line from either end point of AB to the point where the two arcs cut, or intersect, makes an angle of 60° with AB.

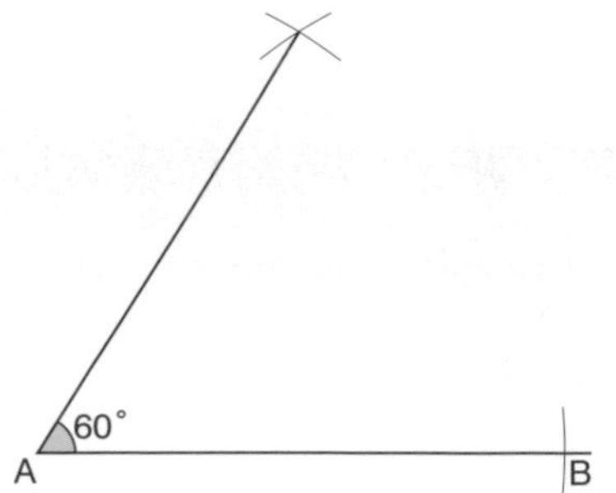

The point where two lines or curves cross is their point of intersection.

Bisecting an angle

Example 7.9

Divide the shape into two equal parts.

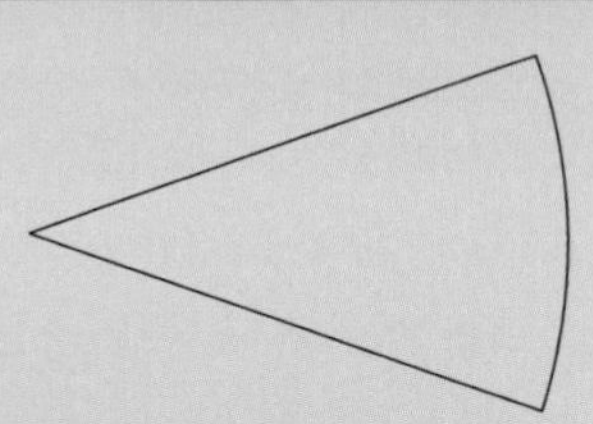

Method

1 Put the point of the compasses on the point of the angle and make an arc on each arm, at A and B.

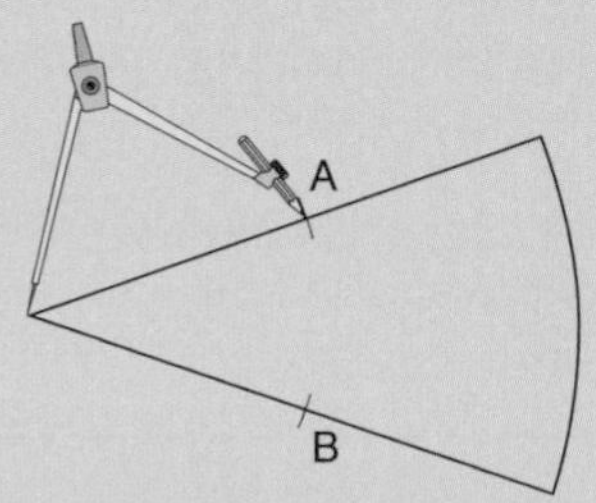

2 Move the point of the compasses to A and B in turn and make a further arc from each. Do not change the radius between drawing from A and drawing from B.

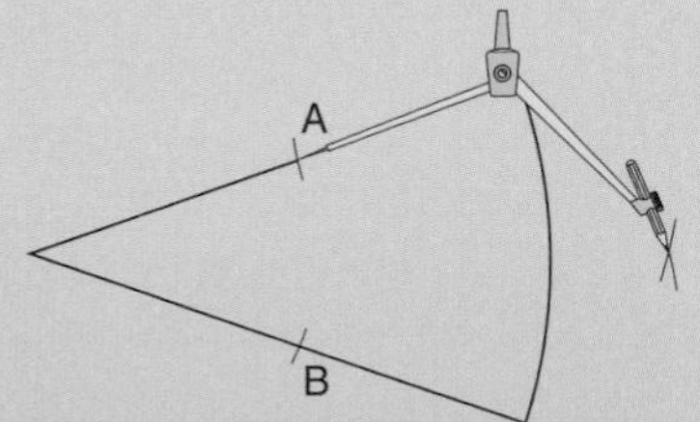

3 Join the cross to the point of the angle to make the bisector of the angle.

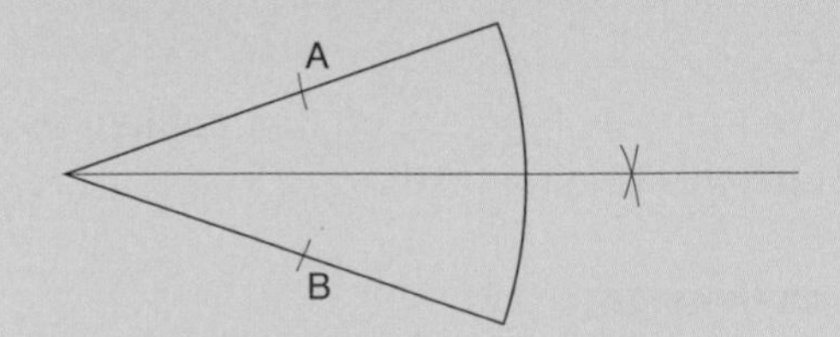

Remember: *You can construct an angle of 45° by constructing a perpendicular, then bisecting it.*

Rounded corners

Example 7.10

Below is a pond measuring 4 m by 3 m. Using a scale of 2 cm to represent 1 m, draw the locus of a point that is exactly 1.5 m outside the pond. Be careful to round the corners using your compases. Shade in the resulting area outside the pond.

Solution

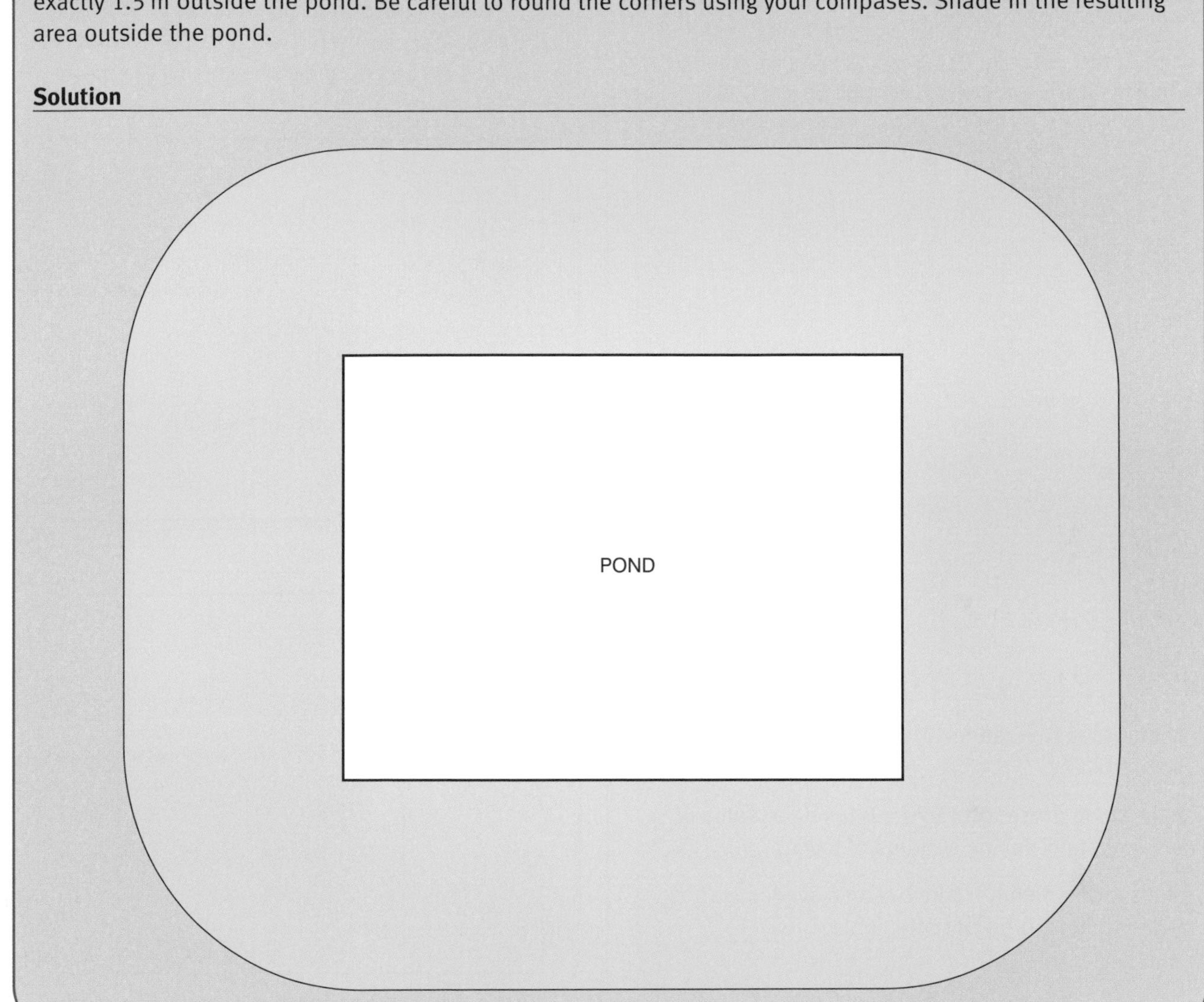

Overlapping regions

Example 7.11

The diagram below illustrates the positions of three of the fairground lights, A, B and C. They illuminate a maximum distance of 50 m, 90 m and 100 m respectively. Using a scale of 1 cm to 20 m, indicate the region which is lit by all three.

A

B

C

Solution

For light A, 50 m is represented by 2.5 cm. Set the compasses to a radius of 2.5 cm and draw an arc centred at A.

Repeat the process for lights B (using a radius of 4.5 cm) and C (using a radius of 5 cm).

The shaded region where the arcs overlap is the region that is lit by all three lights.

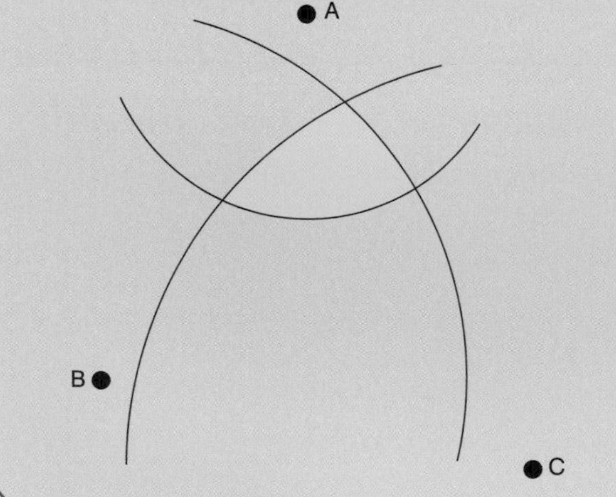

Scale drawings

Example 7.12

The diagram shows the plan of a stall at a Summer Fayre. Players have to throw bean bags at targets and must stand at least 4 m from the stall. Using a scale of 1 cm to 1 m, draw the area where players may not stand.

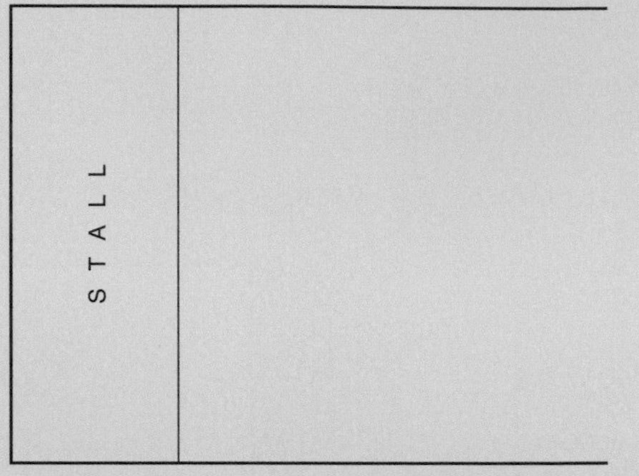

Solution

Plan and elevation

Imagine a solid glass block, with opposite faces equal. The front is a parallelogram and the top, bottom and sides are all rectangles.

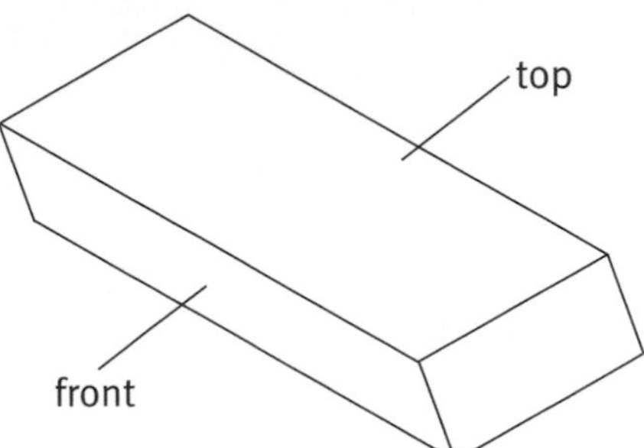

Suppose the block is placed on a flat surface and viewed from above. This is the **plan** view. It looks as if the block is flattened.

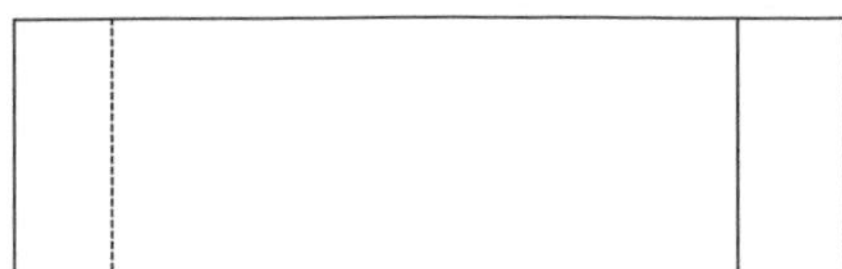

Now suppose the block is viewed from the front. This is the **front** elevation.

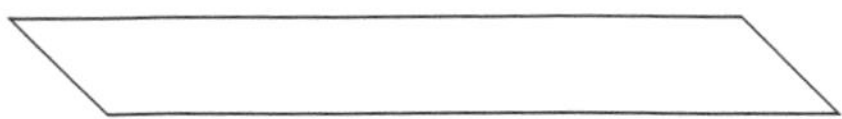

When the object is viewed from the side, this is the side elevation.

Exercise 7.7

1

A

B

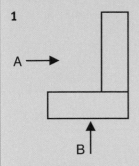

Above is a plan view of two blocks, each 1 cm × 1 cm × 3 cm.

Draw elevation views from:

a) point A

b) point B.

2

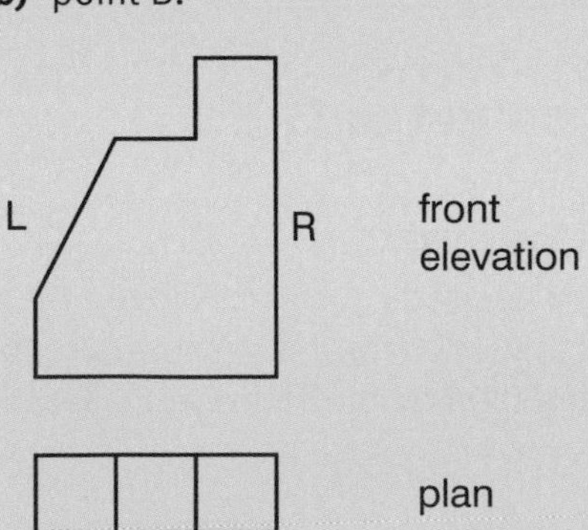

The front elevation and plan of a block are shown. Draw both side elevations.

Answers – 7.7

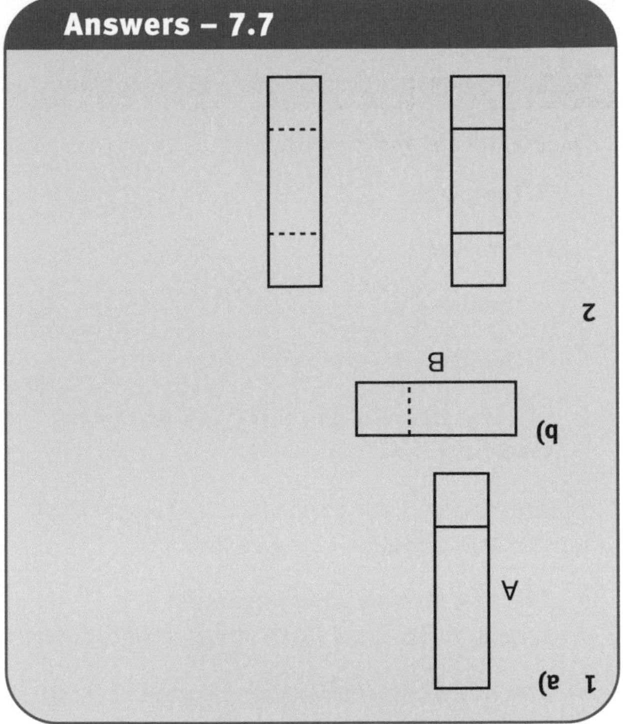

REVIEW

How much have you learnt?
Tick off each topic in the list when you are confident that you can cope with it.

- ☐ **Name the different types of triangle (isosceles and equilateral).**
- ☐ **Identify special angles formed by intersecting lines.**
- ☐ **Name and identify different types of quadrilaterals.**
- ☐ **List the properties of different quadrilaterals.**
- ☐ **Recognise congruent shapes.**
- ☐ **Identify regular and irregular polygons.**
- ☐ **Find the interior and exterior angles of polygons.**
- ☐ **State whether given polygons will tessellate.**
- ☐ **Understand and use circle theorems to find angles**
- ☐ **Construct perpendicular bisectors of lines.**
- ☐ **Construct bisectors of angles.**
- ☐ **Construct equilateral triangles.**
- ☐ **Construct angles of 90°, 60°, 30° and 45°.**
- ☐ **Draw simple loci.**
- ☐ **Make scale drawings and understand and use the terms 'plan', 'elevation' and 'view'.**

Chapter 8 Transformations

PREVIEW

By the end of this chapter you will be able to:

- **describe or draw a reflection**

  in the x-axis

  in the y-axis

  in the line $y = x$

  in the line $y = -x$

  in a line where either x or y is equal to any value, e.g. $x = 3$, or $y = -2$
- **describe or draw a translation of a specified size and direction using vectors**
- **describe or draw an enlargement of a specified size from (0, 0) or any other centre**
- **describe or draw a rotation centred at (0, 0) and of a specified direction and number of degrees not centred at (0, 0).**

In an exam question on transformations, you will probably gain one mark for correctly identifying a translation, reflection, enlargement or rotation. However, extra marks are often awarded and full marks for these questions are easy to score.

This chapter shows you how it's done!

How much do you know already?

Exercise 8.1

1 Carry out the transformations listed below on the following grid.

  a) Reflect the triangle labelled A in the y-axis. Label the reflection B.

  b) Reflect triangle A in the line $y = -x$. Label the reflection C.

  c) Rotate triangle A 90° clockwise, centred at (0, 0). Label the triangle D.

  d) Enlarge triangle A by a scale factor $\frac{1}{2}$, centre (0, 0). Label the enlargement E.

  e) Translate triangle A by a vector of $\binom{3}{-1}$. Label the translation F.

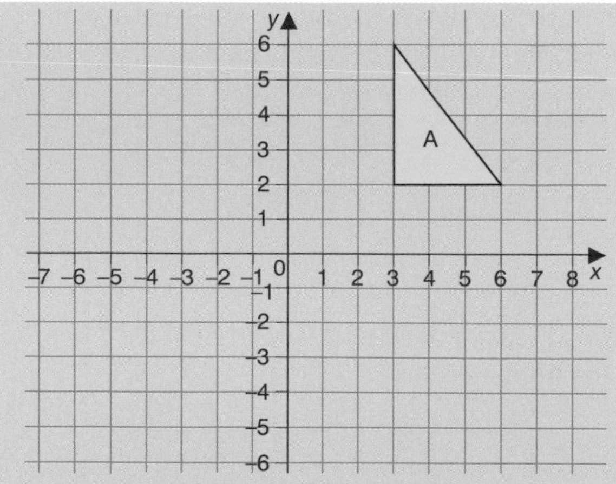

2 What single transformation would map B to D?

3 Describe fully the transformation which maps B to C.

Answers – 8.1

1

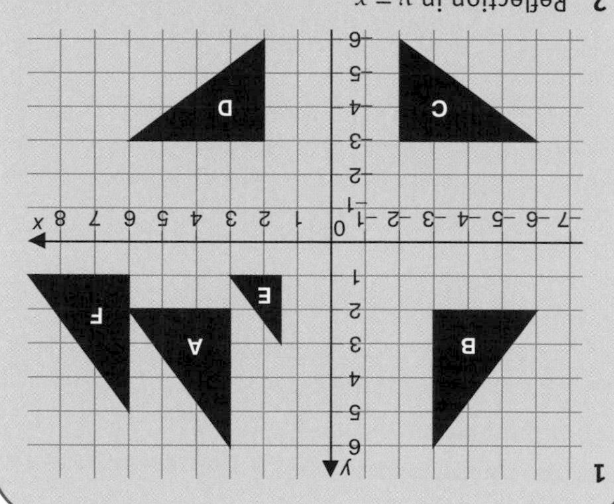

2 Reflection in $y = x$.

3 Anti-clockwise rotation 90°, centred at (0, 0).

How did you get on?

All or most of them right?

If you made any mistakes, just check up on the parts of the chapter that will help you to see where you went wrong, and then try the Shape and space review on page 109.

Don't even ask?

The bad news is that you will need to do some work on this part of the syllabus. The good news is that this is a very short chapter, and an easy way to pick up some valuable marks.

Describing transformations

To get 1 mark you need to identify correctly whether the transformation is a reflection, translation, enlargement or rotation. However, you will usually score more marks by describing the transformation fully. Extra marks are often awarded as follows: reflection 1, translation 1, enlargement 2, rotation 3.

Reflections

You need to identify the reflection or mirror line. This line is sometimes called the **line** or **axis of symmetry**.

It is usually easier to work out a reflection if you get one in the exam, rather than to try to learn all the different combinations. To draw the image of a reflection in a line, you can use tracing paper and fold along the reflection line.

Recognising reflections

These are usually obvious when the line of reflection is either the x-axis or y-axis. They are not always quite so obvious if the reflection line is $y = x$, or $y = -x$.

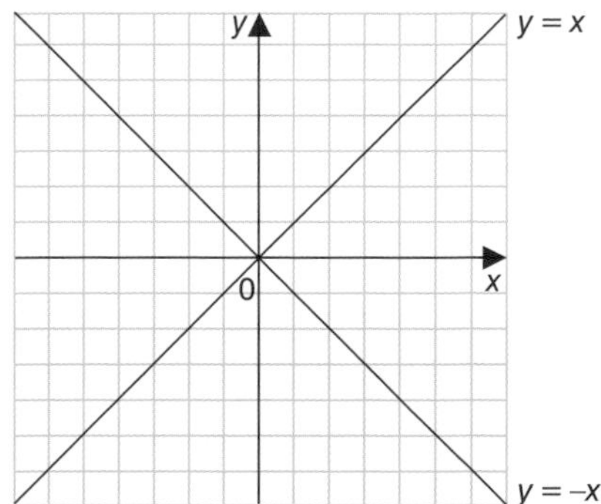

To test for reflection, take each point in turn, and count the squares or measure the distance at right angles to what you think may be the reflection line. If you are correct, the line and its image will be the same distance from the line, but on opposite sides. If the point is already on the line of reflection, it does not change.

Be careful to get these the right way round. If you aren't sure, make up some coordinates.

$x = -2$ Make up two sets of coordinates with $x = -2$, for example, $(-2, 1)$ and $(-2, 3)$. Join them up. The resulting line has the equation $x = -2$.

$y = 3$ Make up two pairs of coordinates with $y = 3$, for example, $(-1, 3)$ and $(2, 3)$. Join them up. The resulting line has the equation $y = 3$.

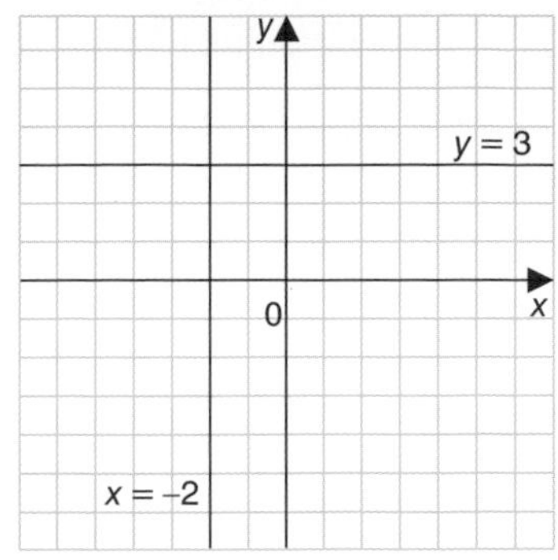

Translations

Translation has nothing to do with foreign languages – even if at times you may think that everything to do with Maths is written in a foreign language.

A translation is a movement. The shape stays the same size and does not rotate or reflect. It merely moves its position.

Vectors

Vectors are used to describe translations. They are written in a column, with the horizontal component (the movement in the x-direction) above the vertical component (the movement in the y-direction) so their form is $\begin{pmatrix} x \\ y \end{pmatrix}$ or $\begin{pmatrix} \text{across} \\ \text{up} \end{pmatrix}$.

Calculations with vectors are similar to those with coordinates. Remember to count across *before* you count up or down. Remember that forwards and up are *positive*, backwards and down are *negative*.

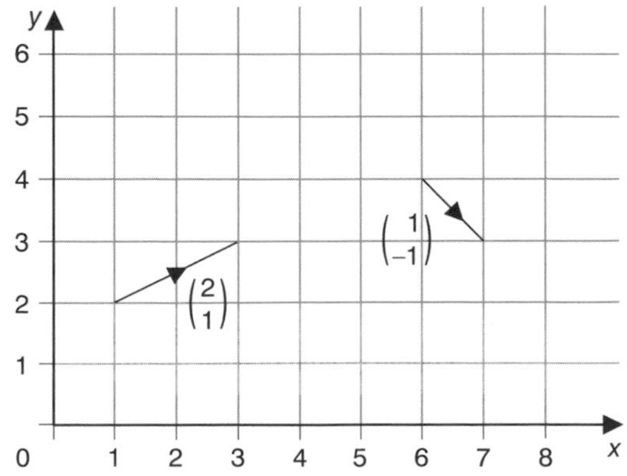

Always follow the direction of the arrow.

To gain that extra mark in the exam, you need to state correctly the translation vector.

The position of a point on an x–y graph can also be written as a vector, with reference to the origin.

For example, (2, 5) is written as $\binom{2}{5}$ with the x-value (*along* the corridor) first, or on top, and the y-value (*up* the stairs) second, or on the bottom.

Remember: *They are written alphabetically, (x first, y second).*

Enlargements

To identify an enlargement, you need:

a) the scale factor
b) the centre of enlargement.

To draw an enlargement, lightly draw lines from the centre of enlargement to each point of the end of the original shape. Multiply this length by the scale factor of the enlargement. Plot the new points along your lines, measuring from the centre of enlargement.

Finding the scale factor of an enlargement

The scale factor equals: $\dfrac{\text{image length}}{\text{original length}}$

If the shape and its image are already drawn, you may be asked for the scale factor of the enlargement.

*Put the **S**econd **O**ver the **F**irs**T** and don't be SOFT in the head and get it wrong.*

Finding the centre of an enlargement

Choose corresponding points in your original shape and its image and join them up. Where they meet will give you the centre of the enlargement.

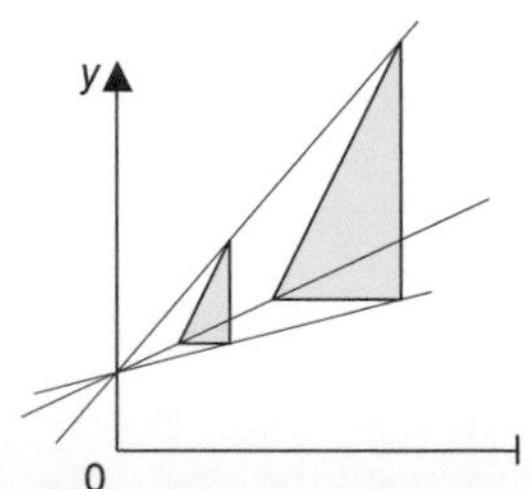

Example 8.1

Describe the transformation from ABC to A'B'C'.

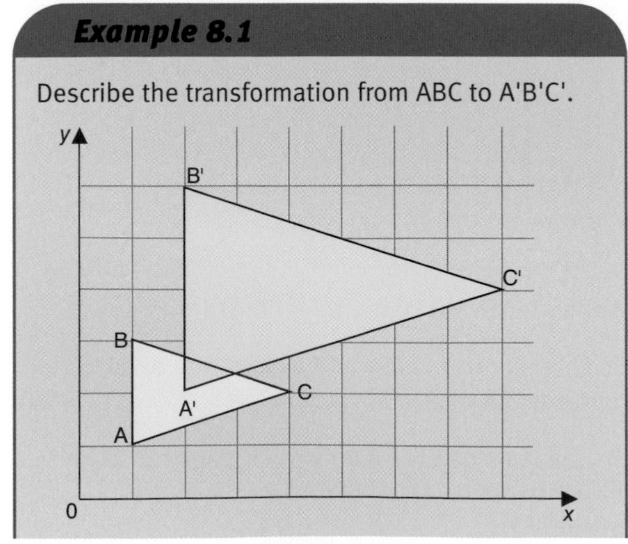

Solution

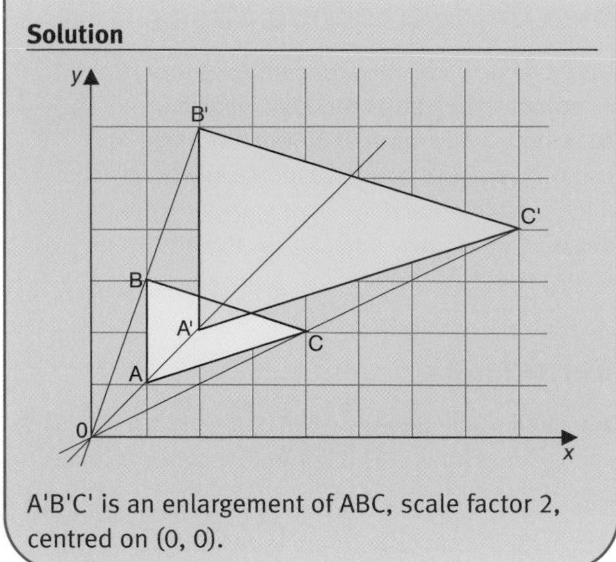

A'B'C' is an enlargement of ABC, scale factor 2, centred on (0, 0).

Enlargements are usually worth an extra two marks if you give the centre of enlargement and the scale factor.

Fractional scale factors

Confusing as it may seem, a shape which is enlarged by a scale factor that is less than 1 is still called an enlargement, even though the resulting shape is smaller than the original.

Example 8.2

Enlarge the triangle with vertices P(4, 6), Q(6, 6) and R(6, 4) by a scale factor of 0.5 centred on the origin.

Solution

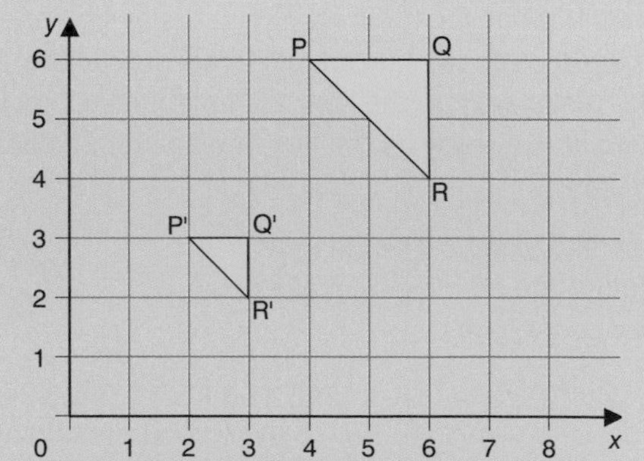

The image of P, P', is at (2, 3), the image of Q, Q', is at (3, 3) and the image of R, R', is at (3, 2).

Rotations

It is easier to draw a rotation if you use tracing paper. Remember, you can always ask for tracing paper in the exam if you do not already have some.

1 Trace the object.
2 Put your pencil on the paper over the centre of rotation and rotate the tracing paper according to the question.
3 Draw heavily over your tracing to make the image.

Example 8.3

On the diagram below, transform triangle T through a rotation of 90° clockwise, centred at (0, 0).

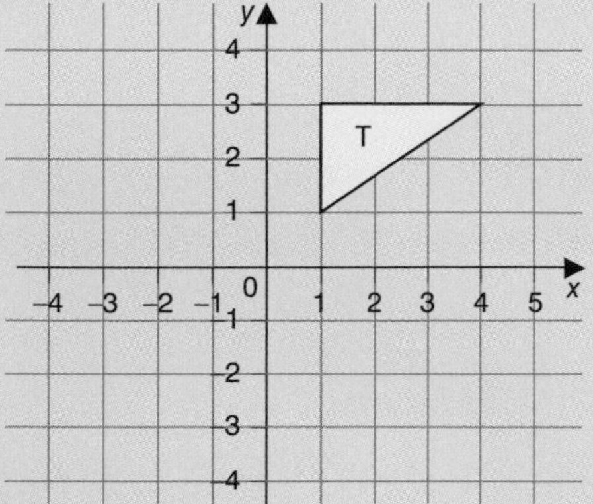

Solution

The triangle will move into the quadrant which is immediately below it.

Turn the page round so that the required quadrant is now at the top right-hand corner.

Now imagine your original triangle in exactly the same place as it was before.

Alternatively, use tracing paper to trace the object. Hold your pencil firmly, with its point at the origin, and keep it there as you rotate the tracing paper through 90° clockwise.

Try looking at each original point and work out its new coordinates using left and right, and up and down.

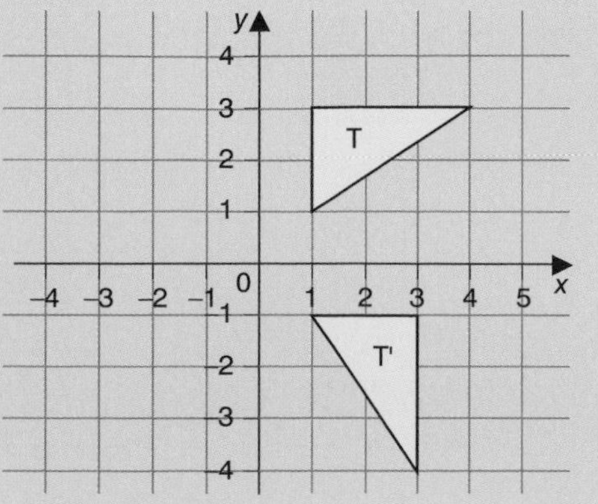

Recognising rotations and their centres

You can often identify a rotation by tracing over the given shape, and then anchoring your tracing at the point which you think is the centre of rotation and seeing if you are right.

Alternatively, choose two corresponding points and construct the perpendicular bisector of the line between them (see page 99 if you have forgotten how to do this). Do the same to another two points.

Where the bisectors meet is the centre of rotation.

Questions involving rotational symmetry can give you three extra marks if you remember to include the centre, the angle of rotation and the direction (unless the angle of rotation is 180°).

Rotational symmetry may be identified by its order or fold number. You may find this confusing as it sounds like lines of symmetry. To make it clearer, a regular hexagon may be described as having rotational symmetry of order 6, or 6-fold rotational symmetry.

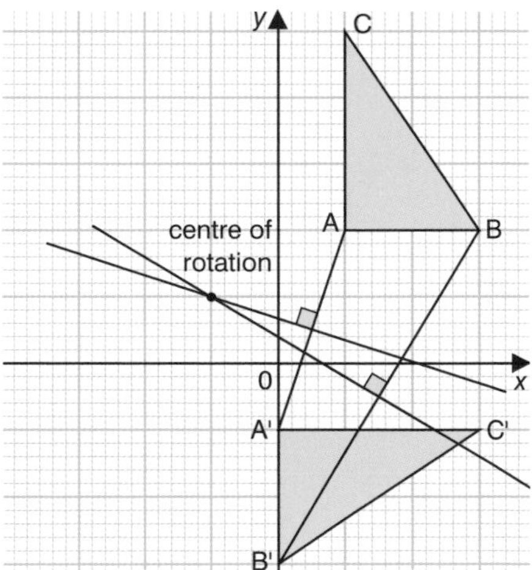

If a rotation is described as 'positive' it means it is in an anticlockwise direction.

Putting it all together

If you want all the marks that are available for questions of this type, you have to describe fully any transformation that you might be given.

REVIEW

How much have you learnt?
Tick off each topic in the list when you are confident that you can cope with it.

- ☐ **Describe or draw a reflection**
  - ☐ **in the x-axis**
  - ☐ **in the y-axis**
  - ☐ **in the line $y = x$**
  - ☐ **in the line $y = -x$**
  - ☐ **in a line where either x or y is equal to any value, e.g. $x = 3$, or $y = -2$**
- ☐ **Describe or draw a translation**
  - ☐ **of a specified size and direction using vectors**
- ☐ **Describe or draw an enlargement**
  - ☐ **of a specified size**
  - ☐ **from (0, 0) or any other centre**
- ☐ **Describe or draw a rotation**
  - ☐ **centred at (0, 0) and of a specified direction and number of degrees**
  - ☐ **not centred at (0, 0)**

If you are confident that you can now handle the topics in chapters 5, 6, 7 and 8, try the Shape and space review on pages 109–110.

1 A ladder 6 m long leans against a wall, with its foot is 2.6 m away from the wall.

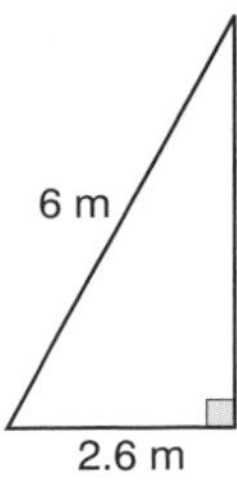

a) Use Pythagoras' theorem to find how far up the wall the ladder extends.
b) Find the angle between the ladder and the wall.

2 Circles with an of area 26 cm^2 are cut from card.
a) What is the radius of each circle?
b) If 24 circles are cut from a rectangle 25 cm by 30 cm, how much card is left?
c) Write this as a percentage of the original amount.

3 You are given that a, b and c refer to lengths. Using dimensions, state which could be a formula for length, area, volume or none of these.
a) $\pi a(b + c)$
b) $2b^2c + \frac{1}{4}ac^2$
c) $\pi c^2 \div a$

4 The library is on a bearing of 240° from the post office. What is the bearing of the post office from the library?

5 Describe the transformation which maps:
a) A on to B
b) C on to A
c) A on to D
d) E on to A
e) C on to B.

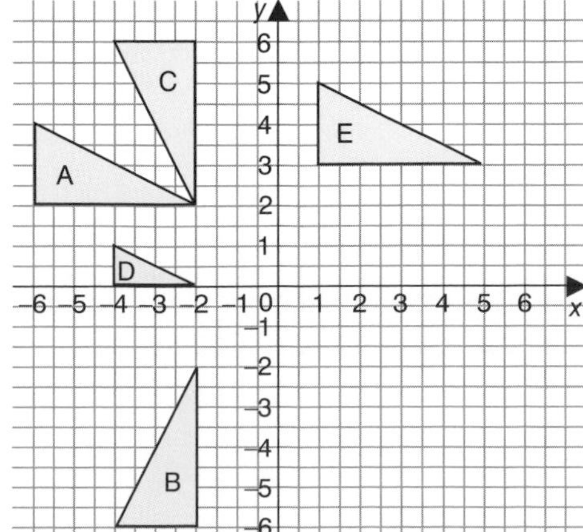

6 From a cliff top, the angle of depression of a rock out to sea is 27°. If the cliff is 45 m high, how far away is the rock from the top of the cliff?

7 Copy the diagram below to a scale of 1 cm to 1 m. It represents a garden with a tree planted at C. Grass is to be planted in the area of the garden which is nearer to C than A, but at least 4 m from the tree.

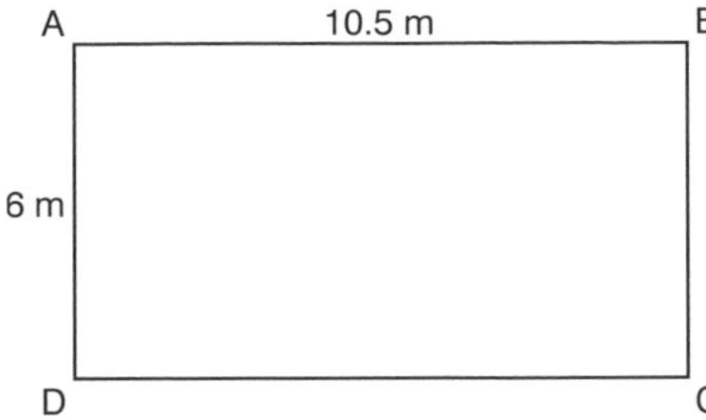

Shade the area where grass may be planted.

8 a) Name two quadrilaterals in which the diagonals do not cross at right angles.
b) Name two quadrilaterals with rotational symmetry of order 2.
c) Name a quadrilateral which always has reflective symmetry, but which has rotational symmetry of order 1.

9 What is the surface area of a solid cylinder of base radius 1.4 m and height 80 cm? Give your answer in m^2 correct to 2 d.p.

10 Triangle DEF is isosceles. DE = 8.4 m and EF = 8 m. X is the midpoint of EF.

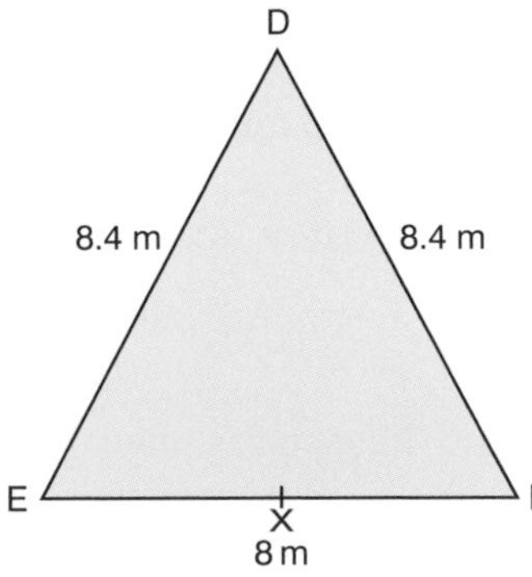

a) Find the length of DX correct to 1 d.p.
b) Find angle DFE correct to 2 s.f.
c) Find the area of triangle DEF.

11 a) Using ruler and compasses only, construct an angle of 60° on the line below.

b) Bisect this angle.

Leave all construction lines on your diagram.

12 The interior angle of a regular polygon is 140°. How many sides does the polygon have?

13 a) In the diagram, BE is parallel to CD. How can you tell that triangle ABE and triangle ACD are similar?

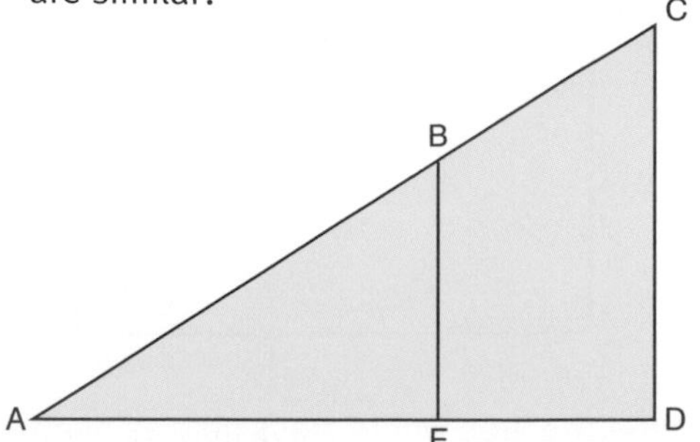

b) The length of AE = 71.1 cm, BE = 57.6 cm and CD = 80.7 cm. Using similar triangles, find AD.

14 a) Find the volume of water held by a full cylindrical glass of radius 3.1 cm and height 9.1 cm. Give your answer correct to 1 d.p.

b) If this water was poured into a cylindrical glass of radius 4.1cm, how deep would it be? Give your answer correct to 1 d.p.

Answers – Shape and space review

1 a) 5.4 m

b) 26°

If your answer was 64°, you found the angle between the ladder and the ground.

2 a) 2.9 cm **b)** 126 cm^2 **c)** 16.8% or 17%

3 a) area **b)** volume **c)** length

4 060° Remember that bearings have 3 figures.

5 a) rotation 90° anti-clockwise, centred at (0, 0)

b) reflection in the line $y = -x$

c) enlargement scale factor $\frac{1}{2}$, centred at (−2, −2)

d) translation $\binom{-3}{-1}$

e) reflection in the x-axis, or reflection in $y = 0$

6 99 m. The angle from the cliff = 63° so you need to calculate 45 ÷ cos 63°. Alternatively, you could use 45 ÷ sin 27°.

7 The diagonal line is the perpendicular bisector of AC. The arc is of radius 4 cm, centred on C.

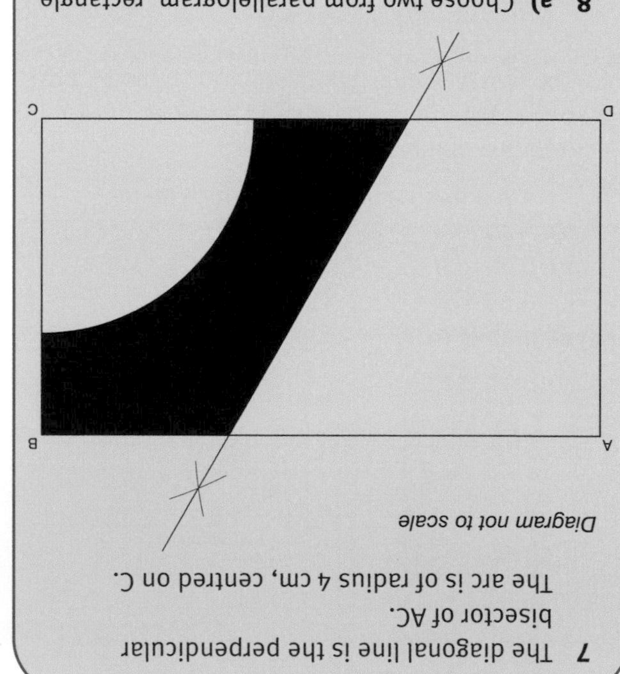

8 a) Choose two from parallelogram, rectangle, trapezium.

b) Choose two from rhombus, rectangle, parallelogram.

c) kite

9 19.35 m^2

10 a) 7.4 m **b)** 62° **c)** 30 m^2 (2 sig. figs.)

11

12 The exterior angle is 180° − 140° = 40°
Number of sides = 360 ÷ 40 = 9

13 a) angle D = angle E and angle C = angle B (BE and CD are parallel.)
Angle A is common to both. Therefore the triangles are similar.

b) AD = 99.6 cm

14 a) 274.7 cm^3 **b)** 5.2 cm

PREVIEW

By the end of this chapter you will be able to:

- **find the mean, median and mode of a set of data**
- **find the range of a set of data**
- **draw a bar chart for a set of data**
- **draw a pie chart for a set of data**
- **complete a frequency polygon**
- **draw up a cumulative frequency table**
- **draw a cumulative frequency graph**
- **find the interquartile range of a set of data**
- **draw and interpret box plots**
- **draw and interpret stem-and-leaf diagrams**
- **calculate moving averages**
- **interpret scatter diagrams**
- **carry out sampling activities**
- **interpret results from sampling activities**
- **carry out surveys**
- **interpret results of surveys**
- **design questionnaires**
- **evaluate questionnaires.**

Statistical tools available to you

- mean
- median
- mode

} averages

- range
- interquartile range

} spread or dispersion

- cumulative frequency
- frequency polygons
- scatter diagrams
- pie charts
- bar charts and histograms
- box plots
- stem-and-leaf diagrams

} charts

- questionnaires
- sampling

} surveys

This chapter shows you how to use them.

How much do you know already?

Exercise 9.1

1 13, 7, 27, 12, 7, 10, 28, 7, 5, 11, 12, 8, 19, 12, 2.

Using the above numbers, find:

a) the mean **b)** the median

c) the mode **d)** the range.

2 The table below illustrates the distance between home and the town centre of a group of 75 students.

Distance in km (d)	No. of students (frequency, f)
1 km or less	6
$1 < d \leqslant 2$	7
$2 < d \leqslant 3$	15
$3 < d \leqslant 4$	18
$4 < d \leqslant 5$	10
$5 < d \leqslant 6$	10
$6 < d \leqslant 7$	7
$7 < d \leqslant 8$	2

a) What is the modal group?

b) Find an estimate of the mean distance from the town centre to home.

3 Use the information in the table provided for question 2.

a) Draw a frequency polygon.

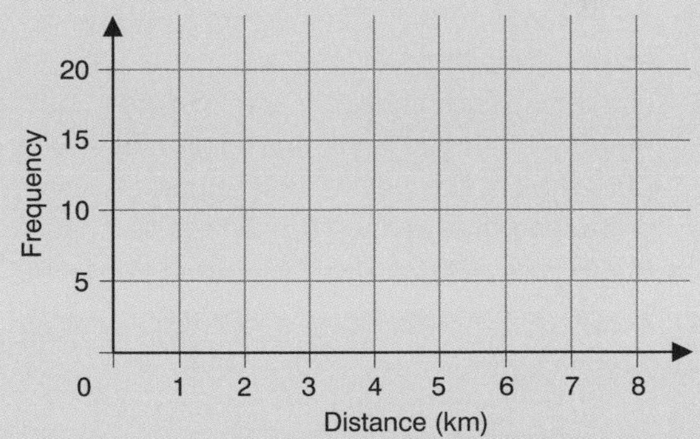

b) Draw a cumulative frequency graph.

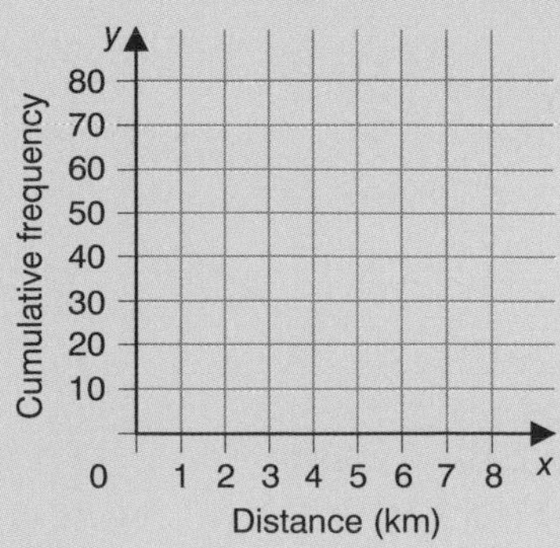

4 Refer to the cumulative frequency graph from question 3b).
  a) Find the median and the interquartile range.
  b) Draw a box-and-whisker plot of the data.

5 The results of a survey carried out on a sample of 450 people were displayed on a pie chart.
  a) How many people would 40° represent?
  b) How many degrees would represent 90 people?

6 The results of a group of students who sat tests in French and Spanish are given below.

French (x)	20	12	64	50	68	37	38	25	31	83
Spanish (y)	36	28	60	50	48	75	38	30	41	64

  a) Display the results on a scatter diagram.
  b) Draw the line of best fit.
  c) One student scored 56 in French, but was absent for the Spanish test. What would a likely score have been? Show clearly how you reached your answer.
  d) What kind of correlation does your graph show?

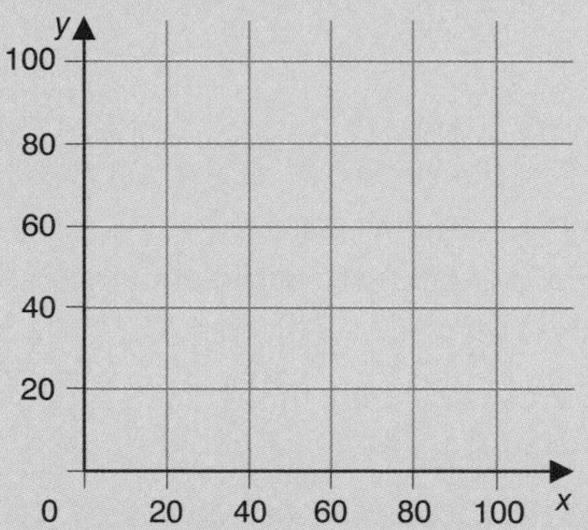

7 Draw stem-and-leaf diagrams for the students' results in question 6.

8 In a survey on homework, Sakina asked ten friends, 'Don't you think that we get too much homework at the weekends?' Suggest two ways to improve the survey.

Answers – 9.1

1 a) 12 b) 11 c) 7 and 12 d) 26

2 a) $3 < d \leqslant 4$ b) 3.66 km

3 a)

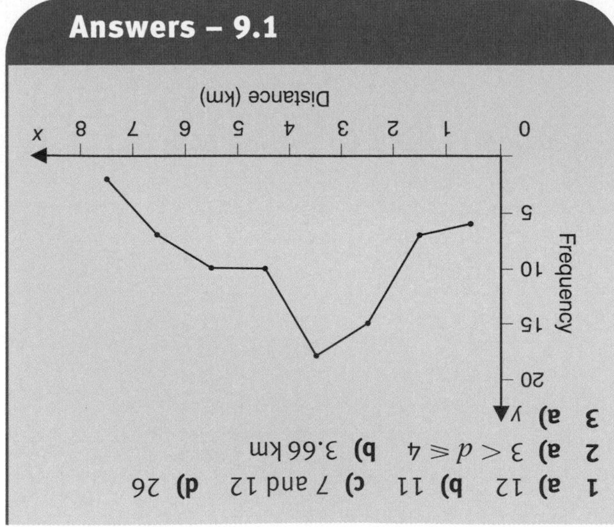

b)

4 a) median = 3.6 km, interquartile range ≈ 3.1

b) 0 2.2 3.6 5.3 8

5 a) 50 b) 72°

6 a) and b)

c) 55 approximately

d) strong positive

7

French		Spanish	
Stem	Leaf	Stem	Leaf
1	2	1	
2	0 5	2	8
3	1 7 8	3	0 6 8
4		4	1 8
5	0	5	0
6	4 8	6	0 4
7		7	5
8	3	8	

8 The question is leading, so change it to, 'Do you think you get too much homework at weekends?'. Secondly, the sample size is very small, so ask more people.

How did you get on?

All or most of them right?

Lucky you – or was it just sheer hard work on your part? Either way it's good news because most exam papers are crammed with questions on this part of the syllabus and a good mark here will stand you in good stead. If you made any mistakes, however trivial, it really is worth reading through this chapter to sort them out.

Don't even ask?

The material in this chapter carries about 20% of the total mark. Although there is a certain amount to remember, the questions are usually easy to understand.

This chapter will show you where most people lose marks in the questions on Statistics, and so where you can manage to boost yours.

Question 1 or 2 on page 111 wrong?

You need to brush up on averages and ranges. Otherwise go to 'Frequency diagrams' on page 114.

Averages and range

The mean, the median and the mode are three ways of expressing an average. The range is the spread of the data. Confused? Read on!

Mean Add together all the values and divide by the number of values you have. (The mean is not necessarily a whole number.)

Median Arrange the values in order of size. The median is the middle value.

Mode This is the most commonly occurring value. (There can be more than one mode.)

Range Find the largest value and subtract the smallest.

The pros and cons of using the mean, median and mode

	Pros	Cons
mean	• most commonly used • easy to calculate	• can be misleading, as, if one term is much bigger or much smaller than the others, it distorts the mean
median	• often gives a truer picture of the situation • not so affected by extreme values as the mean	• not used very often in the real world • takes longer to calculate because values must first be arranged in order
mode	• unaffected by extreme values • very appropriate when you need to find the most common result (e.g. if you were a buyer for shoes you would want to know the most commonly bought sizes.)	• there may be more than one mode • it ignores much of the information

The modal group

The modal group is like the mode. The mode is the most frequently occurring value, and the modal group is the most frequently occurring class. In this case it is $3 < d \leqslant 4$.

Finding the mean of grouped frequency data

First you need to find the mid-interval values as shown in the table below.

Distance in km (d)	No. of students (frequency, f)	Mid-interval value (MIV)
1 km or less	6	0.5
$1 < d \leqslant 2$	7	1.5
$2 < d \leqslant 3$	15	2.5
$3 < d \leqslant 4$	18	3.5
$4 < d \leqslant 5$	10	4.5
$5 < d \leqslant 6$	10	5.5
$6 < d \leqslant 7$	7	6.5
$7 < d \leqslant 8$	2	7.5

To find the mean, multiply the frequency by the mid-interval value and add the results. Then divide by the total frequency.

Distance in km (d)	No. of students (frequency, f)	Mid-interval value (MIV)	$f \times$ MIV
1 km or less	6	0.5	3.0
$1 < d \leq 2$	7	1.5	10.5
$2 < d \leq 3$	15	2.5	37.5
$3 < d \leq 4$	18	3.5	63.0
$4 < d \leq 5$	10	4.5	45.0
$5 < d \leq 6$	10	5.5	55.0
$6 < d \leq 7$	7	6.5	45.5
$7 < d \leq 8$	2	7.5	15.0
Total	75		274.5

Mean = 274.5 ÷ 75 = 3.66 km

Frequency diagrams

If question 3 on page 111 had asked for a bar chart, you would have drawn this.

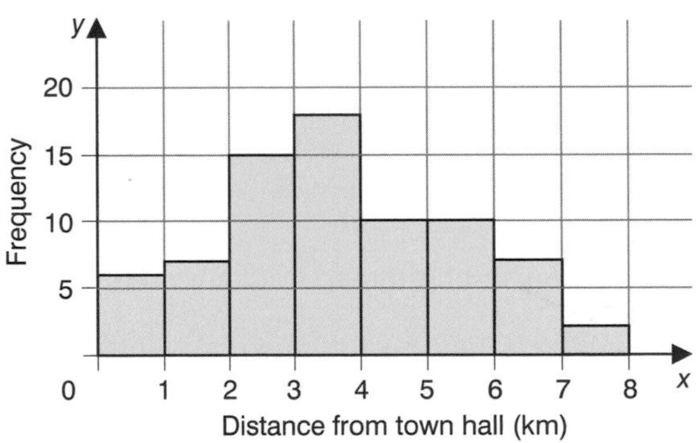

When asked for a frequency polygon, imagine the bars and mark the midpoint at the top of each imaginary bar. Then join the points with straight lines.

Cumulative frequency

To find the cumulative frequency, you accumulate (or add together, or 'roll over') the frequencies.

Distance in km (d)	No. of students (frequency, f)	Cumulative frequency
1 km or less	6	6
$1 < d \leq 2$	7	13
$2 < d \leq 3$	15	28
$3 < d \leq 4$	18	46
$4 < d \leq 5$	10	56
$5 < d \leq 6$	10	66
$6 < d \leq 7$	7	73
$7 < d \leq 8$	2	75

Plot the points on the cumulative frequency graph, and join them with a smooth curve.

Remember: You plot the points at the **end** of the interval and not in the middle.

Median and IQR

To find the median, take the middle value of the frequency.

Usually to find the position of the median you add 1 to the number of values and divide the result by 2. This gives the position of the median when the values are written in order.

However, as the numbers involved here are usually large, you do not need to add one first as you usually do for the median, since the result would be almost identical. Just draw across and down as indicated in the diagram below.

The interquartile range requires the value at the **upper quartile** ($\frac{3}{4}$ way up the frequency) and the **lower quartile** ($\frac{1}{4}$ way up the frequency).

The upper quartile minus the lower quartile gives the **interquartile range**.

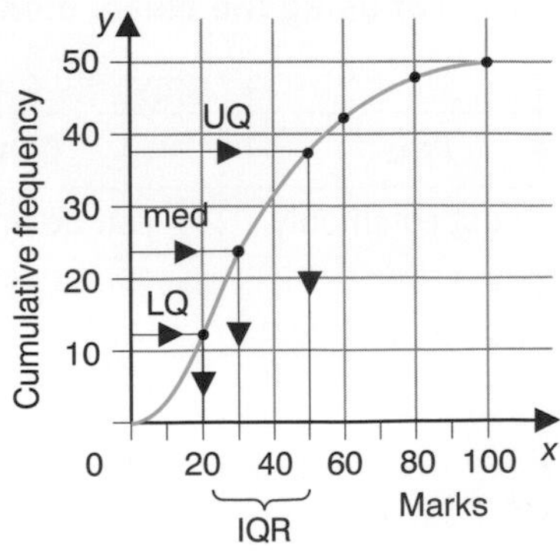

interquartile range = upper quartile − lower quartile

What does the interquartile range tell us?

The interquartile range shows how widely the central half of the sample is spread. A low interquartile range shows that the data is closely grouped together, whereas a higher figure would reflect wider differences between the data (also called a wider spread).

Example 9.1

What do these test results for classes A and B tell you?

Interquartile range	Class A	10
Interquartile range	Class B	25

Solution

The pattern of class A's results shows them to have a more similar ability level than class B – perhaps class A was streamed whereas class B was of mixed ability.

Note that the interquartile range in the last example does not tell you which class had the better performance – one of the measures of the average would tell you this.

Box plots

These are also called 'box and whisker plots'. They display information about a set of data, in the form of a diagram. A box plot looks like this.

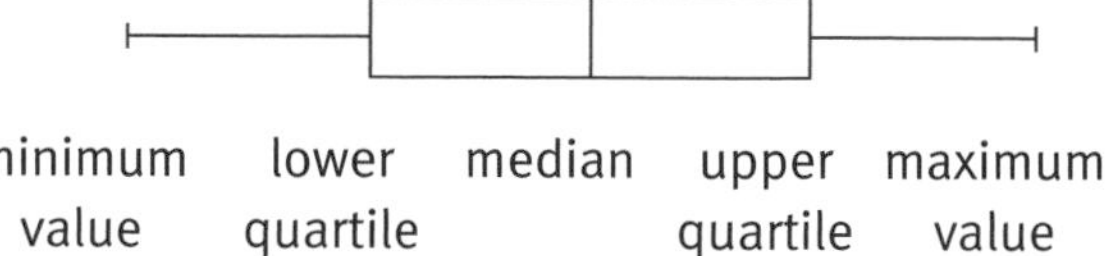

Example 9.2

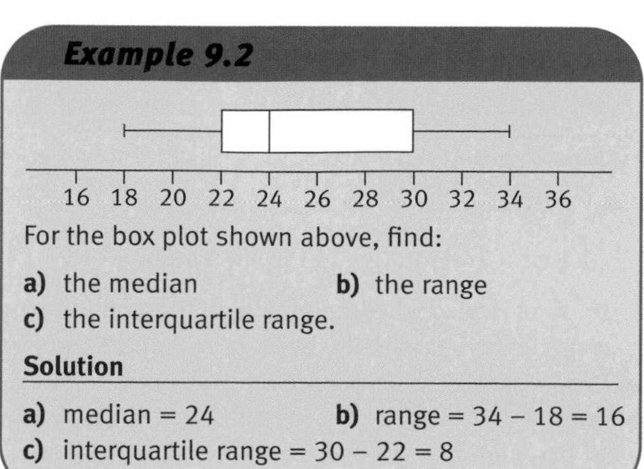

For the box plot shown above, find:

a) the median **b)** the range
c) the interquartile range.

Solution

a) median = 24 **b)** range = 34 – 18 = 16
c) interquartile range = 30 – 22 = 8

Example 9.3

David and Brad are in an archery contest. The plots below show the distribution of their scores. Give two comparisons between their scores.

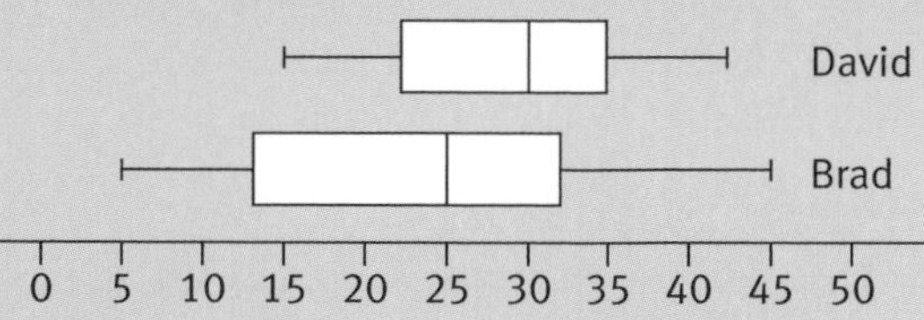

Solution

a) David has a higher median, or average.
b) Brad has a larger interquartile range.

You could compare the ranges instead of comparing interquartile ranges.

Exercise 9.2

The number of arrows shot on target by eleven members of the archery club are shown below.

3 6 9 12 11 7 6 8 10 9 5

a) Find the median.
b) Find the upper and lower quartiles
c) Find the interquartile range.
d) Display the information in a box plot.

Answers – 9.2

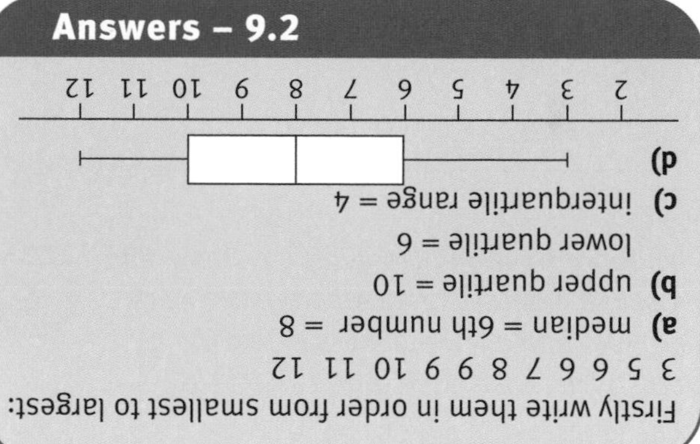
Firstly write them in order from smallest to largest:

3 5 6 6 7 8 9 9 10 11 12

a) median = 6th number = 8
b) upper quartile = 10
lower quartile = 6
c) interquartile range = 4
d)

Stem-and-leaf diagrams

Stem-and-leaf diagrams are used to display data without losing any of the information. They order the data and show how the data is distributed. The diagram can also help find the mode and the median.

Record a mark with the tens in the stem and the units in the leaf: for example, the number 23 would have a stem of 2 and a leaf of 3; 47 would have a stem of 4 and a leaf of 7.

Start by working through the digits and arrange in a preliminary stem-and-leaf diagram, then reorder in a second diagram.

Example 9.4

A class's marks out of 50 in a French test are given below. Display the data in a stem-and-leaf diagram.

10, 41, 33, 27, 36, 32, 39, 21, 15, 11, 20, 31, 33, 42, 33, 25, 28

Hence find the mode and the median.

Solution

For 10, put a 1 in the stem column and 0 in the leaf column, for 41 write 4 as a stem and 1 as the leaf, etc.

Stem	Leaf
1	0 5 1
2	7 1 0 5 8
3	3 6 2 9 1 3 3
4	1 2

Then reorder the leaves:

1	0 1 5
2	0 1 5 7 8
3	1 2 3 3 3 6 9
4	1 2

The mode, the most common number is 33.

The median is the $\frac{(n+1)}{2}$th number.

As n =17, it is the 9th number. Counting along from 0, 1, 5, 0, etc. as the 1st, 2nd, 3rd, 4th numbers, etc., the 9th number is 31.

The above stem-and-leaf diagram shows that most of the data is grouped around the 20s and 30s, with a few numbers in the 10s and 40s. It is like a bar graph on its side.

Exercise 9.3

A class of 21 students gained the following marks in a mathematics test.

14 26 33 34 37 25 28 23 11 6 16
35 7 18 27 24 19 29 17 36 27

1 Construct a stem-and-leaf diagram.

2 Using your stem-and-leaf diagram, or otherwise, find
 a) the range,
 b) the mode,
 c) the median.

Answers – 9.3

1

0	6 7
1	1 4 6 7 8 9
2	3 4 5 6 7 7 8 9
3	3 4 5 6 7

2 a) 37 − 6 = 31
 b) 27
 c) 11th number = 25

Moving averages

These are a method of showing trends. For example, the sales of an ice cream company per quarter would be quite erratic if shown on a graph, as the sales during the summer would be much higher than during the rest of the year. Moving averages graphs smooth out these seasonal changes to show general trends.

Moving averages are calculated by finding the mean of data from consecutive periods.

For example, to calculate a four-quarterly moving average,

Year 1 | Year 2 | Year 3
1st 2nd 3rd 4th 1st 2nd 3rd 4th 1st 2nd 3rd 4th

first find the mean of the first four quarters

then the mean of the 2nd through to the 5th quarter

then the mean of the 3rd through to the 6th quarter

Each point is plotted at the middle of the period being averaged: for example, the average of the 1st, 2nd, 3rd and 4th periods would be plotted midway between the 2nd and 3rd quarters.

For a 12-month moving average,

Year 1 | Year 2
Jan Feb Mar Apr May Jun Jul Aug Sep Oct Nov Dec Jan Feb Mar Apr...

take the mean of the 1st through to the 12th month

then the 2nd through to the 13th month, etc.

Each point is plotted at the middle of the period being averaged: for example, the average of January through to December would be plotted midway between June and July, the average of February through to January would be plotted midway between July and August, and so on.

Example 9.5

The quarterly sales for the school newsletter, in pounds, for the last two years are given below.

Year 1				Year 2			
1st	2nd	3rd	4th	1st	2nd	3rd	4th
540	780	532	448	652	776	552	576

Find the four-quarterly moving averages for the given period. Display the data on a graph.

Solution

The first moving average is

$(540 + 780 + 532 + 448) \div 4 = 575$

The second moving average is

$(780 + 532 + 448 + 652) \div 4 = 603$

and so on.

The moving averages are

575, 603, 602, 607, 639

Plot 575 midway between the 2nd and 3rd periods, 603 midway between the 3rd and 4th periods, and so on.

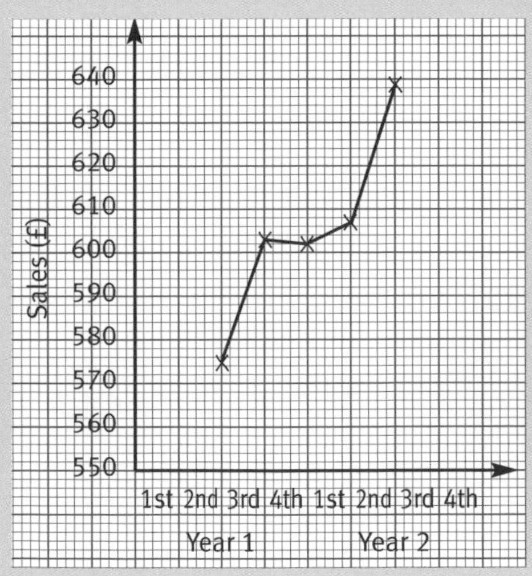

Exercise 9.4

A youth club committee meeting is held every quarter. The attendance figures for the last two years are given below:

Year 1				Year 2			
1st	2nd	3rd	4th	1st	2nd	3rd	4th
104	244	288	172	124	236	200	156

Find the four-quarterly moving averages for the given period. Display the data on a graph.

Answers – 9.4

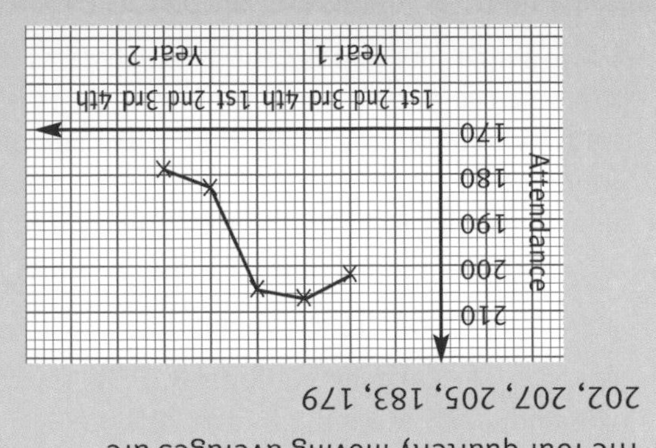

202, 207, 205, 183, 179

The four quarterly moving averages are

Pie charts

Example 9.6

a) Out of a group of 450 people, how many people would be represented on a pie chart by 40°?

b) What angle would represent 90 people?

Solution

a) People Degrees

People	Degrees
450	360
?	40

$$\frac{40 \times 450}{360} = 50 \text{ people}$$

b) People Degrees

People	Degrees
450	360
90	?

$$\frac{90 \times 360}{450} = 72^\circ$$

Some statistical banana skins

1 Mean

- This may be a decimal fraction, and may seem a ridiculous answer. For instance, the mean number of children per family is often stated as 2.4.
- If one or two values are either much bigger or much smaller than the rest, then they will alter the mean significantly.

2 Median

- If you are given some values and asked to find the median, you **must first** arrange them in order of size. To find the median of 7, 2, 6, 5, 4, first arrange them in order of size.
  2, 4, 5, 6, 7
  The median is then clearly seen as 5.

- To find the position of the median value, add 1 to the number of values, and divide this by 2.

  For example, the middle number of 7 items is the 4th, and the middle number of eight items is halfway between the 4th and 5th. (For cumulative frequency, as the numbers involved are usually very large, simply halve the total frequency.)
- If you have an even number of values, the median is halfway between the two middle values.

  For example, take the numbers 3, 7, 8, 10, 13, 19. The midpoint between 8 and 10 is 9.
- Finding the median from a table of grouped values can trip you up.

No. of people in a car	1	2	3	4	5
No. of cars	6	4	3	1	1

The answer is not 3, which is merely the middle group. There are 15 cars in total, and if they were all lined up in order with the least full cars first, the middle car would be the eighth ($\frac{15+1}{2} = 8$). The eighth car would have two passengers.

You may find that it helps to list the data as: 1 1 1 1 1 1 2 2 2 2 3 3 3 4 5 before you find the mean, median and mode.

3 Mode

The mode is the most common value.

- You may be asked a question in which you have to compare two graphs. For instance, which of the following graphs has the higher mode?

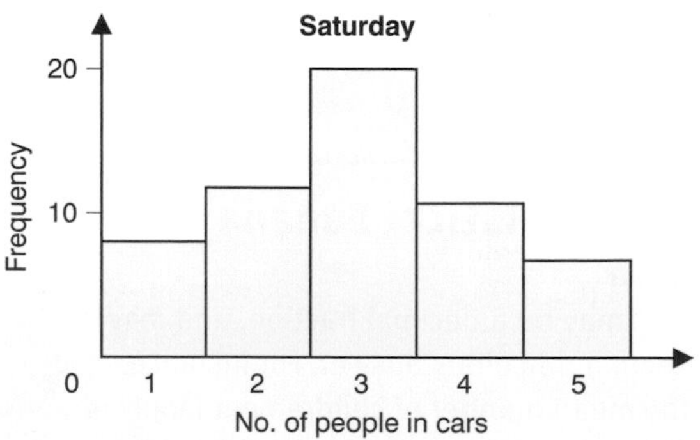

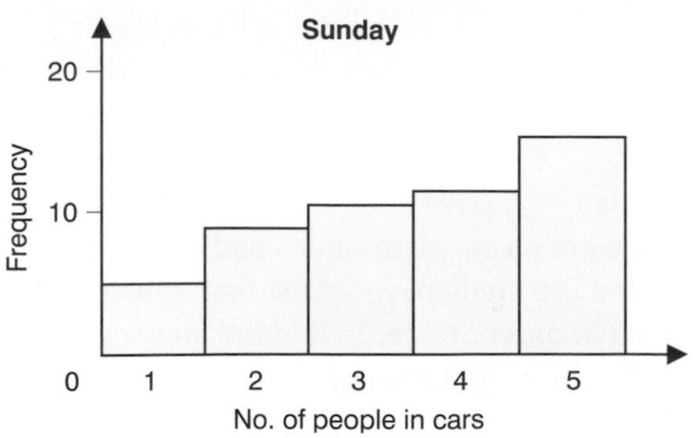

The mode of the Saturday traffic is 3 and that of Sunday is 5. Therefore, Sunday has the higher mode.

To recap ...

- Mode
  There can be more than one mode.
- Mean
  The mean can be altered significantly by very large or very small numbers.
  The mean may not be a whole number.
- Median
  To find the position of the median, take the number of values, add 1 and divide by 2.
  Where the number of items is even, you have to take the midpoint of two values.

TAKE A BREAK

You have now completed most of the work on Statistics. Have a break before continuing to the end of the chapter.

Correlation

The **line of best fit** shows a line which is closest to the majority of the points on a scatter diagram.

When drawing a line of best fit, aim to have approximately the same number of points on each side of the line.

Correlation shows a link between the variables on both axes.

- **positive correlation** – if one variable rises, the other is expected to rise.
- **negative correlation** – if one variable goes up, the other will probably fall.
- **no linear correlation** – there is no linear link between the two variables.

weak negative correlation

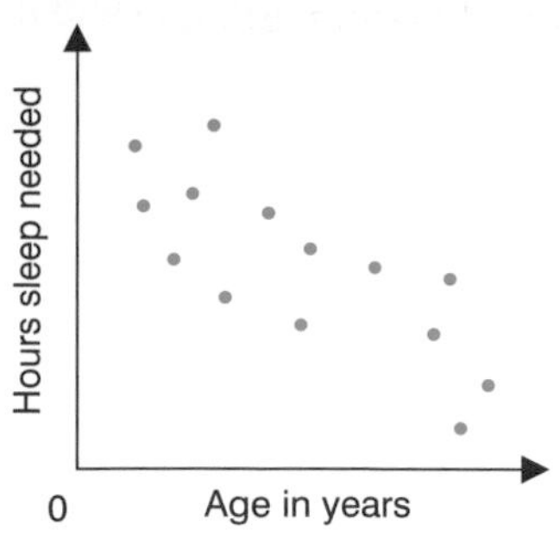

no linear correlation

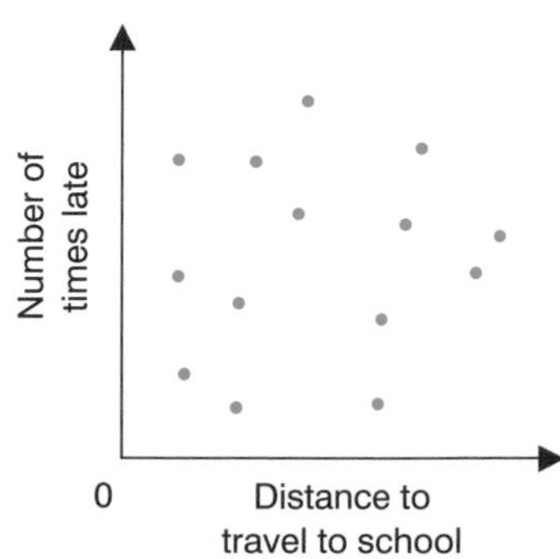

Sampling and surveys

A **sample** is a set of values (i.e. those given in the question). The **frequency** is how often something occurs.

Sampling

In any statistical research, it is impossible to collect data from every possible unit which may be involved. It is necessary, therefore, to take a sample, or group of the people or items that you are investigating.

Random sample
A random sample is a group selected purely by chance. You might, for instance, stop the first 20 people you meet in the street and ask them to complete a questionnaire. A drawback of using this method is that the people you meet may not fully represent the whole group. For instance, people who shop on weekday mornings may be quite different from those who shop on Saturday afternoons. For this reason another procedure is often used to find a more representative group.

Stratified random sample
Although individuals within the sample are still selected randomly, the sample itself is structured so that it represents as many groups as possible. In a survey on shopping habits, for instance, an interviewer might be asked to obtain data from a specified number of teenagers, young single adults, families and pensioners.

Examiners' questions
You are often asked to comment on a sample. There are three main points to consider.

1 **Size** – is the sample big enough?

2 **Representativeness** – are all types represented?

3 **Randomness** – is the sample biased?

Remember this or you'll be ***S****o**RR**y!*

Surveys

Examiners sometimes ask you to give your opinion on surveys and questionnaires. You should comment on the following areas.

1 The way the question is worded

a) Is it a **leading** question?
(Is it trying to push the interviewee into answering in a certain way?)

b) Is it **ambiguous**?
(Could the question be interpreted in more than one way?)

2 The range of responses

This is less common, but you should look at ways that the interviewee can reply to see whether all possible outcomes are clearly and accurately represented.

3 Drawing up questionnaires

a) Ask yourself if the question is easy to understand.
Is the meaning clear, or could there be more than one interpretation?
Is it **a**mbiguous?

b) Is the question **l**eading?
Does it suggest an answer?

c) Do the answer boxes cover the full range of responses?
Are they **i**nclusive?

d) Will the results be fair and un**bi**ased?

Use the above criteria and you'll be OK – you'll have your **alibi**!

Is the question ***A****mbiguous?*
L*eading?*
I*nclusive?*
BI*ased?*

Remember, you always need an ***ALIBI****!*

Exercise 9.5

1 What kind of correlation is shown on the graph below?

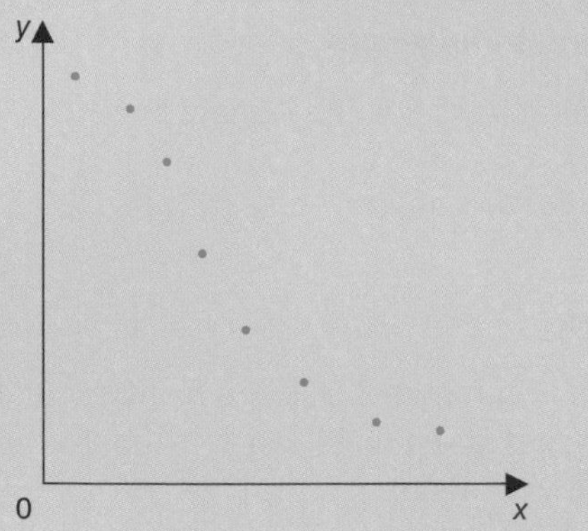

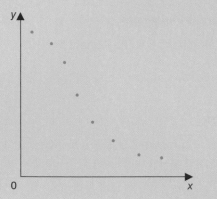

2 The results of a survey on 1440 students who completed a questionnaire on their favourite subject are given below.

Favourite subject	Number of students
Maths	108
English	300
PE	520
Sciences	124
Languages	388

Construct a pie chart to show this information. Calculate the number of degrees required for each subject.

3 The following table represents the test marks achieved for a group of 50 candidates.

Marks, m	Frequency, f
$0 < m \leqslant 20$	12
$20 < m \leqslant 40$	20
$40 < m \leqslant 60$	10
$60 < m \leqslant 80$	6
$80 < m \leqslant 100$	2

a) What is the modal group?
b) Copy the table and complete a column showing the cumulative frequency.
c) Display the information on a cumulative frequency graph, and find the median and the interquartile range.
d) What percentage of students scored above 70%?
e) If the pass mark was 40%, how many students failed?
f) Another group which took the test had a median of 26 and an interquartile range of 35. Which class was streamed and which was of mixed ability? Give a reason for your answer.

4 Using the table in question 3, find the mean mark.

5 Using the table in question 3, draw a frequency polygon.

Answers – 9.5

1 strong negative

2

Favourite subject	Degrees°
Maths	27
English	75
PE	130
Sciences	31
Languages	97

Maths 27°
English 75°
PE 130°
Science 31°
Languages 97°

Maths, English, PE, Science, Languages

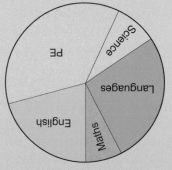

3 **a)** $20 < m \leqslant 40$
b)

Marks, m	Frequency, f	Cumulative frequency
$0 < m \leqslant 20$	12	12
$20 < m \leqslant 40$	20	32
$40 < m \leqslant 60$	10	42
$60 < m \leqslant 80$	6	48
$80 < m \leqslant 100$	2	50

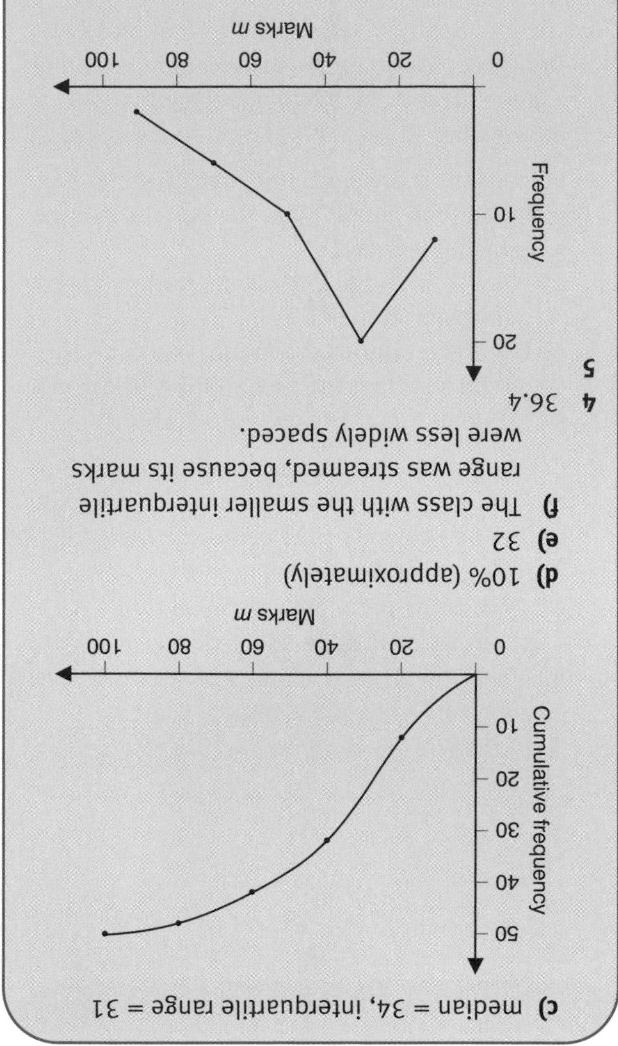

REVIEW

How much have you learnt?
Tick off each topic in the list when you are confident that you can cope with it.

- ☐ **Find the mean of a set of data.**
- ☐ **Find the median of a set of data.**
- ☐ **Find the mode of a set of data.**
- ☐ **Find the range of a set of data.**
- ☐ **Draw a bar chart for a set of data.**
- ☐ **Draw a pie chart for a set of data.**
- ☐ **Complete a frequency polygon.**
- ☐ **Draw up a cumulative frequency table.**
- ☐ **Draw a cumulative frequency graph.**
- ☐ **Find the interquartile range of a set of data.**
- ☐ **Draw and interpret box plots.**
- ☐ **Draw and interpret stem-and-leaf diagrams.**
- ☐ **Calculate moving averages.**
- ☐ **Interpret scatter diagrams.**
- ☐ **Carry out sampling activities.**
- ☐ **Interpret results from sampling activities.**
- ☐ **Carry out surveys.**
- ☐ **Interpret results of surveys.**
- ☐ **Design questionnaires.**
- ☐ **Evaluate questionnaires.**

Chapter 10 Probability

PREVIEW

By the end of this chapter you will be able to:

- **find the probability of an event with a known number of possible outcomes**
- **find the joint probability of two events that are independent**
- **construct tree diagrams**
- **identify mutually exclusive events**
- **calculate the probability of two mutually exclusive events occurring**
- **comment on suggestions about the probabilities of two events that are not necessarily mutually exclusive.**

How much do you know already?

Exercise 10.1

1 In a competition, the probability of winning a prize was 0.35. What was the probability of not winning?

2 1000 tickets were sold in a raffle. If there were 28 prizes, what was the probability of any one ticket winning a prize? Write your answer as a fraction in its lowest terms.

3 Complete the following tree diagram.

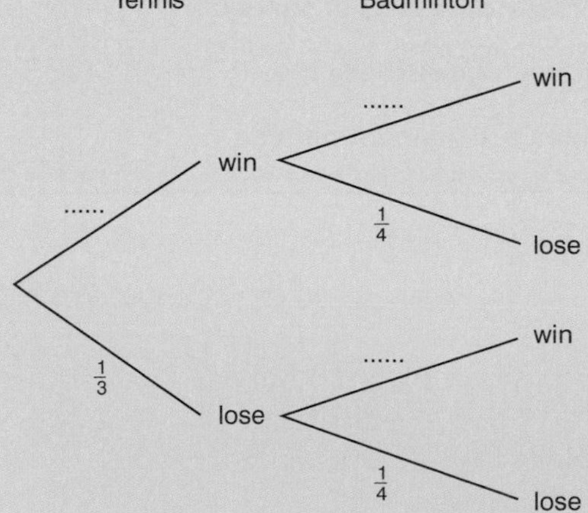

4 If a six-sided dice is thrown, and a coin is tossed, how many different outcomes are there?

5 Steve has been competing in tennis and badminton tournaments. Using the information given in question 3 above, find the probability that he:

a) wins both tournaments
b) wins the tennis, but not the badminton
c) wins only one tournament.

6 The probability of Jane wearing a red dress to work is 0.36, and the possibility of her wearing a green dress is 0.23. What is the probability of her wearing either a red dress or a green dress?

7 In a box there are seven red, five blue and four green buttons. In addition, the buttons may be round, square or oval.

a) What is the probability that a button taken at random is blue?
b) If $\frac{1}{8}$ of the buttons are round, why can you not be sure that the probability of choosing a blue or round button is $\frac{5}{16} + \frac{1}{8} = \frac{7}{16}$?

8 Charlotte only likes chocolates with hard centres. In a box of 30 chocolates, 12 have soft centres, 20 are milk chocolates and 5 are foil wrapped. She takes one at random.

a) What is the probability of Charlotte choosing one with a soft centre?
b) If she wants a chocolate to be a milk chocolate or be foil wrapped, is the probability necessarily $\frac{2}{3} + \frac{1}{6}$? Give a reason.

Answers – 10.1

1 0.65. As the question used decimals, you should give your answer as a decimal.

2 $\frac{28}{1000} = \frac{7}{250}$

3

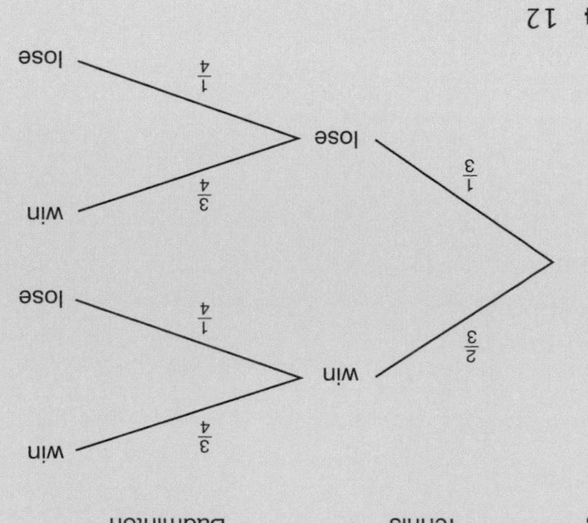

4 12

5 **a)** $\frac{1}{2}$ **b)** $\frac{1}{6}$ **c)** $\frac{5}{12}$

6 0.59

7 **a)** $\frac{5}{16}$ **b)** The events may not be mutually exclusive.

8 **a)** $\frac{12}{30} = \frac{2}{5}$ or 40% **b)** No, because the two events are not necessarily mutually exclusive.

How did you get on?

All of them right?

You should be feeling really pleased with yourself, because almost all exam papers contain probability questions and you should score well here.

Most of them right, but a few mistakes?

The examples in this chapter will help you to see where you went wrong.

Don't even ask?

The good news is that you are by no means alone. Many students start by hating probability. The even better news is that most of them manage to learn it well enough to score highly in the exam, so don't give up on it. If you really have problems with probability, don't try to take in too many rules at one sitting.

Rules of probability

Probability of events is measured on a sliding scale from imposssible to certain.

impossible — certain

0 — 1

1 Each event's outcome can be assessed on a sliding scale from impossible to certain.
2 Impossible events have a probability of 0.
3 Certain events have a probability of 1.
4 All other possibilities, or probabilities, are expressed as a fraction, decimal or percentage.
5 When the probabilities of all possible outcomes are added together, the total must be 1.

In most questions of probability:

OR means ADD
Remember ADORE: ADD = OR

AND means MULTIPLY
Remember SAND TIMER: AND = TIMES

Solutions to questions on page 122

Question 1 – In probability, an event happens or it doesn't, and so the probabilities add up to 1. In this case you either win or you don't, so the probability of not winning is 1 – 0.35 = 0.65.

Question 2 – Your chances of winning are 28 out of 1000. You always write probability as a fraction, decimal, or percentage, never using 'out of'. Note that $\frac{28}{1000}$ cancels down to $\frac{7}{250}$.

Question 3 – Whether you are working with fractions or decimals, the probabilities branching from a common point always add up to 1.

Questions 4, 5 and 6 on page 122

To answer many probability questions you need to know the and/or rules.

Whenever you can say 'and' you multiply the probabilities.

Usually you add when you can say 'or' but the next section tells you when this is wrong.

Question 4 – There are six possible outcomes on a dice, and two on a coin, so you need all the outcomes on a dice and all those on a coin, i.e. $6 \times 2 = 12$

Question 5 – **a)** 'Wins both matches' can be written as, 'Wins the tennis **and** wins the badminton' so you multiply the probabilities.

b) 'Wins the tennis, but not the badminton' would still make sense if it was written, 'Wins the tennis **and** not the badminton', so you can multiply the probabilities.

c) 'Wins only one tournament' means that he wins the tennis **and** not the badminton, **or** that he wins the badminton, **and** not the tennis. Once you have the probabilities associated with winning only one match and losing the other, you add them.

Question 6 – As you can only wear one dress at a time, you add the probabilities, giving a probability of 0.59.

Question 7b) or 8b) on page 122

Sometimes **add** cannot be used for **or.** In question 6, you could add the probabilities, because Jane would only wear one dress at a time. In this situation, events are said to be **mutually exclusive**. Events that do not influence each other are **independent**.

In question 7b), for example, it is not known whether some of the blue buttons are also round, and if you simply add the probabilities, you might be counting some buttons twice.

If you have a question of this type, where you are asked why you cannot add the probabilities, the answer is usually that the events are not mutually exclusive.

Remember: In probability, an event either happens, or it doesn't. Therefore, if you have worked out the probability of an event occurring, the probability of it not occurring is one minus the probability that it does occur.

Exercise 10.2

1 Perdeep went to the fair and tried to win a prize on the coconut shy and at the hoopla stall. If the probability of winning a prize at the coconut shy was 0.15 and at the hoopla stall was 0.3, find the probability that he wins:

a) no prizes
b) a prize at hoopla but not at the coconut shy
c) exactly one prize
d) two prizes.

Hint: you may find a tree diagram helpful.

2 At the zoo, 30% of the staff are animal keepers, and 45% of the staff are women. Why might the probability of finding a female or a keeper not be 45% + 30% = 75%?

3 Shaun likes playing board games. He plays a game where two fair, six-sided dice are thrown simultaneously, and their scores are added together. Find the probability of him scoring:

a) 8 **b)** 1 **c)** 12.

4 a) Sara and Grace make clothes together. If the probability of Sara producing a sub-standard item is 0.1 and that of Grace is 0.3, find the probability that both Sara and Grace make mistakes when producing a garment.

b) In a consignment of 900 garments, how many would you expect to have flaws from both?

5 The chart is an analysis of visitors to a museum one day.

	under 20	20 or over
Men	210	350
Women	270	170

Using the table, find:

a) the probability that a visitor taken at random is a female aged 20 or over
b) the probability that a female visitor is under 20 years old
c) the probability that a male visitor is aged 20 or over. Give your answer as a fraction in its lowest terms.

6 Toby has drawn a diagram showing the possible routes to the cinema. Depending on which turn he takes, he can pass points A, B, C or D.

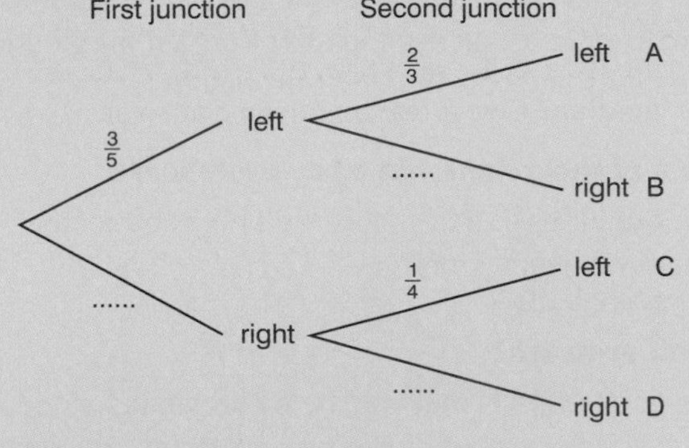

a) Complete the tree diagram.
b) Fay is going to the cinema. Which point is she most likely to pass?
c) Which point is she least likely to pass?

Answers – 10.2

1 a) 0.595 **b)** 0.255 **c)** 0.36 **d)** 0.045

2 The events are not mutually exclusive. There might be at least 1 female keeper.

3 a) $\frac{5}{36}$ **b)** 0 **c)** $\frac{1}{36}$

4 a) 0.03 **b)** 27

5 a) $\frac{17}{100}$ or 17% **b)** $\frac{27}{44}$ or 61% **c)** $\frac{5}{8}$

6 a)

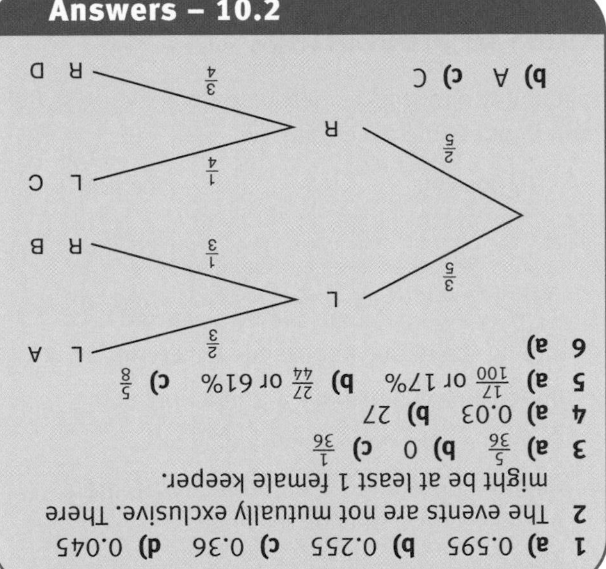

b) A **c)** C

REVIEW

How much have you learnt?
Tick off each topic in the list when you are confident that you can cope with it.

- ☐ **Find the probability of an event with a known number of possible outcomes.**
- ☐ **Find the joint probability of two events that are independent.**
- ☐ **Construct tree diagrams.**
- ☐ **Identify mutually exclusive events.**
- ☐ **Calculate the probability of two mutually exclusive events occurring.**
- ☐ **Comment on suggestions about the probabilities of two events that are not necessarily mutually exclusive.**

When you have ticked off most of the items in the list above, and in the one at the end of the chapter on Statistics on page 121, you can try the Handling data review on page 125.

1 Find the mean, median and range for the following sets of data.

a) 9.6, 10.1, 8.4, 9.8, 6.9, 11.4, 7.2

b) 104, 116, 102, 14, 144, 100

For the second set of data, which is a better measure of the average, the mean or the median? Give a reason for your answer.

2 In an experiment 30 plants were grown in a greenhouse. After two months their heights were recorded. The results are illustrated in the table below.

Height of plant (cm)	22	23	24	25	26	27	28
Frequency	1	0	3	6	9	11	0

a) Find the mean, median, mode and range of the sample.

b) At the same time, 30 similar plants were grown outdoors. The most common height was 24 cm. The range of heights was 8. Make two comparisons between the distributions.

3 An exam was sat by 40 people in class A. The percentage marks (x) scored are shown in the frequency table below.

Mark (x)	No. of students
$0 < x \leq 20$	8
$20 < x \leq 40$	21
$40 < x \leq 60$	6
$60 < x \leq 80$	3
$80 < x \leq 100$	2

a) Calculate an estimate of the mean using mid-interval values.

b) What is the modal class?

c) i) Complete the cumulative frequency table below.

Mark (x)	No.	Cumulative frequency
$0 < x \leq 20$	8	
$20 < x \leq 40$	21	
$40 < x \leq 60$	6	
$60 < x \leq 80$	3	
$80 < x \leq 100$	2	

ii) On the given axes, draw a cumulative frequency curve to represent the information.

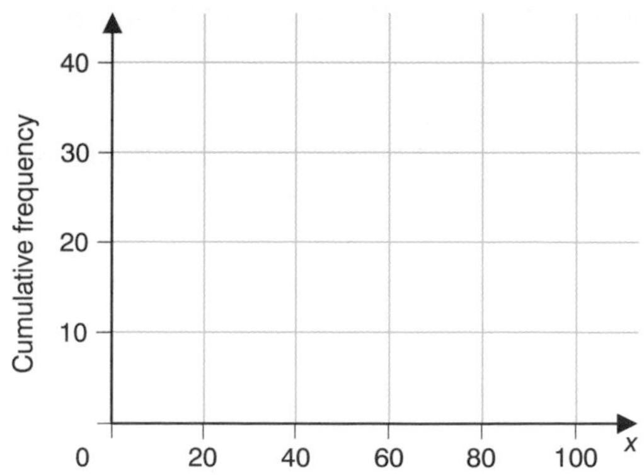

d) Find the median and the interquartile range.

e) Class B sat the same test. The median of their results was 60, and their interquartile range was 35.

i) Which class had the higher average?

ii) Which class was the more consistent?

4 In a survey 720 students were asked how they travelled to school. The results are as follows.

Type of transport	Frequency
On foot	108
By car	180
By bus	252
By train	36
By bicycle	144

a) Draw a pie chart to represent the above information.

b) What was the modal method of transport?

c) What percentage of students walked to school?

5 A school asked 100 boys and 100 girls how far they travelled to school. The results are given in the table below.

Distance from school (d km)	Boys	Girls
$0 < d \leq 2$	26	30
$2 < d \leq 4$	52	36
$4 < d \leq 6$	16	20
$6 < d \leq 8$	6	14

a) Draw two frequency polygons to represent this information, on the diagram below.

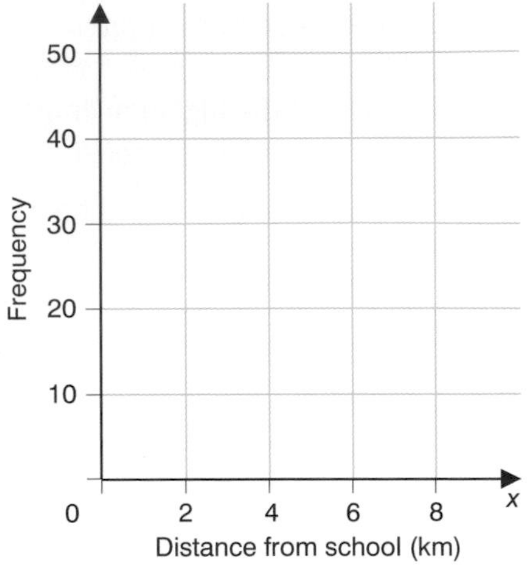

b) Name one similarity and one difference between the graphs.

6 The size of engine, length and fuel consumption of ten cars were recorded. The results are illustrated in the two scatter diagrams below. Describe the correlations shown in the two diagrams.

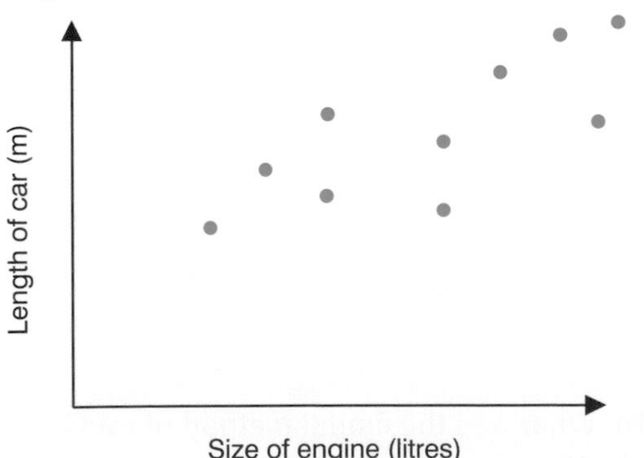

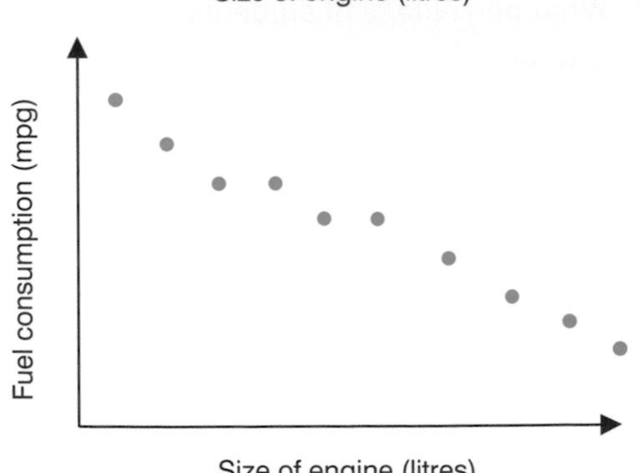

7 In a bag there are seven red, six green, two yellow and five blue marbles. A marble is taken out, the colour noted and it is then replaced. Giving your answer as a fraction in its lowest terms, find the probability that the marble is:

a) green
b) red or blue
c) not yellow.

8 A machine can develop either mechanical or electrical faults. The probability of it developing a mechanical fault is 0.01, and an electrical fault 0.07. These events are independent.

a) What is the probability that it develops both types of fault?
b) How many machines would you expect to develop both faults out of a production line of 130 000?

9 In a class survey, 0.2 of the pupils were left-handed and 0.12 of them wore glasses. These events are independent.

a) What is the probability that a person picked at random is left-handed and wears glasses?
b) Why might it not be correct to say that the probability of a student being left-handed or wearing glasses is 0.32?

10 A test consist of two parts, A and B. It was found that 75% of the candidates pass A, but only 40% pass B.

a) Complete the tree diagram below.

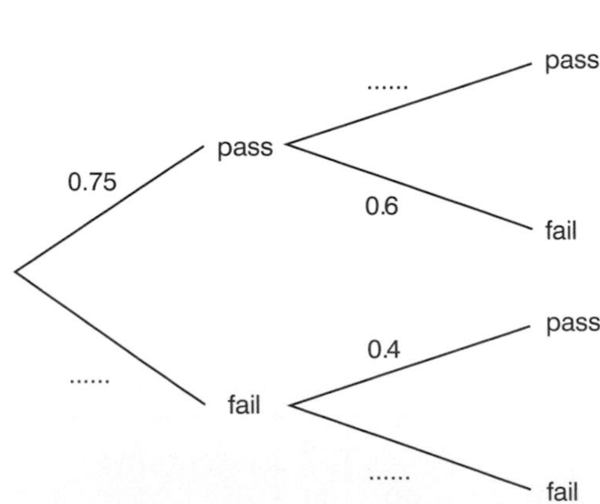

b) What percentage of the students pass both parts?
c) What percentage pass A or B but not both?
d) What percentage fail both parts?

Answers – Handling data review

1 a) mean = 9.1, median = 9.6, range = 4.5

b) mean = 96.7, median = 103 (It is the 3.5th number i.e. the average of 102 and 104.), range = 130
The median is better as the mean is heavily influenced by the number 14.

2 a) mean = 25.8 cm, median (15.5th number) = 26 cm, mode = 27 cm, range = 5 cm
(Don't write your answer as 22 – 27!)

b) The average/mode was higher for the plants grown in the greenhouse.
The range/spread of heights was greater for those grown outdoors.

3 a) 35 **b)** $20 < x \leqslant 40$

c) i)

Mark (x)	Cumulative frequency
$0 < x \leqslant 20$	8
$20 < x \leqslant 40$	29
$40 < x \leqslant 60$	35
$60 < x \leqslant 80$	38
$80 < x \leqslant 100$	40

ii)

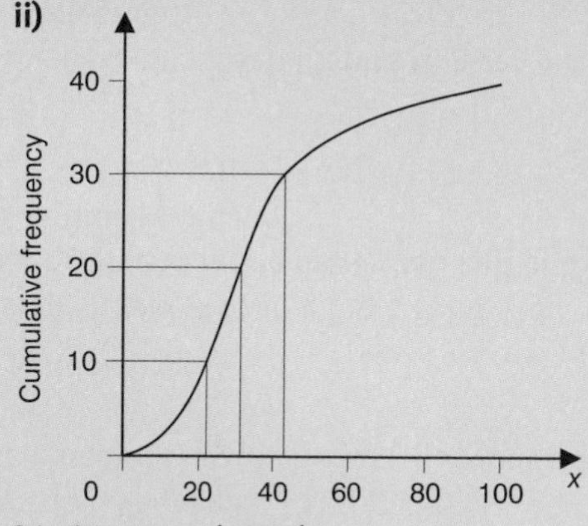

d) 31, 21 approximately

e) i) Class B **ii)** Class A

4 a) foot 54°, car 90°, bus 126°, train 18°, bicycle 72°

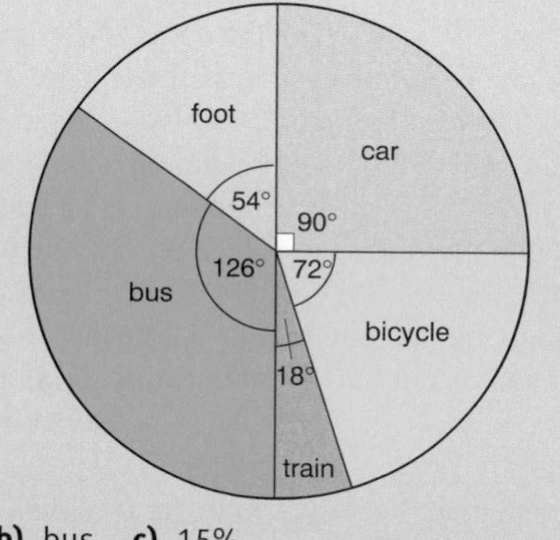

b) bus **c)** 15%

5 a)

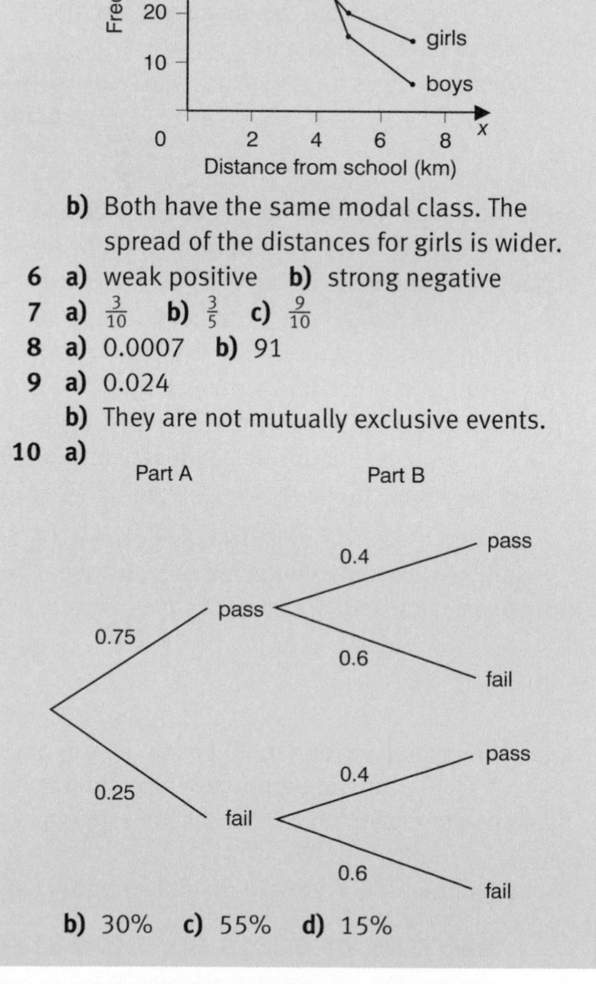

b) Both have the same modal class. The spread of the distances for girls is wider.

6 a) weak positive **b)** strong negative

7 a) $\frac{3}{10}$ **b)** $\frac{3}{5}$ **c)** $\frac{9}{10}$

8 a) 0.0007 **b)** 91

9 a) 0.024

b) They are not mutually exclusive events.

10 a)

b) 30% **c)** 55% **d)** 15%

Three simple steps to success

Some topics come up in exams more often than others.
Some topics usually carry more marks than others.
Some topics are easier than others.
Check up on those first to improve your chance of a good grade.

Step 1

You can use two simple techniques to solve many of the most common questions. Check up on these before you go any further.

- X-Direct – Make a list of all the situations where you can use this method, for example, percentages, proportion, ratio, pie charts. Feel free to add any more that you can think of, and then note down one example of each just to remind yourself of X-Direct in practice.
- Triplets – Again, make a list of any mentioned in this book e.g. for trigonometry, SOH CAH TOA. If you have made up any yourself, add these to the list.

Number

- Percentages – calculator and non-calculator methods, reverse percentages, percentage increase and decrease, including 'double' percentages (for example, a profit of 15% followed by a loss of 6%), profit and loss, compound interest using a multiplier, percentages using fractional or decimal methods
- Ratio and proportion
- Rounding and estimating – significant figures (sig. figs, s.f.), decimal places, largest and smallest values
- Standard index form – calculator and non-calculator examples
- Trial and improvement
- Fractions – equivalent, cancelling, their link with recurring decimals, changing fractions to decimals and vice versa, adding and multiplying simple fractions
- Decimals – ordering according to size, multiplying and dividing decimals

Algebra and graphs

- Substituting numbers into formulae – Make sure that you understand the order in which a **scientific** calculator operates – remember **BODMAS** or **BIDMAS** and take great care if there are negative signs about.
- Basic algebraic notation and simplifying expressions – Make sure that you recognise the difference between an equation, an expression and an inequality.
- Simple equations with one unknown – They only have one kind of variable, unlike simultaneous equations which have two, or quadratic equations which have a squared term.
- Sequences

Shape and space

- Angles – COAST (page 92) and in two dimensional shapes, including interior and exterior angles of polygons
- Area and circumference of circles including giving an answer in terms of π
- Pythagoras' theorem and trigonometry, including use of surds (square roots) in an answer. (Are you sure you know how to use your calculator to find either a side or an angle?)

Handling data

- Mean, median, mode and range. (Remember grouped data too.)
- Cumulative frequency, including box plots/box and whisker diagrams
- Simple probability – watch those fractions and decimals
- Relative frequency

The **first step** should get you off to a flying start, as you should be able to tackle **more than half** of the questions in the exam paper.

Step 2

Here are the next most useful topics to give your marks another boost.

Number

- Changing metric units (for example, cm^2 to m^2) and changing common metric and imperial units. (Remember, 'Journey's end is full of smiles, eight kilometres make five miles.')
- Types of number, for example, prime, triangle, square, square root, cube, cube root. HCF, LCM and expressing a number as a product of prime factors. You should know, or be able to work out, the squares of 2–15 inclusive and the cubes of 2, 3, 4, 5 and 10.

Algebra and graphs

- Simultaneous equations, solved algebraically and graphically
- Factorising using single brackets
- Gradient and equation of a line
- Graphs of real-life situations and of containers filling

Shape and space

- Area and volume, including nets and surface area
- Bearings, including their relevance in trigonometry questions

- Loci and constructions using ruler and compasses – perpendicular bisector, bisecting an angle and so on
- Similar figures and scale factors
- Transformations – translations using vector notation, reflections, rotations, enlargements

Handling data

- Stem-and-leaf diagrams
- Pie charts, histograms and frequency polygons
- More complicated probability – tree diagrams, and the AND/OR rules
- Scatter diagrams and correlation
- Surveys and questionnaires

If you know all of this material and score good marks on all the questions involving it, you should pass. However, to give yourself a safety net, try to cover as many of the step 3 topics as you can, as well. It could make the difference between a C and a D, or a B and a C.

Step 3

Nearly there now. Pick the topics that you find easiest first.

Number

- Powers, indices, square roots and cube roots
- Inverse proportion
- Rates such as distance, speed, time
- Subtracting and dividing simple fractions
- Long multiplication and division. It doesn't matter if you use an unusual method, but you must be able to cope with large numbers when you attempt a non-calculator paper.

Algebra and graphs

- Formula rearrangement
- Factorising and multiplying out double brackets
- Quadratic equations, including the difference of two squares
- Inequalities – on a number line and on a graph
- Simple function notation

Shape and space

- Dimensions
- Tessellation
- Congruent shapes
- Scale drawing
- Circle theorems
- Plan and elevation

Handling data

- Moving averages

To see how much you can remember, try the specimen questions which follow. They are typical of questions that you will meet in the exams.

Finally try out all your new skills on all the past papers that you can lay your hands on – your teacher will probably be only too pleased and flabbergasted to provide you with plenty of material!

Checklist

Avoid these banana skins!

1 When do you plot a graph using end points?

2 What is the difference between significant figures and decimal places?

3 If you have n numbers, which one would be in the median position?

4 What do the interquartile range and range describe?

5 When shouldn't you use X-Direct?

6 When using Pythagoras' theorem and finding one of the shorter sides, what must you remember?

7 Which four points should you remember when finding a bearing?

8 How many items of information must you remember to write for each of the four types of transformation?

9 **a)** In probability, what calculations do you associate with 'and' and 'or'?
b) When must you be careful with using 'or'?

10 Give the formulae for the area and the circumference of a circle.

11 What should you check on your calculator before starting trigonometry?

12 How do you calculate the scale factor of an enlargement?

13 What should you remember when working in algebra with inequalities?

14 How do you find the mean of grouped frequency data?

15 What is the difference between using **SIN** and **SIN⁻¹** on your calculator?

16 What shapes does the net of a closed cylinder consist of?

17 If a number has been rounded to the nearest 50, how would you find the smallest and largest values?

18 How do you know whether shapes tessellate?

19 What three letters can help you remember the rules for corresponding, opposite and alternate angles?

20 When is the mean an unsuitable measure of the average?

You may want to add some of your own banana skins at this point.

Answers – Avoid these banana skins!

1 Cumulative frequency

2 If you are unclear on this, turn to Chapter 2.

3 If n is even, the median is the mean of the $\frac{1}{2}n$th and the $\frac{1}{2}(n + 2)$th value. If n is odd, the median is the $\frac{1}{2}(n + 1)$th value.

4 How widely apart the data is spread.

5 Inverse proportion

6 For Shorter Sides Subtract.

7 Start at 'from', look north, turn clockwise, and always write the angle with three figures.

8 Reflection 1
Translation 1
Enlargement 2
Rotation 3
Look back to Chapter 8, Transformations, if you need to remind yourself about these points.

9 **a)** and = times, or = add
b) When the events are not mutually exclusive.

10 area = πr^2, circumference = $2\pi r$ or πd

11 Check that it is set to degrees.

12 SOFT: Second Over First

13 The inequality reverses when you:
a) swap the inequality around, or
b) multiply or divide both sides by a negative number.

14 Start by finding the mid-interval values. See page 113 if you need more help.

15 Use *sin* if you want to find a length, use sin^{-1} if you have the sine and want to find an angle.

16 Two circles and a rectangle.

17 Halve 50 to make 25, then add it to the given number to make the largest, and subtract it to make the smallest.

18 The angles around the common point should total 360°.

19 F, X and Z respectively

20 When a small part of the sample is much bigger or much smaller than the rest.

Here's a chance to try out all your new skills on exam-style questions. We have tried to make them as close to the real thing as possible. However, as all examiners have their own funny little ways, it is a good idea to do as many past papers as possible. No doubt your Maths teacher will keep you busy.

Hints & Tips

Before you start on the non-calculator questions, here are a few tips.

1. Work right through the paper, doing as many questions as you can. Leave out any questions you can't do straight away, then come back to them.
2. If you are working on a question and you get a sudden brainwave about another question, jot it down somewhere (perhaps on an inside cover) to use later.
3. A lucky guess might gain you some marks. A blank page never does. Also, if you attempt at least part of a question, there is a chance that you will get some marks.
4. Don't get bogged down in any one question. It's better to move on and come back later if you have time.
5. Always show your working. It's surprising how many marks you can pick up, even if you get the wrong answer.

And finally, if you really don't know where to start, remember:

Read the question.
Identify the problem, i.e. what are they asking?
Note the information, i.e. what do I know already, what information are they giving me?
Get on with it.
Or go back and attempt the question again later if you have time.

Set 1 (non-calculator)

1 In a sale, a shop reduced all its prices by 15%.

a) Find the new price of an article which originally cost £55.00.

b) Find the original price if the reduced price is £102.

c) In the week before the sale, the average number of customers per day was 250. During the sale this number increased to 370. What was the percentage increase?

2 Solve the following equations.

a) $10x + 3 = 12x - 7$

b) $4x + 2 = 2x - 12$

c) $4(x - 3) = 2 - x$

d) Use an algebraic method to solve the following simultaneous equations.
$5x + 2y = 29 \qquad 2x + 5y = 41$

3 a) The following table gives some values for the equation $y = 2x - 4$. Fill in the rest of the table.

x	−2	−1	0	1	2	3	4
y	−8			−2		2	

b) Taking values of x between −2 and 4, and values of y between −8 and 4, draw the graph of $y = 2x - 4$.

c) Hence or otherwise, find the gradient and the y-intercept.

4 a) A square has sides of 10 cm. How long is its diagonal? Leave a square root in your answer.

b) The hypotenuse of a right-angled triangle is 5 cm. If one of the other sides is 3 cm, find the length of the third side.

c) The isosceles triangle ABC is right angled at A. Work out the size of angle B, and hence write down tan B.

5 ABCDEFGH is a regular octagon centred at O. Find the size of:

a) angle BCD

b) angle BED

c) angle ABE

d) What name is given to the shape BCDE?

e) What is the order of symmetry of the octagon?

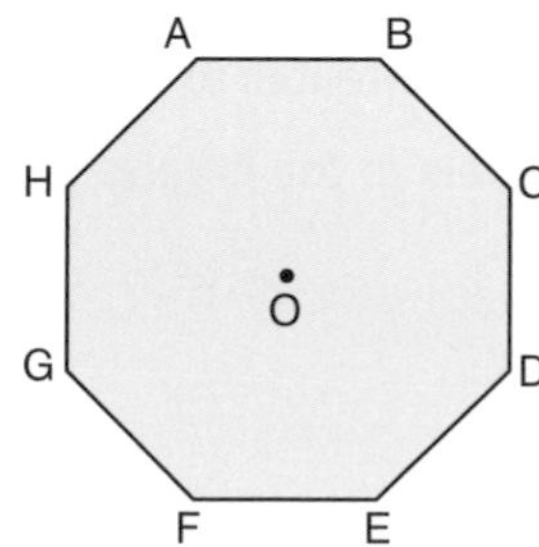

6 i) In the sequence, 15, 19, 23, 27, ... give:

a) the next two terms

b) the 20th term

c) the nth term.

ii) A sequence is made by doubling the previous term and subtracting 2. Give the next three terms.
3, 4, 6, 10, ...

iii) Give the next term and a formula for finding the nth term.
4, 7, 12, 19, ...

7 A millionaire is estimated to be worth £22 000 000 to the nearest million. What is the least value of his wealth?

8 **i)** Simplify where possible.

a) $3(2x + y) - (x - y)$

b) $5x^2 + 2x + 7x + 2y + y^2$

ii) Find the solutions to these equations.

a) $(x - 3)(x + 2) = 0$

b) $x^2 + 8x + 7 = 0$

c) $x^2 - 8x - 20 = 0$

9 You are given that l, h and r are all lengths. Using dimensions, state with a reason whether each of the following is a formula for length, area, volume or none of these.

a) $\pi r^2 + 2lh + r^3$ **b)** $4l(h + r)$

c) $4h + \frac{1}{4}\pi r + \frac{1}{2}l$ **d)** $\pi r^2(l + h)$

e) $\frac{4}{3}\pi r^3 \div h$

10 'Don't you agree that there aren't enough programmes for teenagers on TV?'
Is this a good question to ask when conducting a survey in teenagers' viewing habits?
Give a reason for your answer.

11 A rectangular garden, ABCD, has dimensions AB = CD = 20 m, BC = AD = 14 m. AB is the back wall of a house.

a) Make an accurate scale drawing of the garden, using a scale of 0.5 cm to 1 m. How long should AB be on the plan?

b) A tree is to be planted 6 m from the house and equidistant from AD and CD. Using a ruler and compasses only, mark the spot T where the tree is to be planted.

c) A pond is to be made so that it is to be no more than 13 m from both A and C. Indicate the region where it is to be dug.

12 Match the labels to the graphs below.

a) $y = x^3$

b) $y = -x$

c) $y = x^2 + 2$

d) $y = 2x - 3$

i) **ii)**

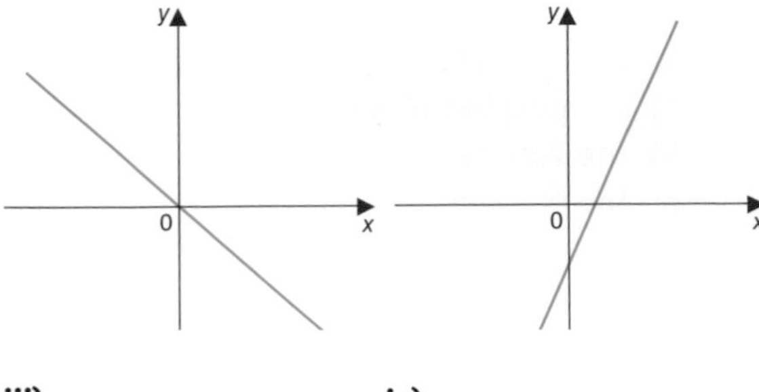

iii) **iv)**

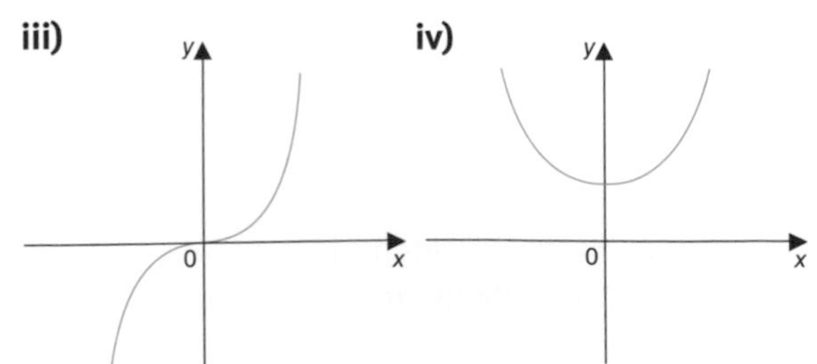

13 **a)** $5\frac{2}{5} - 3\frac{1}{2}$ **b)** $4\frac{1}{3} \div 2\frac{1}{6}$

c) $2\frac{5}{8} \times 2\frac{1}{2}$ **d)** $4\frac{1}{3} + 5\frac{1}{6}$

14 **a)** Write 56.8×10^3 in standard form.

b) Work out $(1.2 \times 10^{-4}) \times (9.8 \times 10^{-5})$

15 The probability that a train is late on any given day is 0.3. The probability that a bus is late on any given day is 0.2. If the two events are independent, find the probability that on any given day

a) the train and the bus are late

b) either the train or the bus is late, but not both.

16 Using the equation $y = 2x - 3$, write down

a) the gradient

b) the y-intercept.

Set 2 (calculator)

1 1 litre is approximately equal to 1.75 pints and 8 pints make 1 gallon.

a) How many gallons are approximately equal to 40 litres?

b) How many litres are approximately equal to 15.75 gallons?

2 **a)** The probability of a student taking French is 0.3 and of taking German is 0.4. What is the probability that a student takes German but not French?

b) The probability of a girl being picked for the girls' netball team is 0.4. The probability of a boy being picked for the boys' rugby team is 0.3. The probability of a student being picked for the school chess team is 0.2.

i) Why might it be incorrect to say that the probability of being chosen for either the netball or the chess team is 0.4 + 0.2?

ii) What further information would you need to be able to estimate the probability of being chosen for either the netball or the chess team?

3 Find the angle marked x below, to the nearest degree.

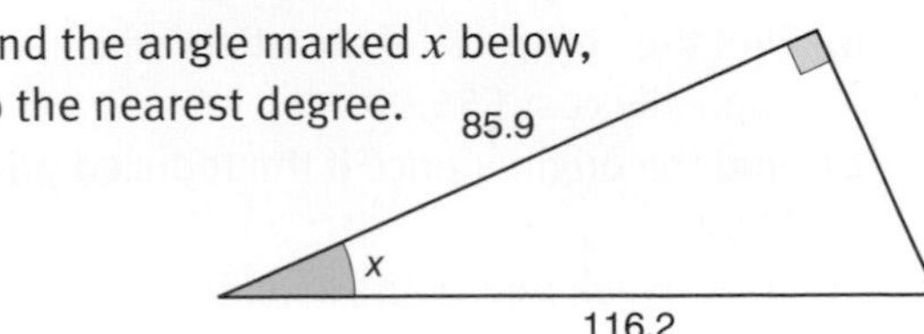

4 An employer advertised a part-time job at the rate of £50.00 per week plus £6.00 per hour.

a) If w stands for the wage in pounds, and h stands for hours worked, write a formula in terms of w and h to show this information. Begin the formula: $w =$

b) Rearrange the formula to make h the subject.

c) If an employee earned £170.00 in a week, how many hours had she worked?

5 A fish tank is made in the shape of a cuboid. with a base measuring 60 cm by 40 cm. If it contains 72 litres of water, how deep is the water in the tank?

6 A closed cylindrical tank has a base radius of 1.7 m, and a height of 3.4 m.

a) Find its volume.

b) Find its surface area.

7 **i)** Work out the following. Give your answers in standard form correct to 3 significant figures.

a) $(3.7 \times 10^8) \times (1.4 \times 10^4)$

b) $(8.6 \times 10^{12}) \div (3.2 \times 10^5)$

ii) Use a calculator to work out the following. Give your answers correct to 1 decimal place.

a) $\dfrac{3.7 + 9.2}{1.4 \times \sqrt{0.16}}$

b) $\dfrac{\sqrt{17 \times 3.7^2}}{12.6 - 2.5}$

c) $\dfrac{2.1^2 + 15.8}{7.1 - 2.2}$

iii) Without using a calculator, show how you can give a rough estimate of the answer to:

$\dfrac{2.1^2 + 15.8}{7.1 - 2.2}$

iv) Now, using a calculator, work out the answer to:

$\dfrac{2.1^2 + 15.8}{7.1 - 2.2}$

Write down

a) all the digits on your calculator display

b) your answer correct to 2 decimal places.

8 In the diagram below calculate:

a) AB

b) BC

c) the area of triangle ACD.

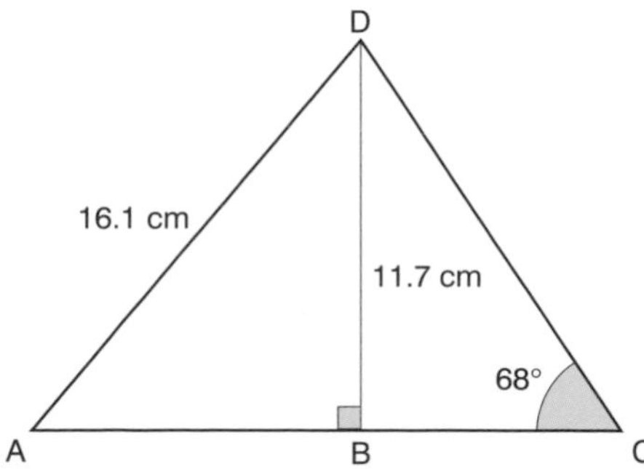

9 A survey, carried out on the ages of 80 members of a sports' club, gave the following information.

No. of years, x	Frequency	Cumulative frequency
Less than 10	2	
$10 < x \leqslant 20$	16	
$20 < x \leqslant 30$	30	
$30 < x \leqslant 40$	16	
$40 < x \leqslant 50$	10	
$50 < x \leqslant 60$	6	

a) Complete the column showing the cumulative frequency.

b) Draw a cumulative frequency graph, and use it to find the median and the interquartile range.

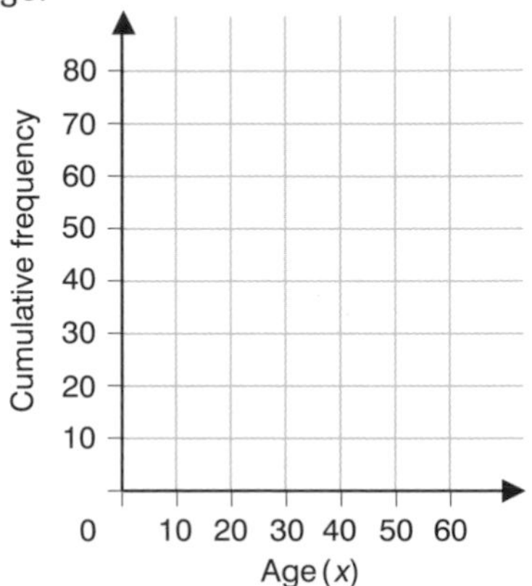

c) Using the information given in the table above, state the modal group, and find an estimate of the mean.

d) In which group does the median value lie?

10 Describe fully the transformation which maps:

a) P on to Q **b)** P to R **c)** P to S.

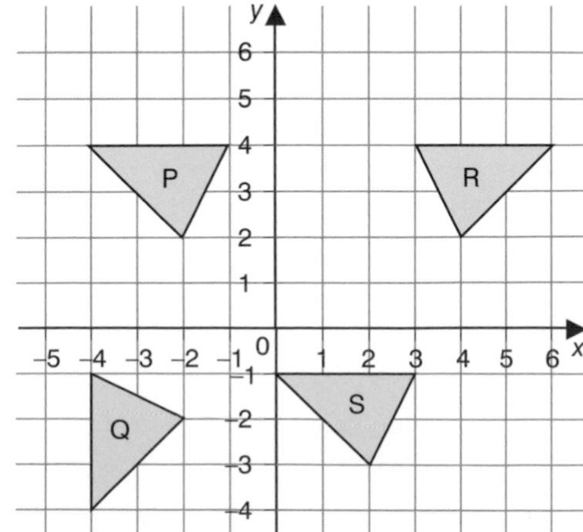

11 **a)** Express 780 as a product of its prime factors.

b) $18\,000 = 2^x \times 3^y \times 5^z$. Find x, y and z.

12 On the diagram below, shade the region indicated by the following inequalities.

$x \leqslant 3$
$y \geqslant 1$
$y \leqslant x$

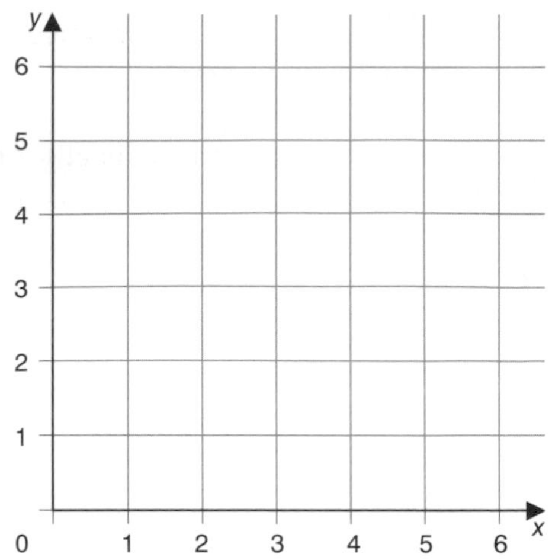

13 Find:

a) the mean
b) the median
c) the range

of these numbers.

7, 8, 3, 9, 6, 30

d) Is the mean or the median a better indicator of the average? Give a reason.

14 Solve the following inequalities to find all the integer values of x.

$10 - x < 3x + 3 \leqslant x + 11$

Answers – Set 1

1 a) £46.75 **b)** £120.00 **c)** 48%

2 a) $x = 5$ **b)** $x = -7$
c) $x = 2.8$ **d)** $x = 3, y = 7$

3 a)

x	−2	−1	0	1	2	3	4
y	−8	−6	−4	−2	0	2	4

b)

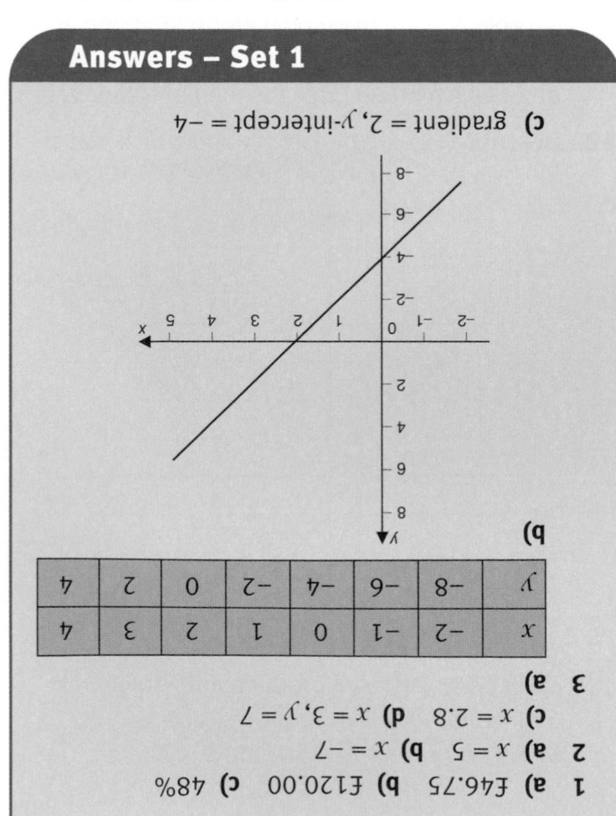

c) gradient = 2, y-intercept = −4

4 a) $10^2 + 10^2 = 200$ The diagonal is $\sqrt{200}$ cm
b) You have the hypotenuse and one of the shorter sides, so you need to subtract the squares.
$5^2 - 3^2 = 16$. The missing side is 4 cm long.
c) If angle A = 90°, angle B + angle C = 90°. As the triangle is isosceles, angle B = angle C = 45°. Also, the opposite and the adjacent are the same length, so the tan is 1. (If you find this confusing, sketch a triangle marking angles A and B and the equal sides.)

5 a) 135° **b)** 45° **c)** 90° **d)** trapezium
e) Order 8 or 8-fold rotational symmetry

6 i) a) 31, 35 **b)** 91 **c)** $4n + 11$
ii) 18, 34, 66
iii) 28, $n^2 + 3$

7 £21 500 000 or £21.5 million

8 i) a) $5x + 4y$ **b)** $5x^2 + 9x + 2y + y^2$
ii) a) $x = 3, x = -2$ **b)** $x = -7, x = -1$
c) $x = 10, x = -2$

9 a) none (area + area + volume)
b) area (length × length)
c) length (length + length + length)
d) volume (area × length = length × length × length)
e) area (volume ÷ length = area)

10 This is a bad question, because it is leading, i.e. it is suggesting a particular response to the interviewee.

11 a) 10 cm
b) and **c)**

D C
Not drawn to scale
T
A B

12 a) (iii) **b)** (i) **c)** (iv) **d)** (ii)

13 a) $1\frac{9}{10}$ **b)** 2 **c)** $6\frac{9}{16}$ **d)** $9\frac{1}{2}$

14 a) 5.68×10^4
b) First work out 12 × 98, or 98 × 12 if it's easier. 98 × 12 = 1176. Then put in the missing decimal point. 1.2 x 9.8 = 11.76 Now deal with the powers of 10.
$10^{-4} \times 10^{-5} = 10^{-9}$. Putting both parts together gives 11.76×10^{-9}. However, $11.76 = 1.176 \times 10^1$, so the final answer is $1.176 \times 10^{-9} \times 10^1 = 1.176 \times 10^{-8}$

15 a) $0.3 \times 0.2 = 0.06$
b) You need to work out (train late and bus not late) or (train not late and bus late).
$(0.3 \times 0.8) + (0.7 \times 0.2) = 0.24 + 0.14 = 0.38$

16 a) 2 **b)** −3

Answers – Set 2

1 **a)** 8.75 gallons
b) 72 litres

2 **a)** 0.28
b) **i)** The probabilities are not mutually exclusive.
ii) You would need to know how many girls are in both groups.

3 42°

4 **a)** $w = 50 + 6h$ **b)** $h = \dfrac{w - 50}{6}$
c) 20 hours

5 30 cm

6 **a)** $30.9\,\text{m}^3$ **b)** $54.5\,\text{m}^2$

7 **i)** **a)** 5.18×10^{12} **b)** 2.69×10^7
ii) **a)** 23.0 **b)** 1.5 **c)** 4.1
iii) $4 + 16 = 20$, $7 - 2 = 5$, $20 \div 5 = 4$
iv) **a)** 4.124489796 **b)** 4.12

8 **a)** 11.1 cm
b) 4.7 cm
c) $92.4\,\text{cm}^2$

9 **a)**

No. of years, x	Frequency	Cumulative frequency
Less than 10	2	2
$10 < x \leqslant 20$	16	18
$20 < x \leqslant 30$	30	48
$30 < x \leqslant 40$	16	64
$40 < x \leqslant 50$	10	74
$50 < x \leqslant 60$	6	80

b) median = 27, IQR = 16 (approximate answers)

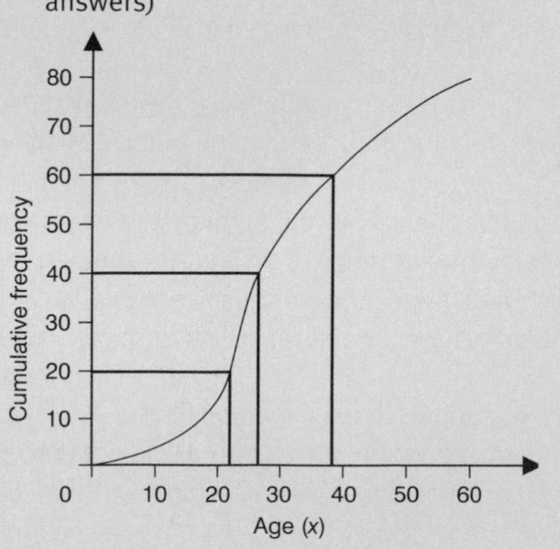

c) $20 < x \leqslant 30$, mean = 29.25
d) $\dfrac{80 + 1}{2} = 40.5$ The median value is halfway between the 40th and 41st values. These are found in the $20 < x \leqslant 30$ group.

10 **a)** rotation anti-clockwise, 90°, centre (0, 0)
b) reflection in the line $x = 1$
c) translation $\binom{4}{-5}$

11 **a)** $780 = 2^2 \times 3 \times 5 \times 13$
b) $x = 4, y = 2, z = 3$

12

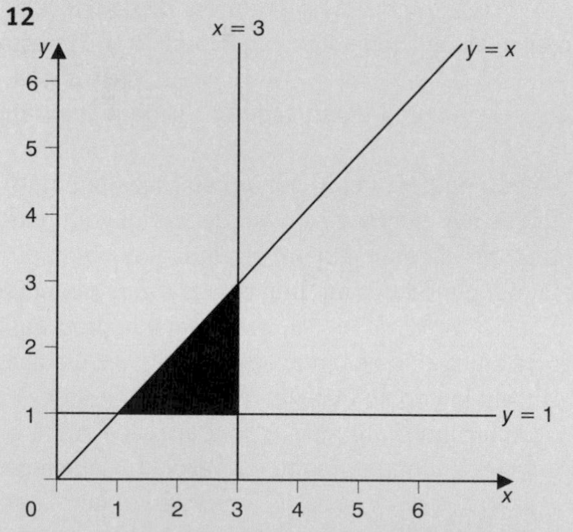

13 **a)** mean = 10.5, median = 7.5, range = 27
b) The median is better, as the mean is distorted by the one much larger value.

14 Split the inequality and deal with each half separately.
$10 - x < 3x + 3 \leqslant x + 11$
$10 - x < 3x + 3 \quad 7 < 4x \quad 1.75 < x$
$3x + 3 \leqslant x + 11 \quad 2x \leqslant 8 \quad x \leqslant 4$
Putting both parts together gives $1.75 < x \leqslant 4$
The possible integers are 2, 3, 4.

Glossary

The following is a list of the usual mathematical words which you will need for the Intermediate syllabus. It also includes translations of some jargon which examiners love to use. Questions are much easier to answer if you can understand what they are asking you to do!

arc of a circle The length between two points marked on the circumference of a circle. The larger length is a **major arc** and the smaller a **minor arc**. (See **sector of a circle**.)

bisect cut in half.

coefficient The fixed number in front of a variable, e.g. the coefficient of $3y$ is 3, the coefficient of $12ab$ is 12. Strictly speaking, you do not need to remember this for GCSE, but you may come across the word in a text book.

compound interest To find the compound interest, add the interest to the original amount and then find the interest on the new amount, and so on. (Alternatively, use the multiplier method from Chapter 1.)

congruent shapes Shapes that are identical in size and shape.

constant A number which does not change in value, e.g. in the expression $x^2 + 3x + 5$, 5 is the constant. If you are drawing a graph to show $y = x^2 + 3x + 5$, you would substitute different values for x, but you would always finish by adding 5. This word will not be used in an Intermediate exam, but you may come across it in a text book.

correlation A relationship between two or more variables. Plot the coordinates showing the relationship on a graph. If the result is a straight line sloping up, the correlation is **positive,** if it slopes down it is **negative.** If you cannot see a pattern resembling a straight line, there is no **linear** correlation.

cross-section A 'slice' from a prism sometimes called the 'cross-sectional area'.

denominator The bottom number of a fraction.

depreciates Loses value.

equivalent fractions Two or more fractions which are worth the same amount.

evaluate To find the value of.

expand This usually refers to brackets and means to multiply them out.

expression This is a formula. If, for example, a boy is three years older than his sister, who is n years old, then the boy's age is $n + 3$. Do not confuse an expression with an equation. If you are told $n + 3 = 10$, this is an equation and you can solve it to find the value of n.

factor A whole number which divides into another number exactly.

hence If you see this word in a question, it implies that some information which you have already worked out could be useful in helping you to discover the answer. Sometimes you will see, 'hence or otherwise'. This means that you could use the information from an earlier part of the question, or you could also use another method to find the answer.

hexagon Any two-dimensional six-sided shape.

highest common factor (HCF) The largest factor which two or more numbers have in common e.g. 6 is the HCF of 12 and 18.

histogram At Intermediate level, treat a histogram in exactly the same way as you would a bar chart.

improper fraction A fraction in which the numerator is larger than the denominator. You may see this called a 'top-heavy' fraction.

index/indices In the number 4^3, for example, 3 is the index or power. The plural of 'index' is 'indices'.

inequality Any value which is larger ($>$) or smaller ($<$) than another value. If the inequality sign has an extra line, e.g. $\geqslant$ or $\leqslant$, it means greater than/less than *or equal* to another value. If you have to draw the equation of a line and then indicate the region which is greater than or less than the equation, simply shade the area above or below. If illustrating a range of values on a number line, remember that the circle at each end of the line is open if the inequality is $>$ or $<$ and closed if the inequality includes 'or equal to', i.e. $\geqslant$ or $\leqslant$.

integer Any whole number including negative numbers and zero.

inverse A reverse process which 'undoes' an operation, e.g. addition and subtraction are inverses, as are multiplication and division. Inverse sin, cos or tan ($\sin^{-1}$, $\cos^{-1}$, $\tan^{-1}$) are used in trigonometry to find angles when you know two sides of a right-angled triangle. Use the INV, SHIFT or 2ndF button on your calculator.

line segment In theory, any line goes on for ever with no beginning or ending, so the part referred to is a line segment. You will not need to use the words 'line segment' but you may meet them in Maths questions.

locus (plural **loci)** The path taken by a point following a given rule, e.g. the locus of a point P which is always 3 cm from a fixed point O is a circle of radius 3 cm, centred at O.

lowest common multiple (LCM) The smallest number into which two or more numbers will divide exactly, e.g. the LCM of 12 and 18 is 36. Finding the lowest common denominator when adding or subtracting fractions is the same as finding the LCM.

mixed number A number comprising a whole number and a fraction. At the end of a calculation involving fractions, you often need to change an improper fraction back to a mixed number.

numerator The top number of a fraction.

octagon Any eight-sided, two-dimensional shape.

pentagon Any five-sided, two-dimensional shape.

perpendicular Lines that meet at right angles, e.g. the perpendicular height of a triangle is a line from an angle which meets the opposite side at right angles.

polygon A two-dimensional, straight-sided shape e.g. triangles, hexagons, octagons are all polygons. A **regular polygon** is a polygon in which all sides and angles are equal.

primary data Data collected at source, e.g. in a questionnaire.

prime number A number which has exactly two factors: itself and one. The first, and only even prime number, is 2. 1 is not a prime number as it has only one factor: itself.

prism A three-dimensional shape which can be cut into any number of identical slices.

quadrilateral Any two-dimensional four-sided shape.

reciprocal A number 'turned upside down', e.g. the reciprocal of $\frac{2}{3}$ is $\frac{3}{2}$. Your calculator has a button marked either $\frac{1}{x}$ or x^{-1}. The mathematical definition is a number by which another number is multiplied to obtain the answer 'one', e.g. $\frac{1}{2}$ or 0.5 is the reciprocal of 2 and vice versa because $2 \times \frac{1}{2} = 1$.

recurring decimal (or **repeating decimal)** A decimal with a pattern which recurs for ever, e.g. 0.33333 ..., 0.121212 ...

secondary data Data generated from primary data, e.g. you might decide to sort all the responses from a set of questionnaires into categories dependent on the age or sex of the members of the sample.

sector of a circle A triangular 'slice' of a circle enclosed by two radii and the arc of the circumference which joins them.

similar shapes Shapes where one is an enlargement of the other. The sides increase or decrease by the same scale factor or multiplier, but the angles in each are identical. Be careful to distinguish between similar and congruent. Congruent shapes are identical in size and shape. The lengths of similar shapes are different, but their lengths are enlarged in the same ratio.

simplify If this refers to an expression, collect together all the terms which are of the same kind. Sometimes you will need to multiply out (expand) brackets. If it refers to a fraction, cancel the fraction.

simple interest To find the simple interest, work out the percentage interest on the original amount and multiply that number by the length of time given.

subtend You may meet this word in questions involving circle theorems. The lines at the end of two points meeting at an angle are said to subtend the angle.

surd A number in root form, e.g. $\sqrt{2}$. You may be asked in a question on a non-calculator paper to leave your answer in surd form, e.g. the answer to the length of a side in a question involving Pythagoras' theorem could be $\sqrt{42}$.

term In a sequence, each number is a **term**. Finding a formula for the nth term means finding a formula which would enable you to find what the number is in any specified position in the list – e.g. 4th, 18th, 75th etc. It is also used to describe an equation or expression. The expression $x^2 + 3x + 2$ has three terms.

terminating decimal A decimal which terminates or finishes, e.g. 0.5, 0.007, 0.23 etc. Terminating decimals are easily turned into fractions by writing the decimal part as the numerator and writing the decimal by replacing the decimal point followed by the same number of digits as there are in the question.

tetrahedron (plural **tetrahedra)** A pyramid on a triangular base, so it has four sides.

variable A quantity which varies in size, often expressed by the letters x or y. For example, in the equation $y = 2x + 4$, x and y will vary according to the values chosen. If $x = 10$, $y = 24$, if $y = 16$, x must be 6.

Index